CHANGES IN RICE FARMING IN SELECTED AREAS OF ASIA

THE INTERNATIONAL RICE RESEARCH INSTITUTE

LOS BANOS, LAGUNA, PHILIPPINES P.O. BOX 933, MANILA, PHILIPPINES.

Correct citation: International Rice Research
Institute, 1975. Changes in Rice Farming in
Selected Areas of Asia. Los Banos, Philippines

The International Development Research Centre,
Canada provided a major portion of the
financial support for this project.
The responsibility for all aspects of this
publication rests with the
International Rice Research Institute.

Contents

Preface

In early 1971, a group of development specialists in agricultural economics, rural sociology and related fields from the International Rice Research Institute (IRRI) and the University of the Philippines at Los Baños began to consider ways to undertake research to improve our understanding of the changes occurring and the problems associated with the adoption of the new rice technology at the farm level. This group believed that a research project could be planned, organized, and implemented to collect and analyze data from a number of locations in different rice farming areas in South and Southeast Asia that would be useful to research workers, program planners, and policy makers in these countries.

To develop such a research project, with the support and coordination of IRRI and the International Development Research Center of Canada (IDRC) about 20 Asian social scientists who were experienced in conducting farm level research were invited to join the initial planning group in two workshops (May and September 1971) at IRRI. Together they explored, and expanded on the initial plan for a study of changes in rice farming in selected areas of Asia that had been affected by modern rice technology.

During these workshops, a research proposal was developed to investigate the effect of changing technology on rice farming and farmers, and on how factors such as the physical environment, traditions, and established institutions affected the adoption of modern technology. The basic format of the study was outlined, and proposed participants were identified. Twelve Asian institutions and the IDRC agreed upon the financial support arrangements for the project. Subsequently, two additional sites were added to the project, both located in Mindanao in the southern Philippines and supported by the Ford Foundation.

During the course of the study, a third workshop was held in June 1972 to review the progress and problems and discuss the initial findings. The final workshop was convened in May 1973 to discuss, assess, and evaluate the findings of the study. A plan of action was developed for preparing the research findings and their assessment into the following report.

Studies of each area were prepared and are presented in the following chapters. In addition, data from each of the sites were provided to staff of the Department of Agricultural Economics of IRRI and analyzed by them both at IRRI, Cornell University, and at the Stanford Food Research Institute. Computer analysis at Cornell was financially supported through a 211d grant provided by the United States Agency for International Development.

This research undertaking, with its broad-gauged objectives and wide geographic scope, was in no small measure an experiment that was marked with both successes and failures. Organizing and coordinating a research project in a dynamic, diverse, and at times politically unstable area of the world has presented many challenges and opportunities. Initially social scientists in eleven countries in Asia were contracted, but for various reasons full participants were ultimately found in six countries. Even as the project progressed, political problems and professional advancements periodically threatened to eliminate many of the study sites.

Equally important, if not more important than the substantive and methodological lessons learned from the project, is the study's contribution to the strengthening of social science research in South and Southeast Asia. The rice study was not just another research project. It served as a means for developing a network of working relationships among Asian social scientists who are concerned with similar problems. It has afforded an opportunity for senior and junior researchers and graduate students to participate in a regional study, the positive ramifications of which may extend through this decade. The accompanying workshops have provided an avenue for personal and professional contact and for the resolution of mutual problems through sharing experiences, expertise, and counsel.

A list of participants in the project follows:

Name	Country	Institution
ADULAVIDHAYA, K.	Thailand	Kasetsart University
ANDEN, T.	Philippines	International Rice Research Institute
ARELLANO, A.	Philippines	Ateneo de Davao Colleges
BARKER, R.	Philippines	International Rice Research Institute
CASTILLO, G.	Philippines	University of the Philippines, Los Baños
CHAUDHARI, H.	West Pakistan	Pakistan Agric. University
CONTADO, T.	Philippines	University of the Philippines, Los Baños
DAVID, C.	Philippines	Stanford University
HERDT, R.	Philippines	International Rice Research Institute
HERRERA, R.	Philippines	University of the Philippines, Los Baños
IHALAUW, J.	Indonesia	Satya Wacana Christian University
ISVILANONDA, S.	Thailand	Kasetsart University

JAIME, R.	Philippines	University of the Philippines, Los Baños
KANUNGO, K.	India	Indian Agricultural Research Institute
KEARL, B.	Singapore	A/D/C Asia Office, Singapore
KRISHNA MURTHY, A.	India	University of Agric. Sciences
LOCKWOOD, B.	Fiji Island	University of South Pacific
MOHY-UD-DIN, Q.	West Pakistan	Pakistan Agric. University
MUSTAPHA, N.	West Malaysia	Malaysian Research & Dvpt Institute
PAL, T.	India	Central Rice Research Institute
PARTHASARATHY, G.	India	Andhra University
PRABOWO, D.	Indonesia	Gadjah Mada University
RAJAGOPALAN, V.	India	Tamil Nadu Agric. University
RASHID, A.	West Pakistan	Pakistan Agric. University
SAJOGYO	Indonesia	Agro-Economic Survey
SHARMA, J.	India	G. B. Pant University of Agric. & Tech.
SRISWASDILEK, J.	Thailand	Kasetsart University
TAMIN, M.	West Malaysia	University of Malaya
TAN, E.	Philippines	Notre Dame University
UTAMI, W.	Indonesia	Satya Wacana University
WELSCH, D.	Thailand	Kasetsart University
WICKHAM, G.	Philippines	University of the Philippines, Los Baños

Introduction

THE NEW RICE TECHNOLOGY is making its impact felt throughout tropical Asia. Accompanying this so-called "green revolution" is a corresponding harvest of rhetoric and controversy as to what else the new technology has brought along with it. Much has been written about the changes that are occurring. Despite this it is difficult to find comparable village level studies which document these changes in production and production practices, and in the socio-economic factors such as income gain, the sharing of benefits, and employment.

In search of insights into some of the issues that have arisen an investigation of changes in rice farming in South and Southeast Asia was initiated by the International Rice Research Institute in 1971. This project has involved the leadership and research participation of the agricultural economists and rural sociologists from six countries who are listed in the preface. Information was gathered from a total of 36 rice-growing villages in 14 separate study areas (see map).

The primary objective of this research was to provide information on farm changes associated with the introduction of the new rice technology. Answers were sought to the following questions:

- To what extent have the modern or so-called high yielding varieties been accepted in the study areas? Were changes in other farm practices associated with the introduction of modern varieties?

- What are the major obstacles to further growth in rice production? Are these a function of physical environment, socio-economic factors, or a combination of both?

- How has the new technology affected the level and structure of employment? Has the labor requirement increased? Is labor saving equipment being adopted?

- Who has benefited from the new technology, and how have these benefits been spent? To what degree are profits capitalized into rising land values? How has the relationship among various tenure groups (landowner, tenant, landless laborer) changed?

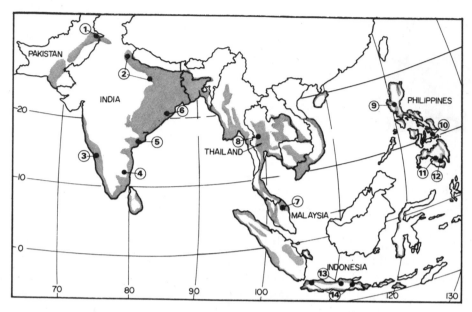

Project locations for study of changes in rice farming in selected areas of Asia (1. Punjab, 2. Uttar Pradesh, 3. Mysore, 4. Tamil Nadu, 5. Andhra Pradesh, 6. Orissa, 7. Kelantan, 8. Suphan Buri, 9. Nueva Ecija, 10. Leyte, 11. Cotabato, 12. Davao, 13. Central Java, 14. East Java and West Java). Shading indicates approximate areas of intensive rice production.

It was expected that while this study would probably find more questions than answers, some trends and patterns would emerge that would not only be of interest, in their own right, but also help to point out the need and direction for more detailed research on specific subjects.

PROCEDURES

Procedures to be followed in each of the study areas were developed during the course of two workshops held in May and September 1971. In designing the present project, one aim was to reach a compromise between conformity and flexibility. While a common core of information was to be obtained in all areas, at the same time participants were encouraged to investigate those issues that might be unique, but extremely important in their specific area. This provided the flexibility to cope with the extreme heterogeneity in physical and socio-economic environment among the various sites.

Thus, 14 separate case studies have been conducted with a common theme and a degree of uniformity in procedure, in the hopes that taken individually or as a unit, these studies would provide useful insights on the issues at hand. Basic decisions agreed upon at the planning workshops prior to initiating the project included: the choice of objectives, the criteria for selection of villages and sampling of farms, the common core of data to be gathered in all areas, and the time schedule for the project.

From one to three villages were to be chosen in each of the study areas by the project leader in each area. In *at least one* of the localities chosen most farmers interviewed would have had realistic reasons for considering the adoption of the new rice technology. More specifically, these localities should have: (1) a supply and control over water that would permit the farmers to plan on producing two or more crops each year, (2) ready physical access to the inputs required in the new technology, and (3) reasonably good access to markets for produce. However, they should not have been the object of a selective, intensive campaign. In short, those areas where change is likely to take place fairly rapidly, and those which are likely to be more favorably situated with respect to the adoption of the new rice technology — not the typical rice growing areas — were to be selected. The reader should keep this point constantly in mind as he examines the research findings.

From 150 to 250 farms would be sampled in each study area. It was initially planned that a complete enumeration of farmers in each of the villages would be made and a sample be drawn from this enumeration. However, in several cases it proved more expedient to sample from existing farm lists. A simple random sample of farmers was drawn from most villages, but in some areas the sample was stratified to obtain adequate representation of certain groups of farmers.

The procedures used to collect the common core of data in each area (including the farm questionnaire) are presented in Appendix A. Two rounds of interviews were conducted between late 1971 and early 1973. For most study areas the survey year is the crop year 1971/72. However, in two cases, the survey year was the calendar year 1972 because there was unavoidable delay in initiating the project.

THE NEW RICE TECHNOLOGY

Terms such as "green revolution", "seed-fertilizer revolution," "high-yielding varieties," "modern inputs," and "improved package of practices," have been used to describe the introduction of the new rice and wheat technology in Asia. But these terms are frequently more misleading than enlightening. More specifically, the "Green revolution" denotes the large increases in crop yields that in recent years resulted mainly from the development and adoption of new plant hybrids and the improved technology associated with their culture.

There is, of course, the notion that there has been no revolutionary change, but rather an evolution and in the aggregate sense, this is certainly true. However, this transition has been characterized by very rapid change in some areas and almost no change in others.

The study sites were chosen for their potential for rapid change. The environment of the study site represented no major obstacle to farmers who might have wished to adopt the new varieties and the associated package of practices, which includes fertilizer, methods and agricultural chemicals to control weeds, diseases, and pests (insects, rats, and birds) with the input requirement differing for each location. When used under the right environmental conditions, these inputs allow the new varieties to express their yield potential. Without these inputs the grower cannot expect a good yield. A major difference between modern and traditional varieties is in their response to inputs and good cultural practices. The yields of the modern varieties can be increased with inputs such as fertilizer while this is usually not true for traditional rice varieties.

There is an important interaction between input requirements and varietal improvement. Breeding research in the early and mid-1960s produced varieties such as IR8 and Jaya which were characterized by a major departure in plant type (short stature and stiff straw) from the traditional indica varieties and were noted for their responsiveness to high levels of nitrogen input under optimum conditions. But in some situations these so-called high-yielding varieties give yields equal to or less than the yields of existing varieties.

Subsequent varietal improvement research has emphasized the incorporation of insect and disease resistance and quality in the varieties. Developing varieties with insect and disease resistance reduces the requirement for chemicals and hence, the cost of the input package. IR20 is an example of a variety which combines good yield potential with improved resistance and quality. It has been accepted in many areas where earlier varieties such as IR8 were rejected by farmers.

More recently rice researchers are selecting and breeding varieties for tolerance to such unfavorable environmental conditions as drought, deep water, poor soils, and cold temperature. These developments are largely in the experimental stage, but it would appear that some of these new varieties will differ markedly from their predecessors in plant type and other characteristics. The newly released Thai variety, RD5, for example, is 150 cm compared with about 100 cm for IR8. The planting of this variety is expected to spread to some areas in Thailand where water is too deep for the shorter rice varieties.

The new rice varieties are environment specific with respect to their performance. The term high-yielding variety (HYV) tends to give the erroneous impression that a rice variety is high yielding under all conditions. No single term or phrase can adequately describe the increasingly diverse characteristics of the new rice varieties. This study is concerned with changes that have been associated with the introduction of varieties developed and released to farmers since 1965, and so the term *modern* or *new* is used in this report to refer to those varieties. It suggests a chronology of plant development which is important when studying change.

Those varieties that were developed through breeding programs before 1965 are referred to as *improved local* varieties, and others are referred to as *traditional* varieties. A glossary describing the rice varieties mentioned in the text appears in Appendix C.

The adoption of these terms is not meant to suggest that important improvements did not occur in rice technology before 1965. On the contrary, the results show that improved local varieties are still important in many of our study areas because they possess characteristics which farmers regard as superior to those of available modern varieties. For example, Mahsuri, a variety developed in the 1950's and still widely planted in Malaysia, was introduced into Andhra Pradesh, India only recently, but it is gaining popularity in the wet season among the farmers in that study area.

THE STUDY AREAS

The 14 farm surveys have been conducted over a broad geographic area reflecting a wide range of differences in farming conditions. The following is a brief discussion of certain critical variables in the study areas that influence farming conditions – climate, farm structure, and irrigation. Each of the study sites can be located on the map, and average rainfall data for selected sites are shown in Figures 1a and 1b. Some of the basic characteristics of the sample villages are shown in Tables 1 and 2.

Climate. Nine of the 14 sites, including those in India, Pakistan, Thailand, and the northern Philippines, lie between 10 and 30° North latitude where the heaviest rains occur between June and November and the main crop is normally harvested in November and December. The five sites lying between 15 and 25° North latitude (West Godavari

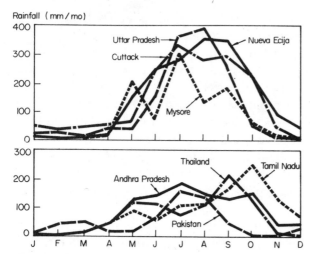

Fig. 1a. Average monthly rainfall, 1967-1971, at different study sites.

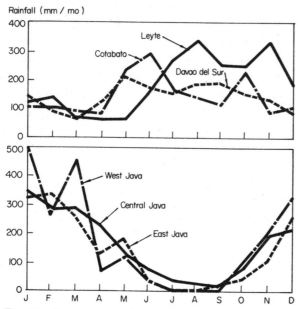

Fig. 1b. Average monthly rainfall, 1967-1971, at different study sites.

and Cuttack in India, Suphan Buri in Thailand, Nueva Ecija and Leyte in the Philippines) are subject to typhoons and heavy rains which occasionally severely damage the main rice crop.

The three study areas in Malaysia and the southern Philippines lie between 0 and 10° North latitude where both rainfall and solar energy are more evenly distributed throughout the year. The wet and dry seasons are less distinct than in the previously mentioned five sites.

The Indonesian sites fall between 5 and 10° South latitude where the heaviest rainfall occurs from December through May. The main crop is harvested in April and May. In the two study areas in North India and Pakistan, cold weather during the winter favors the production of wheat as the dry season crop. In all other areas where crops are grown under irrigation rice is the principal second crop.

Farm structure. There was considerably greater variation in the size of the farm operating unit than in family size among the survey villages (Table 1). The average village farm size was 2.9 hectares and ranged from 0.5 hectare in Java to 7.8 hectares in Thailand and Pakistan. The

Table 1. Size and tenure characteristics in sample villages.

location	farms in sample (no.)	size of household (members)	size of farm (ha)	pure owners (%)	pure tenants (%)
India					
Andhra Pradesh					
Pedapulleru	185	5	4.7	41	32
Tamil Nadu					
Kariyamangalam	52	6	4.1	86	10
Palvarthuvenran	33	6	2.0	100	0
Manmalai	66	6	1.8	96	2
Uttar Pradesh					
Dhanpur-Vijaypur	51	6	6.0	100	0
Tarna	43	8	1.2	100	0
Barain	57	7	1.2	100	0
Mysore					
Gajanur	48	7	2.4	n.a.[a]	n.a.
Hosahally	43	8	4.8	n.a.	n.a.
Ashoknagar	51	7	2.8	n.a.	n.a.
Orissa					
Kandarpur	57	6	0.6	49	9
Korpada	112	6	0.6	62	5
Indonesia					
Central Java					
Nganjat	60	5	0.5	80	4
Kahuman	60	6	0.6	67	2
Pluneng	66	6	0.5	71	2

Table 1. (Cont'd)

location	farms in sample (no.)	size of household (members)	farm (ha)	pure owners (%)	pure tenants (%)
East-West Java					
Sidomulyo	75	6	0.5	86	7
Cidahu	77	4	0.5	90	1
West Malaysia					
Kelantan					
Salor_	175	6	0.9	58	11
Meranti	133	5	1.0	43	17
West Pakistan					
Punjab					
Aroop	80	9	6.7	65	4
Maraliwala	80	11	7.8	23	41
Thailand					
Suphan Buri					
Rai Rot	47	6	7.0	75	6
Nong Sarai	59	6	7.8	66	5
Sa Krachom	44	6	7.8	64	13
Philippines					
Nueva Ecija					
San Nicolas	55	7	2.5	16	56
Malimba	66	6	3.1	9	59
Mahipon	72	6	3.8	25	26
Leyte					
Canipa	49	7	1.7	17	77
Marcos	66	6	1.5	14	86
Tab-ang	56	5	1.2	33	57
Davao					
Beynte Nuwebe	66	6	1.7	8	92
Sinayawan	93	7	2.2	14	86
Cotabato					
Bulucaon	40	6	2.0	6	91
Maluao	36	6	2.9	44	53
Capayuran:					
Christians	36	6	1.9	14	86
Muslims (Cabpangi)	48	7	3.9	100	0

[a]Tenure information was not available since sample farmers in this area were reluctant to disclose their tenure status.

majority of the 2,428 rice farms surveyed were small, 35 percent were less than 1 hectare, 46 percent from 1 to 4 hectares, and only 19 percent were larger than 4 hectares.

High rates of tenancy were found principally in the Philippine study areas. Here the traditional tenure pattern is based on a 50-50 sharing of cost and rice output between landlord and tenant, although in recent years it has shifted toward fixed cash rent or leasehold under a government land reform program. Elsewhere, in Pedapulleru, India and in the Pakistan villages the tenancy rate was also high. The rights of tenure appeared to be less stable than those in the Philippines both in terms of sharing arrangement and in claim to work a given piece of land.

In all areas the principal crop was rice. In about half of the villages rice was the only crop of any significant hectarage. In the other half of the villages, the most important other crops were sugarcane, tobacco, corn, and wheat.

Water resources. In the selection of the study areas water control was standardized to a degree, although the quality of water delivery systems varied widely among the villages. Villages were scored according to the quality of irrigation and drainage (Table 2). The scoring was subjective, it was based upon field observations and the description of the sites furnished by the project leader in each area. The best irrigated areas received a score of 1, while at the other extreme the rainfall villages received a score of 5.

The majority of areas were served by canal or gravity irrigation systems, most of which had no water storage capacity but served a limited command area during the dry season. Thus there was the possibility of too much or too little water (depending upon the season) on at least a portion of the irrigated farms in many of the survey areas.

In Pakistan and in Uttar Pradesh in northern India, the command areas were overextended, and pump irrigation was widely used in the survey area to supplement or substitute for the canal water supply. Two of the three Tamil Nadu villages were entirely served by pumps, and the third village had a combination of pumps and tank irrigation.

Large government operated pumps supplied water directly from the Kelantan River to a gravity irrigation network in northern Malaysia. Small privately operated pumps were used for the same purpose in one of the Leyte villages in the Philippines.

The most reliable irrigation and drainage systems were found in Java (particularly Klaten in Central Java) and in Mysore, India where a storage reservoir constructed along the Tunga River in 1952 supplied water to the study area.

Table 2. Cropping and irrigation characteristics in sample villages.

location	avg rice area (ha)		rice area irrigated (%)		quality of irrigation[a]	double-cropped rice area(%)
	wet	dry	wet	dry		
India						
Andhra Pradesh						
Pedapulleru	4.4	3.8	100	100	3	66
Tamil Nadu						
Kariyamangalam	1.4	0.8	100	100	2	61
Palvarthuvenran	1.3	1.2	100	100	3	91
Manmalai	0.7	0.6	100	100	2	89
Uttar Pradesh						
Dhanpur-Vijaypur[b]	3.2	–	65	–	3	–
Tarna[b]	0.5	–	92	–	3	–
Barain[b]	0.7	–	31	–	4	–
Mysore						
Gajanur	1.7	1.1	100	100	2	60
Hosahally	1.9	1.5	100	100	2	61
Ashoknagar	2.2	1.9	100	100	2	84
Orissa						
Kandarpur	0.6	0.5	100	97	3	83
Korpada	0.6	0.5	98	100	3	83
Indonesia						
Central Java						
Nganjat	0.5	0.5	100	100	1	100
Kahuman	0.6	0.6	100	100	1	100
Pluneng	0.5	0.5	100	100	1	100
East-West Java						
Sidomulyo	0.4	0.3	100	100	2	98
Cidahu	0.5	0.5	100	100	2	100
West Malaysia						
Kelantan						
Salor	0.8	0.8	100	100	3	100
Meranti	0.9	0.9	94	94	3	100
West Pakistan						
Punjab						
Aroop[b]	3.7	–	100	–	2	–
Maraliwala[b]	6.0	–	100	–	2	–

Table 2. (Cont'd)

location	avg rice area (ha)		rice area irrigated (%)		quality of irrigation[a]	double-cropped rice area(%)
	wet	dry	wet	dry		
Thailand						
Suphan Buri						
Rai Rot	5.3	1.4	98	100	3	19
Nong Sarai	6.1	1.1	73	100	4	13
Sa Krachom	5.4	0	0	0	5	0
Philippines						
Nueva Ecija						
San Nicolas	2.5	2.5	100	100	2	93
Malimba	3.1	3.1	100	100	3	92
Mahipon	3.8	0	0	0	5	0
Leyte						
Canipa	0.8	0.8	90	90	3	100
Marcos	0.4	0.4	99	99	3	100
Tab-ang	0.7	0.7	99	99	3	100
Davao						
Beynte Nuwebe	1.7	1.7	100	100	4	100
Sinayawan	1.9	1.9	100	100	4	100
Cotabato						
Bulucaon	1.8	2.0	100	100	3	100
Maluao	1.6	1.6	90	84	5	100
Capayuran:						
Christian	1.3	1.2	100	100	3	100
Muslims (Cabpangi)	1.4	1.3	100	100	5	95

[a] 1 = very good; 5 = poorly irrigated or wholly rainfed.
[b] Second crop: wheat.

WHAT FOLLOWS

Chapter 2 is based upon an analysis of data obtained from each study area. No attempt was made to analyze all the available data or to discuss all the issues reported in the individual studies; rather, the chapter focuses on the more important issues. The 14 case studies have a somewhat similar format. Each chapter includes a map, a diagram of the cropping cycle, and one standard table describing the characteristics of the sample in each study area. Following a brief discussion of that information the emphasis given to specific topics varies widely from chapter to chapter reflecting the preference of the authors and the variability in significant issues from one study area to another. A final chapter summarizes the key findings from all of the individual studies.

Factors influencing the use of modern rice technology in the study areas

Randolph Barker and Teresa Anden

THIS CHAPTER PROVIDES an analytical overview of the data from each of the study areas. An analysis of the yield variance showed that approximately 58 percent of the variance was amung villages and 42 percent occurred within villages. In the first section those factors which cause variation in yield and the use of new rice technology among villages are identified and discussed. This is followed by a description of the relationship between the changes in farming practices and labor use. Lastly, farm size influences on the use and benefits of new technology are examined among farms within villages.

BARRIERS TO HIGH YIELD

For analytical purposes the villages were classified into two types: the *monoculture* rice village where 90 percent or more of the cropped area that is suitable for rice production (i.e. excluding upland and tree crop areas) is planted to rice in both the wet and dry seasons; and the *mixed farming* villages, where at least one crop such as sugarcane, tobacco, corn, and wheat, in addition to rice was of major economic importance. These other crops were grown either in rotation, such as rice followed by wheat or corn, or on different portions of the farm area during the same season, such as rice in combination with sugarcane or tobacco.

The difference in cropping patterns between these two types of villages reflects differences in environmental conditions. A rice-growing village that can grow a crop in addition to or in combination with rice is likely to have a more favorable environment even for rice production

Randolph Barker and Teresa Anden are agricultural economist and research assistant, respectively, Agricultural Economics Department, the International Rice Research Institute, Los Baños, Laguna, Philippines.

as a result of better irrigation and drainage facilities. By contrast, the monoculture villages tend to have, for largely environmental reasons, no alternate or supplementary crop to rice. Most of the monoculture villages are located in the heart of the traditional rice-growing areas. Except where otherwise noted, four poorly irrigated or rainfed villages that were studied (Mahipon, Sa Krachom, Cabpangi, and Maluao) were not included in the analysis to make the group more homogenous.

The introduction of modern varieties. The adoption of modern varieties by monoculture and mixed-farming villages is shown in Table 1. Since nearly all villages in the study were considered to be well suited (favorable rainfall patterns, good topography, access to irrigation, etc.) to the modern varieties, it is not surprising that most farmers have tried the modern varieties at least during one season or another. In 29 of 32 irrigated villages 90 percent or more of the farmers reported having tried modern varieties. However, the modern varieties are more commonly planted in the dry season, and more frequently used in mixed farming villages than in monoculture villages during the wet season. The high level of solar energy, in the dry season which allows maximum

Table 1. Farmers adopting modern varieties and area planted to modern varieties (MV) in study villages, 1971–72.

season/type of farming	villages (no.) reporting			villages (total no.)	average rice area in MV (%)
	90% and above	50 to 90%	below 50%		
Farmers who had ever planted MV					
	29	3	0	32	
Farmers planting MV in year of survey					
Wet season	16	13	3	32	
Dry season	24	0	3	27	
Rice area planted to MV					
Wet season					
monoculture[a]	8	0	9	17	60
mixed farming	4	8	3	15	71
Dry season					
monoculture	11	4	2	17	87
mixed farming[b]	6	2	2	10	82

[a]Monoculture rice villages are those where 90 percent or more of the land suitable for growing rice is planted to rice. [b]Five villages in Pakistan and Uttar Pradesh plant wheat during the dry season.

photosynthetic activity and frequently is accompanied by a low incidence of insect and disease promotes maximum realization of the full yield potential of the modern varieties.

Less than 50 percent of the total rice cropland was planted to modern varieties in 12 of the 32 villages in the wet season and in 4 of 27 villages in the dry season. The reason for this low adoption rate can best be understood by examining specific situations. In five mixed-farming villages where less than 50 percent of the rice areas were planted to modern varieties, the local varieties commanded a higher price than did the modern varieties. Price seemed to be the main reason for the popularity of the local varieties in Nganjat, Central Java during the wet season, in Kahuman, Central Java during the dry season, and in Aroop and Maraliwala in the Pakistan Punjab during the wet season. In Pakistan the local Basmati rice provides substantial foreign exchange earnings. A high-yielding Basmati rice for export has not yet been developed, so the government has found it profitable, in terms of foreign exchange earnings, to raise the local price of Basmati rice to as much as twice the level of the modern varieties.

Among the remaining 11 monoculture villages where less than 50 percent of the rice land was planted to modern varieties, the price of local rice varieties relative to that of modern varieties did not seem to be an important factor. In villages in Cuttack and Andhra Pradesh, located in the flood plains along the eastern coast of India, high-yielding rice varieties suitable for the wet season were not yet available. In an experiment comparing Mahsuri with modern varieties in Andhra Pradesh in the 1972 wet season, Mahsuri yielded 4.4 t/ha without added nitrogen, while the average yield of Jaya and IR8 was 2.3 t/ha without added nitrogen. Neither showed any response to added nitrogen at rates up to 200 kg/ha. In the village of Cidahu in West Java about half of the wet season crop was destroyed by gall midge. Farmers noted that the pest attacks were more severe on modern varieties, such as IR5, than on the local varieties, and so they reverted to growing the local varieties. While similar severe losses due to tungro virus were reported in several areas of the Philippines, resistant modern varieties were available, which replaced the susceptible varieties.

Low adoption of modern varieties was also reported in Kelantan, Malaysia, and in Suphan Buri, Thailand. In Malaysia, where the completion of the Muda River Irrigation Project has moved the country close to self-sufficiency in rice, new technology was not emphasized in areas like Kelantan. Only one modern variety — a Malaysian selection of IR5 which gave an uneven stand — was available to farmers in Kelantan

Table 2. Preference of farmers for specific varietal groups, 1971–72.

type of farming	villages (no.)	farmers (%) preferring		
		local	modern[a] (1966-68)	modern[b] [c] (1969-71)
		Wet season		
Monoculture	17	47	25	28
Mixed farming	15	28	49	23
		Dry season		
Monoculture	17	34	33	33
Mixed farming	10	22	71	7

[a]Includes the following varieties first released from 1966–68: IR8 and IR5 (known officially in Indonesia as PB8 and PB5), C4-63, Jaya, and IR6 (known officially in Pakistan as Mehran 6). [b]Includes the following varieties first released from 1969–71: IR20, IR22, IR24, Ratna, Pankaj, RD1, and RD5. [c]Although Jaya and IR20 were released in 1969, Jaya which has characteristics very similar to IR8 has been classified in the early modern group, while IR20 bred specifically for resistance to insects, has been classified in the late modern group.

at the time of a 1970–72 survey. As in Andhra Pradesh, Mahsuri tended to perform better than the modern varieties that were tested.

In Thailand, as in Pakistan, priority has been given to protecting existing export markets and foreign exchange earnings. RD1 and RD3, the first modern varieties developed in Thailand, were released in 1970. They were bred specifically to meet the standards of the export market. While these varieties were widely planted in the dry season, they occupied less than half of the rice growing area in the two irrigated villages in Suphan Buri during the wet season, and later were grown even less in these villages. This suggests that environmental factors, specifically the frequent flooding that occurs in these areas, may be discouraging the use of the short modern varieties that become in- undated in the wet season (the latest Thai variety released, RD5, is 50 percent taller than RD1 and RD3). Also, Suphan Buri had the most un- favorable fertilizer-rice price ratio of all the study areas.

The farmers surveyed were asked in both the wet and dry season what rice variety they preferred, and their responses were grouped as: local varieties, modern varieties released from 1966 to 1968, and modern varieties released from 1969 to 1971 (Table 2). The early modern varieties are distinguished from the later modern varieties primarily by the greater disease and insect resistance and the higher market quality that was bred into the more recent releases. During this 1972 survey, the early modern varieties were still dominant in the mixed-farming villages in both seasons. But in the monoculture villages, the local varieties were preferred, particularly during the wet season. Furthermore, the preference for more recent rice releases was about equal to that for the early modern varieties in both the wet and dry seasons. The new releases are expected to continue to replace the early modern varieties. However, local varieties will remain popular in some areas until modern varieties that are suitable to local environmental conditions are developed or until the preferential price support policy for local varieties is altered.

In summary, three factors seem to account for the differences among villages in relative area planted to modern rice varieties: (1) the availability of modern varieties suitable for a particular locale, (2) differences in the rice-growing environment (including climate, soils, irrigation, and drainage), and (3) the price relationships between improved and local varieties. Although an effort was made to quantify the relationship between the adoption of new varieties and the above three factors, the results were unsatisfactory primarily because the adoption rates were very high in most of the villages that were surveyed. Taken together, these three factors reflect both the profitability and risk associated with the use of modern varieties. While the suitability of available varieties is closely related to the environment, government policy as it influenced price and availability of modern varieties was a significant factor in determining the rate at which these varieties became available and were accepted by farmers.

Constraints to higher yield and fertilizer use. The relationship between the use of modern varieties and the other associated modern inputs needed to achieve the high yield potential of these varieties was examined. In those villages where both modern and local varieties were still being grown, the modern varieties frequently outyielded the local varieties by a ton or more per hectare. This was due in part to the use of more fertilizers on modern varieties, and generally the modern varieties seemed to receive better management and were planted on better soils than were the local varieties. These results do not imply, however, that the area where local varieties are being grown should be shifted to modern varieties.

The present analysis is confined to a comparison of the performance of modern varieties among the survey villages. The yield and nitrogen input for monoculture and mixed farms in the wet and dry season is presented in Table 3. The major difference in yield level and in fertilizer input occurred between monoculture and mixed farming villages rather

Table 3. Average yield and nitrogen input for modern varieties in mono-culture and mixed farming villages, 1971–72.

type of farming	villages (no.)	yield (t/ha)	nitrogen (kg/ha)
		Wet season	
Monoculture	17	2.9[a]	45
Mixed farming	15	4.5[a]	104
		Dry season	
Monoculture	17	3.2	54
Mixed farming	10	5.1	112

[a] Adjusted for serious damage due to tungro virus and gall midge in some of the villages.

Table 4. Yield, nitrogen input, and percent area in modern varieties by nitrogen level and type of farming, 1971–72.

nitrogen level[a]	villages (no.)	area in MV (%)	nitrogen (kg/ha)	yield (t/ha)
		Wet season		
Low nitrogen	11	77	24	2.9
High nitrogen				
Monoculture	9	39	69	3.0
Mixed farming	12	73	122	5.0
		Dry season[b]		
Low nitrogen	9	99	17	2.8
High nitrogen				
Monoculture	9	76	86	3.6
Mixed farming	9	80	123	5.4

[a] Low nitrogen — village average of less than 45 kg/ha N. Low nitrogen villages includes 8 monoculture and 3 mixed farming villages in the wet season, 8 monoculture and 1 mixed farming village in the dry season.
[b] Data not available for the two Davao del Sur villages in the dry season.

than between seasons. The potential of the monoculture areas appeared to be well below that of the mixed farming areas, which is what had been expected when the villages were categorized according to type of farm.

Table 5. Nitrogen level and proportion of farmers viewing selected factors as constraints to higher yield in the wet season, 1971–72.

villages characterized by nitrogen use	villages (no.)	farmers (%) viewing as constraint				
		obtaining seed	obtaining fertilizer	obtaining credit	poor irrigation	diseases, insects, pests
Low nitrogen	11	7^a	21	16^a	21^a	66
High introgen						
Monoculture	9^b	16	19	22	26	84
Mixed farming	12	12	37	31	20	64

[a] Data available for 9 of the 11 villages. [b] Data available for 7 of the 9 villages.

In identifying those factors that were associated with high yield, the yield potential of the environment was found to be an important factor. Additionally, the correlation between average yield and nitrogen input of the villages was high, 0.86. Thus, efforts were made to determine why in some villages farmers were applying only low levels of nitrogen on rice varieties.

The first step was to separate the villages where only low levels of nitrogen were used from the other villages and gather information about their location and characteristics. Experiments at IRRI have shown that 60 kg N/ha can be profitably used on modern varieties, excluding risk factors, even under wet season conditions.[1] Thus, an average rate of nitrogen use below 45 kg/ha was assumed to be a low level of input. Eleven villages (8 monoculture, and 3 mixed farming) fell into this category of "low nitrogen village" in the wet season, and 9 villages (8 monoculture and 1 mixed farming) in the dry season (Table 4). Despite the significantly lower levels of nitrogen input, the yield difference between the low nitrogen and the high nitrogen monoculture farms in the wet season was not significant. The basic question of whether the low levels of fertilizer input in these villages reflect a physical or a socio-economic constraint remains to be answered.

When farmers were asked what factors they considered to be the major constraints to higher rice yields (Table 5), the control of diseases, insects, and other pests was identified as the most serious problem in most villages. There appeared to be other problems which were considered more acute in the low-nitrogen villages compared with the other villages.

The 11 low-nitrogen villages are located in the southern Philippines, in Thailand, and in Pakistan. In two of the three southern Philippine areas

[1] International Rice Research Institute Annual Report, 1972, pp. 48–50.

more than half of the farmers were not applying any fertilizer although nearly all of the farm area was planted to the modern varieties. In Thailand and Pakistan about 20 percent of the farmers was applying no fertilizer. In all other areas, at least 90 percent of the farmers used fertilizer. A close examination of each of these areas furnished a partial explanation for why such a sharp contrast in fertilizer use exists.

In the Philippines, Central Luzon has received far more infrastructure development and other facilities to promote agricultural development than the outer regions. In the outer regions, the cost of inputs is higher and the market price received from rice is lower. For example, in the Cotabato study area, the price of nitrogen was 50 percent higher and the price of rice a third lower than in Gapan, Central Luzon. Further-

Table 6. Estimated regression equations for yield and for nitrogen input on modern varieties based on data from 36 villages in the wet season and 29 in the dry season.

variable[a]	yield		nitrogen	
	coefficient and t-value	mean and $S_x{}^b$	coefficient and t-value	mean and $S_x{}^b$
Nitrogen (N)	.016	67.58		
	(4.97)	(6.10)		
Maximum N (M)			0.767	130.15
			(7.44)	(4.07)
Rainfall (R)	−0.006	17.05		
	(−.66)	(1.32)		
Type of farming (T)	−0.440			
	(−2.09)			
Irrigation (I)	−0.301	2.86	16.50	2.86
	(−2.28)	(0.14)	(−4.52)	(0.14)
Credit (C)	0.009	25.80	0.33	25.80
	(1.81)	(2.84)	(2.07)	(2.84)
Price ratio (P)			−9.45	3.30
			(−3.44)	(0.14)
Intercept	3.46		38.20	
	(5.49)		(1.95)	
R^2	0.78		0.79	

[a]See text for definition of variables. $^b S_x{}^b$ = standard deviation of the specified variables.

more, less than 5 percent of the farmers in Cotabato borrowed from institutional or formal credit sources, while in Gapan over 20 percent did. Unfavorable price relationships and high interest rates have resulted in low profits from fertilizer use in Cotabato. Despite the low level of fertilizer use in the southern Philippine study areas, all the farmers there had adopted modern varieties, and most were using insecticides, but usually in very small amounts.

Suphan Buri, Thailand, and Gujranwala, Pakistan are located in the center of major-rice producing areas. Nevertheless, they have the least favorable nitrogen/rice price ratios among all the study villages. Furthermore, the average farm size is larger in these two sites than in any of the other study areas. Farm size tends to be inversely correlated with the intensity of cultivation, and rice responds to intensive care. Contrast, for example, a 6-hectare farm in Rai Rot, Suphan Buri with a 0.6-hectare farm in Kahuman, Central Java. Farms in each area are the major means of support for families of six to seven. A Rai Rot farmer with a minimal yield of 2 t/ha on 6 hectares will in one season produce only twice the annual output of a Kahuman farmer obtaining a 5 t/ha yield twice a year on 0.6 hectare. Thus Rai Rot farmers require 10 times more land to obtain only twice the crop yield achieved by Kahuman farmers. Farmers in Kahuman use a much higher level of labor as well as cash inputs per hectare. Under optimum economic conditions a yield much higher than 2 t/ha in Rai Rot would be expected.

A regression model to explain the variance in yield and in nitrogen level among villages was developed from a knowledge of the factors associated with low yield and low nitrogen input. Data from all villages were used to estimate the equations (including the four rainfed and poorly irrigated villages excluded from the previous analysis). There were a total of 65 observations, 36 for the wet season and 29 for the dry season. There was no dry season rice crop in seven villages.

The variables used in this analysis are defined below, and the regression coefficients are presented in Table 6:

Y = metric tons of rough rice per hectare
N = kilograms of nitrogen per hectare
P = the nitrogen to modern variety rough rice price ratio
C = percent of farmers in each village borrowing from formal sources of credit — banks, cooperatives, and government agencies
I = quality of irrigation where 1 = well irrigated and 5 = poorly irrigated or rainfed
T = the type of farming in the village where monoculture = 1, and mixed farming = 0
R = the average millimeters of rainfall per month from 1967 to 1971

for the harvest month and the month before harvest as a percent of the average total annual rainfall. Rainfall is inversely correlated with solar energy; thus, high rainfall at harvest should mean a lower yield.

M = the nitrogen input in kilograms per hectare needed to obtain maximum yield based upon the results of the experiment stations nearest to each of the study areas.

I and T are qualitative variables. The ranking in irrigation quality is subjective based upon field observations of the authors and the site descriptions prepared by participants in the project.

As a further explanation of the variable "M" it should be noted that at IRRI there are available many published and unpublished reports on experiments conducted at experiment stations throughout Asia showing the yield response of modern rice varieties to applied nitrogen. In most cases, the information was available from stations reasonably near the study areas. Where the information was lacking an educated guess was made with the authors' best judgement based upon a knowledge of the area in relation to similar areas. An estimate was made of the amount (round to the nearest 30 kg) of nitrogen per hectare required for maximum yield. The range varied from a low of 30 kg to a high of 180 kg of nitrogen. This variable takes into account both soil and climatic factors. For example, the soils in India tend to be older and less fertile than those of the Philippines. Consequently, much heavier doses of nitrogen are required to produce maximum yields. The maximum yield that can be achieved and the nitrogen required to achieve that yield are normally higher in the dry season than in the wet season.

The models were constructed with the hypothesis that economic, institutional, and environmental factors are all important in explaining the yield differences. The variables N, P, and C can be changed by altering the economic, social, or institutional structure. But the degree to which these changes will lead to higher production and profit is governed to a large degree by I, the quality of irrigation, which can be upgraded over time, and by environmental factors, reflected in the variables R, M, and T, which cannot be altered. However, rice varieties can be selected or bred to give improved performance under adverse environmental conditions.

Yield (Y) was estimated as a function of nitrogen input (N), the quality of irrigation (I), the percent of farmers using formal credit (C), type of farming (T), and rainfall at harvest (R). Not surprisingly, nitrogen is the most significant variable explaining the variance in yield; the high correlation between nitrogen and yield was noted previously.

It therefore seemed reasonable to estimate another equation with nitrogen as the dependent variable. The nitrogen/rough rice price ratio (P) was one of the independent variables, maximum nitrogen (M), was substituted for the variables R and T since all three variables related to differences in the physical environment. Regressions were estimated in both linear and logarithmic form, but the linear equations provided the best fit.

This second equation may be viewed as a demand function for nitrogen. The price elasticity of demand at the mean is approximately -0.5. However, because the physical and institutional environment vary widely among villages caution should be exercised in interpreting this in the usual fashion (i.e., a 1-percent change in the price ratio would lead to a 0.5-percent change in nitrogen input in the opposite direction).

The variables used in explaining the difference in nitrogen input, (a) between the high and the average level nitrogen village, and (b) between monoculture rice and mixed farming villages, and their relative importance are presented in Figure 1. Again, there is need for caution in

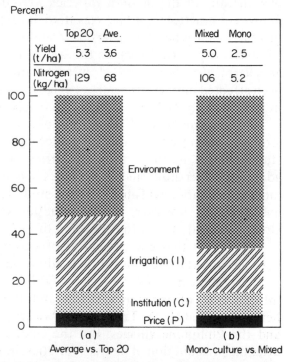

Fig. 1. Factors explaining differences in level of nitrogen inputs: (a) between average and 20 highest users of nitrogen, and (b) between mono-culture and mixed farming. [Based on nitrogen regression in Table 6.]

interpreting the results. Although the equations treat the explanatory variables as independent, an assessment of the individual village situations reveals a complementarity between the environment, the quality of irrigation, and the level of development of credit facilities and other institutions. The key question is what steps must be taken and in what order to relieve the constraints to production in a specific situation. The dominant role of irrigation and environment, two variables which are very hard to change, in explaining the variation in yield and demand for fertilizer among villages, is graphically illustrated in Figure 1.

CHANGES IN FARMING PRACTICES AND LABOR USE

To determine the relation between the introduction of modern rice varieties and the adoption of other modern inputs, the adoption rates were analyzed at three stages: (1) before modern varieties were introduced, (2) the year of their greatest first adoption, and (3) after the year of their greatest first adoption. Only farmers who had tried planting any of the modern varieties were included in the analysis. The improved practices can be classified into potentially yield-increasing practices such as new seeds, fertilizer, and insecticide use, and potentially labor-saving practices such as the use of tractors, mechanical threshers, and herbicides. Since the adoption of modern inputs seemed to have been affected more by differences in national policies than by differences in farm type, the villages were grouped according to country.

The governments of India, Indonesia, and the Philippines have strongly promoted the use of modern yield-increasing inputs. In the study villages in these three countries, a substantial increase in the adoption of fertilizer and insecticides accompanied the introduction of modern rice varieties (Table 7). In the study villages in Malaysia, Pakistan, and Thailand, however, the introduction of modern varieties was less closely associated with the adoption of yield increasing technology. The results suggest that government efforts to promote modern inputs have been an important reason for their adoption.

There appeared to be relatively little relationship between the introduction of modern varieties and the adoption of tractors and herbicides (Table 7). Tractors are widely used in Malaysia, Pakistan, and the Philippine villages. But the tractors were adopted in Malaysia after the introduction of modern varieties; in Pakistan they were adopted before modern varieties; and in the Philippines the growth in tractor use began before modern varieties and continued with their introduction. Herbicides have been popular only in the Philippines.

Table 7. Adoption of new practices by farmers who have tried modern varieties, 1971–72.

location	villages (no.)	users before modern varieties[a] (%)	first adopters (%) in[a] year of greatest adoption of modern varieties	later year	total users in survey year[a] (%)
			Chemical fertilizers		
India	12	55	34	11	100
Indonesia	5	76	20	4	99
Malaysia	2	72	10	18	94
Pakistan	2	80	2	0	76
Philippines	9	45	30	9	72
Thailand	2	57	17	8	69
All villages	32	58	26	9	88
			Insecticides		
India	12	34	34	14	80
Indonesia	5	71	23	5	93
Malaysia	2	48	10	0	49
Pakistan	2	48	4	6	58
Philippines	9	48	45	5	97
Thailand	2	61	15	6	71
All villages	32	47	31	8	83
			Tractors		
India	12	7	3	13	23
Indonesia	5	1	2	12	3
Malaysia	2	10	10	80	96
Pakistan	2	70	1	5	71
Philippines	9	27	19	14	58
Thailand	2	18	7	12	22
All villages	32	16	8	17	37
			Herbicides		
India	12	0	1	3	4
Indonesia	5	0	0	0	0
Malaysia	2	0	9	0	6
Pakistan	2	0	0	0	0
Philippines	9	33	31	9	66
Thailand	2	10	1	3	8
All villages	32	10	9	4	21

[a] Among those who were modern variety adopters in the wet season.

Table 8. Reported changes in pre-harvest labor requirements following the introduction of modern varieties by location, 1971−72.

location	villages (no.)	farmers (%) reporting change in					
		family labor		hired labor			
				from village		from outside	
		more	less	more	less	more	less
India	10[a]	27	2	82	3	65	0
Indonesia	5	26	2	18	12	11	4
Pakistan	2	8	0	2	0	0	0
Malaysia	2	51	18	36[b]	15[b]	−	−
Philippines	9	62	15	65	7	20	7
All villages[c]	28	40	8	56	6	32	3

[a] Data from two Indian villages not available. [b] Includes hired labor from outside the village. [c] Data from two Thai villages not available.

Table 9. Percent of farms reporting increase in pre-harvest labor requirement and area in modern varieties, 1971−72.

labor increase[a]	villages (no.)	rice area (%) in modern varieties
Lfl − Lhl	10	88
Lfl − Shl	2	48
Sfl − Lhl	8	64
Sfl − Shl	8	58

[a] fl = family labor; hl = hired labor; L = large percent of farms ($\geqslant$ 40%) reporting increase; S = small percent change (< 40%) reporting increase; from prior to the introduction of modern varieties to the time of the survey.

A large portion of farmers reported an increase in the use of family or hired labor following the adoption of modern rice varieties (Table 8). Villages with a high proportion of farms reporting an increase in pre-harvest labor requirements tended to have a high portion of their rice area planted to modern varieties (Table 9).

The increase in pre-harvest labor requirement was related to the adoption of other pre-harvest improved practices (Table 10). Villages with a high portion of farms reporting a large increase in labor requirements also had a high percentage of farmers reporting the adoption of

Table 10. Change in pre-harvest labor requirement and adoption of specified improved practices following adoption of modern varieties, 1971–72.

labor change[a]	villages (no.)	adopters (%) of				
		fertilizer	insecticide	straight-row planting	herbicide	tractors
Lfl – Lhl	10	50	52	23	33	33
Lfl – Shl	2	42	35	1	2	40
Sfl – Lhl	8	46	43	14	5	14
Sfl – Shl	8	12	13	10	7	13

[a] As defined in Table 9.

fertilizer use, insecticide application, and straight-row planting. Surprisingly, these same villages had a large percent adoption of herbicides and tractors with the adoption of modern varieties, indicating that the labor-displacing effects the labor-saving practices had were more than offset by the increased labor requirement of the pre-harvest labor tasks (including some of those not mentioned in Table 9, such as hand weeding and water management).

FARM SIZE AND NEW TECHNOLOGY

This section examines the relationship between farm size and selected factors relating to the adoption of new varieties, constraints to input use, and the benefits from the new rice technology. Farm size can be important in both a relative and an absolute sense. For example, a close association between absolute farm size and labor saving or labor using technology is apparent from Table 11 Rotary and hand weeding are less commonly practiced on large farms, while herbicides were rarely used on the sample farms 1 hectare or smaller. Tractors and threshers were more common on the larger farms. By contrast, yield increasing technology – fertilizers, insecticides, and modern varieties – were widely used on all farms regardless of size. Small farms are generally expected to have an ample supply and low opportunity cost for family labor which leads to intensive cultivation and hence higher yields than on large farms. But this labor advantage may be offset by the relative disadvantage of the small farmer in obtaining the necessary inputs. The present hypothesis postulates that access to and benefits from the new technology are likely to be related to the relative size of the farm within the village.

Table 11. Use of specified practices and farm size, 1971–72.

	farms (%) using		
	less 1 ha	1–3 ha	over 3 ha
Modern varieties			
Wet	84	86	93
Dry	89	91	89
Fertilizer			
Wet	76	75	82
Dry	84	83	85
Insecticide	79	81	83
Herbicide	6	20	29
Hand weeding	82	83	87
Rotary weeding	3	20	37
Tractors	13	41	57
Mechanical thresher	36	43	63

To make relative comparisons of farm size among villages, farms were classified into large or small farms on the basis of the median of farm size within each village. Then the Gini coefficient was computed to reflect the degree of equity in the distribution of operating units in each village. This coefficient was computed by first estimating the percentage of farms and the percentage of total land area for each of seven farm size categories ranging from small operating units (less than 0.41 ha) to large (over 3.1 ha). The Lorenz curve for the two villages with the highest and lowest Gini coefficients is shown in Figure 2. If all of the operating units were of equal size, then the Gini coefficient would be zero. Alternatively, if the bulk of the land were operated as a few very large units, but there were many small holdings, the coefficient would approach 1 as a maximum.

The effect of relative farm size on selected factors within the low and high ranges of the Gini coefficient was examined. Farm size was expected to become a significant factor only in those villages with relatively high Gini coefficients, that is, with a relatively unequitable distribution of land among the operating units.

The data were limited, not only in terms of villages, but also in terms of the variables that would lend themselves to this type of analysis. Ideally there should be quantitative data on farm income and resource

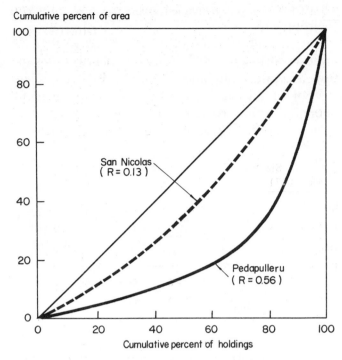

Cumulative percent of area

Cumulative percent of holdings

Fig. 2. Lorenz curves showing percent distribution of holdings for villages having the highest and lowest of Gini ratios.

use for each farm sample. Instead the study was limited primarily to qualitative variables with respect to adoption, constraints, and benefits from the new technology.

In summary, the analytical framework consisted of a hierarchichal classification in which relative farm size was examined as it related to other factors, such as the adoption of modern varieties, for villages grouped according to the level of the Gini coefficient. The farm samples were pooled within each village group to derive two-way classification tables. Chi square was used to test the significance of the relationship between farm size and selected factors.

Farm size and tenure status. The farm size distribution and tenure pattern in the various study areas tell much about the way in which the benefits of the new technology are likely to be distributed. While there are differences in size distribution and tenure status among villages in each of the study areas, the major contrast is found among study areas. Table 12 lists 16 villages, one from each study area, and one additional village each from Uttar Pradesh and East and West Java where the study villages are far apart and represent distinctly different environments.

The 16 villages are ranked according to their Gini coefficients. The highest coefficient is 0.56 for Pedapulleru, India and the lowest 0.13 for San Nicolas, Philippines (Fig. 2). In Pedapulleru approximately 20 percent of the largest farmers operate 60 percent of the land. While operating units are fairly uniform in size in many of the Philippine villages, the Philippine study areas had the highest rate of tenancy. The

Table 12. Size distribution and tenure of operating farm units in selected study villages, 1971—72.

location	Gini ratio	pure owners (%)	pure tenants (%)	farm size (ha)	operating units (%)		
					less than 1 ha	1−4 ha	above 4 ha
Pedapulleru, India	0.56	41	32	4.7	16	49	35
Manmalai, India	0.52	96	2	1.8	41	50	9
Tarna, India	0.42	100	0	1.2	37	58	5
Aroop, Pakistan[a]	0.38	65	4	6.7	1	43	56
Marcos, Philippines	0.38	14	86	1.5	39	56	5
Cidahu, Indonesia	0.36	90	1	0.5	82	18	0
Hosahally, India	0.34	n.a.	n.a.	4.8	7	40	53
Kandarpur, India	0.32	49	9	0.6	79	21	0
Kahuman, Indonesia	0.30	67	2	0.6	81	19	0
Beynte Nuwebe, Philippines	0.28	8	92	1.7	15	84	1
D. Vijaypur, India	0.28	100	0	6.0	0	39	61
Bulucaon, Philippines	0.25	6	91	2.0	0	100	0
Sidomulyo, Indonesia	0.25	86	7	0.5	100	0	0
Salor, Malaysia	0.24	58	11	0.9	66	34	0
Rai Rot, Thailand	0.18	75	6	7.0	0	17	83
San Nicolas, Philippines	0.13	16	56	2.5	0	92	8
Village average					35	45	20
Southeast Asia − 1960[b]					49	36	15

[a]Not based upon a random sample, but a sample of adopters only. The Gini ratio may be biased downward and the average farm size biased upward.
[b]Based upon Country Census of Agriculture, 1960 as reported in the FAO Yearbook.

landowners in these villages would be the major beneficiaries from gains in productivity and growth in income. For example, in Beynte Nuwebe, Philippines five individuals owning 20 hectares or more account for 80 percent of the land.

There appeared to be no relationship between the degree of equity in the size distribution of operating units and the village average size of farm. For example, the Gini coefficient was relatively high when the average farm size was large in Aroop, Pakistan, and small when average farm size was small in Cidahu, West Java. In Rai Rot, Thailand, on the other hand, the coefficient was low despite the large average farm size.

Many factors useful in a comparison of the villages are not revealed by the figures in Table 12. For example, Kandarpur in Orissa and Kahuman in Central Java have similar farm size and distribution of holdings. But there the similarity ends. Kandarpur is located in one of the poorer rice growing areas of India. Farms are not only small but highly fragmented. Despite the proximity of the Indian Government's Central Rice Research Institute to the village, local government efforts to support agriculture have been inadequate. By contrast, Kahuman is located in one of the most progressive districts of Indonesia and has been the beneficiary of major government programs to increase agricultural production.

Farm size and the introduction of modern varieties. Farmers in each village were asked in what year they first planted any of the modern varieties (wet or dry season). Taking the first year of adoption in each village as the base year, the cumulative frequency distributions of adoption for four village groupings were plotted (Fig. 3).

Group I consists of only one village, Pedapulleru, India, which was singled out and treated separately in this and subsequent analyses. It is unique among the study villages (although undoubtedly not unique in Asia) in that there was a strong interaction between farm size and a number of factors relating to the introduction of the modern rice technology.

Group II consists of 10 villages in India and Pakistan (excluding three villages for which data were not available). The remaining villages in Southeast Asia were divided into two groups: Group III with six villages with Gini ratios 0.3 or above and Group IV with 10 villages with Gini ratios below 0.3. (Data were not available for the two Malaysian villages.)[2]

The relationship between farm size and adoption of modern rice varieties was most striking in Pedapulleru, India where over 90 percent of the large farms but less than half of the small farms had planted new

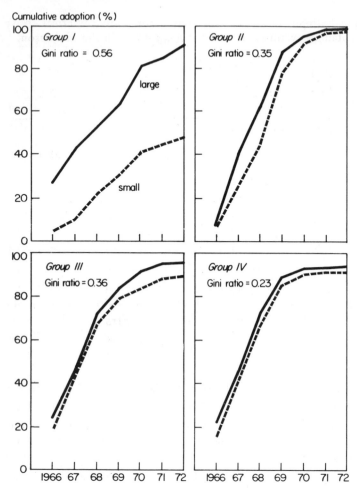

Fig. 3. Gini coefficient, farm size, and year of adoption of modern varieties.

varieties. Small farmers in Group II lagged behind the large farmers at the start, but caught up rapidly in the fourth and fifth year. In group III small farms seem to have lagged in percentage adoption after the third year. The degree of equity in operational farm units clearly is not the only factor influencing the lag in adoption by small farms.

[2]For Fig. 3 the list of villages by group are as follows: Group I – Pedapulleru, India; Group II – Kandarpur, Korpada, Gajanur, Hosahally, Ashoknagar, Tarna, Barain, D. Vijaypur in India and Aroop, Maraliwala in Pakistan; Group III – Marcos, Tab-ang, Sinayawan in the Philippines, and Cidahu, Kahuman, Nganjat in Indonesia; Group IV – Malimba, San Nicolas, Canipa, Bulucaon, Capayuran, and Beynte Nuwebe in the Philippines; Sidomulyo, Pluneng in Indonesia, and Nong Sarai, Rai Rot in Thailand.

Table 13. Relationship between Gini coefficient and proportion of farmers reporting difficulty in obtaining fertilizer or credit as a constraint in the wet season.

village group	villages (no.)	Gini coefficient	farmers who reported constraint (%)	farmers (%) reporting constraint by farm size		Chi-square significance level
				small	large	
Fertilizer						
I	1	.56	54	63	37	.001
II	3	.38	71	65	35	.001
III	6	.27	42	48	52	n.s.
Credit						
I	1	.56	11	85	15	.01
II	3	.38	70	60	40	.01
III	6	.27	38	52	48	n.s.

[a]I = Pedapulleru in India; II = Tarna; Barain, D. Vijaypur in India; III = Malimba, Capayuran, Beynte Nuwebe, Sinayawan, in the Philippines, Pluneng in Java, and Meranti in Malaysia.

Farm size and yield constraints. The relationship between farm size and yield of the modern varieties followed no consistent pattern among the villages. Many factors influenced yield, and these factors may be positively or negatively related to farm size, or may be unrelated to farm size. For example, the absolute area planted to modern varieties is negatively correlated with yield in many situations, since the smaller area frequently receives a heavier input of both labor and capital and because rice responds well to intensive care. However, in this analysis the major concern is with the negative consequences of correlation between farm size and factors influencing yield, such as access to inputs.

Farmers were asked whether they experienced difficulty in obtaining fertilizer or credit. In many villages the number of farmers reporting difficulty was low. This was due in part to the fact that the villages surveyed were generally well situated with respect to input supplies. Therefore, only those villages where at least 20 percent of the farmers reported difficulty in obtaining fertilizer or credit were included in the analysis discussed below.

Following the previous pattern, farms were grouped according to the level of the Gini coefficient, singling out Pedapulleru (Group I) from the other villages (Table 13). Group II consists of the three villages in

Uttar Pradesh, all of which reported a serious problem in obtaining these inputs. Group III consists of villages from Southeast Asia only one of which had a Gini coefficient above 0.3.

There was a significant relationship between the level of the Gini coefficient and the effect of farm size in obtaining inputs (Table 13). The problems relative to farm size appear to occur more in South Asia than in Southeast Asia.

Farm size and benefits. Farmers were asked if their profits from rice and their general level of living had increased in the period following the introduction of modern varieties in their village. They were also asked whether the change in the level of living was due to increased rice profits, and a majority of those who reported a higher level of living answered yes. In 15 villages between 20 and 80 percent of the farmers reported a higher profit from rice or a higher level of living. Data from these villages were further analyzed.

Table 14. Relationship between Gini coefficient and percent of farmers reporting increase in profit from rice and level of living.

village group[a]	villages (no.)	Gini coefficient	farmers reporting increase (%)	farmers (%) reporting increase in profit by farm size		Chi-square significance level
				small farm	large farm	
Profit from rice						
I	1	.56	34	26	74	001
II	2	.38	75	43	57	.05
III	5	.38	52	49	51	n.s.
IV	7	.24	52	51	49	n.s.
Level of living						
I	1	.56	28	23	74	.001
II	2	.38	48	35	65	.01
III	5	.38	38	44	56	.10
IV	7	.24	45	50	50	n.s.

[a] I = Pedapulleru in India; II = Kandarpur, Barain in India; III = Marcos, Tab-ang, Sinayawan in the Philippines and Cidahu, Nganjat in Indonesia; IV = Malimba, Canipa, Bulucaon, Beynte Nuwebe in the Philippines; Rai Rot, Nong Sarai in Thailand, and Meranti in Malaysia.

Villages were grouped following the previous pattern, with Group I and II representing South Asia, and Group III and IV (divided into high and low Gini coefficient levels) Southeast Asia (Table 14).

The percentage of farmers who reported an increase in profits from rice tended to be higher than the percentage who reported a higher level of living. There was a distinct difference between Groups II and III despite identical Gini coefficients, indicating that the level of the Gini coefficient is not in itself an adequate indicator of the importance of farm size.

SUMMARY AND CONCLUSIONS
In identifying some of the factors that may account for the differences among villages in the adoption of modern varieties and the yields obtained from these new varieties, it was first necessary to describe the factors that appeared to be critical in explaining the differences. Then a regression model could be developed to quantify these relationships. The reader will gain more insight into the problems by reading the individual study papers rather than studying the regressions. However, the regression analysis does emphasize the dominant role of environment and irrigation in determining the level of nitrogen application and hence establishing a yield potential for a given area.

In the southern Philippines, fertilizer inputs were extremely low despite the universal adoption of modern varieties. In the flood plains of eastern India the new varieties had not been widely adopted, particularly in the wet season, because their performance was not equal to that of available local varieties. These areas appear to need more intensive farm level investigation by both agricultural and social scientists to obtain a clearer identification of the physical and socio-economic constraints. Such an investigation should point toward the development of a strategy or sequence of steps which could be systematically followed to raise the production potential in some of the less productive areas.

The adoption and increased use of yield-increasing practices – fertilizers, insecticides, etc. – is closely associated with the adoption of modern varieties. In contrast, the adoption of labor-saving technology – herbicides, tractors, etc. – has been far more location-specific, and in many of the study villages had not occurred at all. The villages where labor saving technology had been most widely adopted since the introduction of modern varieties also reported the largest number of farmers with increased employment of family and hired labor. Thus, any savings in labor appears to have been more than offset by increased labor requirements due to the new technology.

There has been much discussion in the literature about the relationship between farm size and the use of modern technology. This study distinguished between relative and absolute farm size, and hypothesized that within the village relative farm size would significantly affect access to and benefits of the new rice technology only where there was a comparatively unequitable distribution in size of farm operating units. For each village a Gini coefficient was computed as a measure of the degree of equity in the distribution of land. The results suggest that not only the equity in the distribution of operating units, but also the socio-economic structure within the village, influence the degree of acceptance of new technology among large and small farmers. In this context, there was a stronger relationship between farm size and new technology in South Asia than in Southeast Asia even in those villages where the Gini coefficients were comparable. There was a high rate of tenancy in all of the surveyed villages in the Philippines, where the equity issue was clearly related to the tenure structure and not to farm size.

The question is frequently raised as to the degree that the new rice technology aggravates the inequity in income distribution. Clearly a technology that requires more cash inputs will tend to reinforce this inequity in some of the study villages. Technological innovations cannot be expected to correct serious inequities in access to and benefits from resources. One mitigating step that can be taken is for agricultural scientists to build more resistance to pests and pathogens and tolerance to adverse growing conditions into the variety itself and thus reduce cash requirements, particularly for agricultural chemicals. Increasing emphasis is being given to this problem in rice research.

THE STUDY AREAS

INDIA

West Godavari, Andhra Pradesh

G. Parthasarathy

The shift to modern varieties has been neither dramatic nor universal. The most severe constraints to adoption are the difficulties in water management in the wet season and the widespread concern about pests and diseases. The bias of the new technology in favor of owners, and the unfavorable position of small owners and tenants in the input, credit, and factor markets have increased the existing inequalities of income.

FOR DECADES THE DELTA FARMERS of West Godavari District have been counted among India's most progressive rice farming communities. Farm management studies conducted during the late 1950's and early 1960's show that they were quick to adopt what they found suitable and profitable from the various rural development programs mounted in the district — and the label "progressive" which was attached to the district ensured that it received rather more than the usual amount of program attention.

Of special note in this respect was the selection of West Godavari as one of the original six districts included in the Intensive Agricultural District Program by the government of India and the Ford Foundation in 1961/62. The program was one of the first attempts in India to raise farm productivity by concentrating attention on the individual farm and devising for it a "package" of inputs and practices including good quality, treated seed of improved local varieties, the use of chemical

G. Parthasarathy is the head of the Department of Cooperation and Applied Economics Andhra University, Waltair, Andhra Pradesh.

The author wishes to acknowledge the help extended by N. Bhaskara Reddy, P. Viswanatha-Raju, and C. Sambamurthy who conducted the field investigations; D. S. Prasad and P. Rajith Kumar who helped in analyzing the data; L. Bullayya, the Vice Chancellor of Andhra University who took keen interest in the project and provided the necessary facilities and of course the farmer-participants of Pedapulleru village for their cooperation.

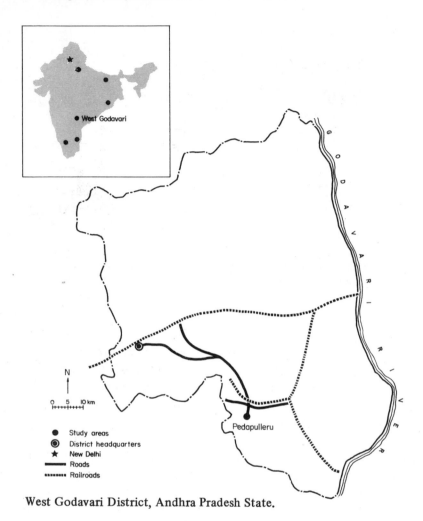

West Godavari District, Andhra Pradesh State.

fertilizer based on soil testing for individual farms, and the use of insecticides and other plant protection measures. Between 1961/62 and 1964/65, the quantity of fertilizers used in the district tripled and there were impressive gains in the use of treated seed and other ingredients of the package. As a result, rice yields rose significantly: the two main local varieties used (SLO13 and SLO19) gave around 3 t/ha and over 4 t/ha was obtained with the varieties introduced after 1965.

West Godavari farmers were well prepared for the introduction of dwarf high-yielding modern rices which came through the High Yielding Varieties Program (HYVP) in 1965/66. By this time many delta farmers

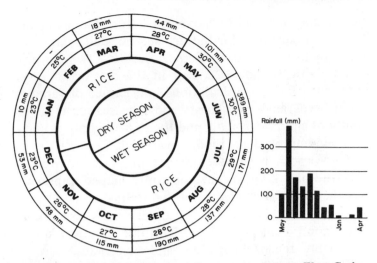

Average monthly rainfall and minimum temperature, West Godavari (Maruteru Experiment Station, 1967-1971), Andhra Pradesh, India.

were not only progressive but also rather prosperous, which insured considerable interest in the new package based on the high potential yields of the modern varieties. But at the same time, farmers could afford to be cautious and selective over the offerings of the HYVP because they were obtaining fairly high yields in the wet season with Mashuri, on which much less fertilizer was usually applied, and which was well adapted to the delta irrigation system and the seasonal cropping pattern of the district.

Rice farming in the delta is dominated by the canal irrigation system and the seasonal distribution of rainfall. Both are decisive influences on the timing of farm operations and on the area that can be planted to rice in the dry season. The improved local varieties are better suited to these conditions than are the modern varieties presently available. For instance, the wet-season crop is planted in June–July and modern varieties such as IR8 are mature and ready for harvest in September–October, a period of heavy rainfall, while Mashuri matures in late November and early December when rainfall is much lower. In consequence, IR8 and other modern varieties are not popular in the wet season. Of the varieties released since 1965 only Mashuri is gaining ground. The agricultural administration is also encouraging the use of Mashuri in the wet season and has included it under the state's HYVP. Mashuri is considered a modern variety throughout this paper.

It is a different matter in the dry season (December–April). Short duration modern varieties have an advantage over improved local varieties in that they can be harvested before the heavy rains start again in May. Consequently, for the dry season, delta farmers are mainly interested in the available modern varieties – IR 8, Jaya, Ratna, and more recently, IR 20 and IR 22. But in the dry season several other factors enter into farmers' calculations and choice of varieties: availability of water, experience with pests and diseases, costs of production, availability of inputs and credit, and the expected prices and price differences between improved and modern varieties.

The various rural development programs in West Godavari district over the past 20 years have not only helped improve farm production but they have also set up and maintained a sound rural infrastructure. Most villages, have reasonably good access to markets, credit, and inputs, good contact with agricultural administration and extension, reasonably reliable irrigation, and electricity.

The village. The environmental limitations, both physical and institutional, to the adoption of modern varieties in the delta are fairly well understood at a general level, but there is still need for studies in detail in specific situations and environments. We examined the adoption record of different classes of farmers in one village. While the HYVP is available to all farmers in theory, certain classes are found to be largely excluded in practice due to socio-economic rigidities in the village.

Pedapulleru village in Akividu block was chosen as the study site as it is fairly typical of the delta villages which have reasonably good resources for growing modern varieties of rice. Its rice fields are reasonably well drained and the irrigation system is dependable. It has a monoculture rice economy. Modern varieties have been grown in both seasons since 1965/66. Pedapulleru is unexceptional and should not be regarded as a special case among delta villages.

Like many delta villages, Pedapulleru has good road access to trading and administration centers in the vicinity. An all-weather road reaches into the village. Quite a few villagers own motor scooters, three cycle rickshaws are available to take villagers to and from nearby towns, and there are two shops where bicycles can be rented by the hour. The administrative headquarters for the block is at Akividu about 6 kilometers away. There is a seed farm at Undi about 3 kilometers away, and a soil testing laboratory at Tadepalligudem some 30 kilometers away. A village-level worker lives in the village and is responsible for explaining and facilitating the various government rural services and programs.

The Pedapulleru co-operative credit **society** has a long and sound history. It supplies fertilizers and insecticides and in 1967 it opened a rice mill which acts as a buying agent for the Food Corporation of India. There is also a small privately owned mill which processes rice retained in the village for consumption. Pedapulleru has its own community center with a radio, and several households have their own radios — a few even have telephone connections. Telegu and English language newspapers are delivered regularly to several households. The village is no isolated backwater, and at least the better-off households are well aware of and interested in the world beyond.

The sample. All 185 farm households in Pedapulleru were included in the study so no further sampling procedure was necessary. Interviews were conducted in June and July 1972 after an earlier survey which prepared the ground and collected basic information about the farm population (Table 1).

Owner-operators formed the largest block in the village: 42 percent of all farmers were in this category and they farmed 45 percent of the rice land (Tables 2 and 3). If we include with these, the landowners who either leased out part of their holdings or added to their operational holding by leasing extra land, we embrace two-thirds of all farm households and as much as 85 percent of all farm land. A third of the farm households were pure-tenants who cultivated just over 15 percent of the land.

While the average farm household operated 4.8 hectares, three quarters of all farm households operated less than this. The average landowner (including owner-rentiers and owner-tenants) operated with 6 hectares, while the average pure tenant worked only 2.4 hectares. Landowners operated nearly 90 percent of the farms larger than 4.8 hectares. The largest farm in the village comprised 34.5 hectares and three others were over 30 hectares; all were farmed by landowners. The largest pure-tenant farm was just over 8 hectares. At the other end of the range there were 39 farms under 1 hectare, only seven of which were operated by pure tenants; and to go lower still, four farms were under 0.2 hectare and only one of these was cultivated by a pure tenant.

The areas referred to are operational holdings and as this is a well-irrigated monoculture village, they are close to the areas actually planted to rice in the wet season. The dry-season rice plantings were considerably lower on most farms, however. In the agricultural year studied, one-third less land was sown in the dry season than in the wet season, and 17 percent of the farmers who had planted rice in the wet season were unable to grow a dry-season crop (Table 4).

Table 1. Characteristics of Pedapulleru farms.

farms	
farms (no.)	185
growing rice (no.)	
wet season	185
dry season	151
avg size (ha)	4.7
avg size of farm household	5
cropping	
avg rice area (ha)	
wet season	4.4
dry season	3.8
irrigation (%)	
wet season	100
dry season	100
area double cropped in 1971/72 (%)	66
principal form of irrigation	canal
modern varieties	
farmers planting in 1971/72 (%)	
wet season	12
dry season	45
area planted in 1971/72 (%)	
wet season	9
dry season	44
year of greatest adoption	
farms over 6 ha	1966
farms between 4 and 6 ha	1969
farms under 4 ha	1970

ADOPTION OF MODERN RICE VARIETIES

Modern rice varieties were introduced into the village through the HYVP in the dry season of 1965/66. Taichung Native 1 was the first modern variety released, but it was replaced during the following year with IR8 which formed the backbone of the program until 1969/70 when Jaya and Ratna were made available. In 1970/71 small areas were planted to IR20 and IR22.

Table 2. Distribution of farms by size and tenancy 1971/72.

farm size[a] (ha)	farmers[b] (no.)				
	all farms	owner-operators	pure tenants	owner-rentiers	owner-tenants
wet season					
below 2	69	36	29	1	3
2 – 4	47	13	21	2	11
4 – 6	20	6	5	2	7
over 6	46	21	5	6	14
total	182	76	60	11	35
dry season					
below 2	55	27	24	1	3
2 – 4	34	9	14	0	11
4 – 6	18	4	5	2	7
over 6	44	21	5	6	12
total	151	61	48	9	33

[a] Operational holding, not area planted in each season. [b] Who planted rice in the relevant season.

None of the modern varieties met with much favorable response from farmers in the wet season (Table 5). Most farmers have been reluctant even to experiment with them — by 1971/72 only a quarter of the Pedapulleru farmers had ever planted any modern variety in the wet season. Furthermore, only 12 percent were growing modern varieties in 1971 and most of these farmers were growing Mashuri rather than IR8 or similar modern varieties. SLO 13, an improved local variety, accounted for about 85 percent of the wet-season rice area. It was not responsive to fertilizer, but nonetheless yielded around 3 t/ha. Mashuri was next in importance. It was responsive up to about 75 kg/ha N and yielded over 4 t/ha. The other modern varieties IR8, IR5, Jaya, and Ratna together accounted for less than 1 percent of the total wet-season rice area.

Since the modern varieties planted in the wet season mature during the period of heavy rainfall, Pedapulleru farmers lost interest in them. The longer duration Mashuri was still too new to be regarded as an

Table 3. Distribution of land by farm size and tenancy 1971/72.

farm size (ha)	area[a] (ha)				
	all farms	owner-operators	pure tenants	owner-rentiers	owner-tenants
wet season					
below 2	71	32	35	b	4
2 – 4	123	36	53	4	30
4 – 6	94	29	23	9	34
over 6	582	291	33	91	167
total	870	388	143	104	235
dry season					
below 2	52	20	28	b	4
2 – 4	76	20	32	0	24
4 – 6	69	17	21	9	22
over 6	378	196	24	71	87
total	575	253	105	80	137

[a] All land sown to rice in the relevant season. [b] Less than 1 ha.

established variety and was grown mainly by the larger farmers, but it promised to become a major wet-season variety. It gave about 1 t/ha more than the existing major variety; it required relatively little fertilizer at least in comparison with the modern varieties such as IR 8; and it was classified as a fine grain.

Modern varieties have become much more important in the dry season. Although the dry-season rice area was only about two-thirds of the wet-season area in 1971/72, the area planted to modern varieties in the dry season was three times larger. And three times as many farmers were growing modern varieties. Half the area of modern varieties in the dry season was planted to Jaya, a quarter to IR 8, 9 percent to Mashuri, and most of the rest to Ratna, IR 20, and IR 22. Altogether, about 45 percent of the Pedapulleru farmers cultivated modern varieties in the 1971/72 dry season, and these varieties accounted for about 44 percent of the rice area. While the short duration of the modern varieties counted against their use in the wet season, it was a considerable advantage in the dry season.

The use of modern varieties in 1971/72 is associated with farm size in both seasons, although the association is more marked in the wet season when there was very little adoption by farmers with less than 4

Table 4. Rice planting in the wet and dry seasons 1971/72.

	farmers not planting a dry season crop (%)	wet season rice area not replanted with dry-season rice (%)
	by tenancy group	
owner-operators	20	35
owner-rentiers	18	23
owner-tenants	6	42
pure tenants	20	26
	by farm size groups	
below 2 ha	20	25
2 – 4 ha	28	38
4 – 6 ha	10	28
over 6 ha	4	35
all farms	17	34

hectares. This can be seen clearly in Table 5 which presents the data for the two large tenancy groups in the village, the owner-operators and pure tenants. The general picture does not change if owner-rentiers and owner-tenants are included.

Owner-operators and pure tenants also differed in adoption. In the wet season, 7% of the pure tenants and 13% of the owner-operators cultivated modern varieties, and in the dry season, 31% and 44% respectively, did.

Both these associations are reflected in the percentage of the total rice area planted to modern varieties. But the association between tenure and the extent of adoption, when separated from the influence of size, is not statistically significant. The relations of size to extent of adoption is not clearly inverse, but owner-operators above 6 hectares have perceptibly higher rates of adoption as measured by numbers as well as area.

Of the farmers cultivating modern varieties, during the wet season only 18 percent had made a complete switch, that is, planted these varieties only. But in the dry season, half the adoptors grew the modern varieties exclusively. Complete adoption, in the area sense, was more frequent on farms under 4 hectares (80 percent of adoptors in both

Table 5. Planting of modern rice varieties, 1971/72.

size of holding (ha)	farmers growing modern varieties (%)			rice area planted to modern varieties (%)			
	owner-operators[a]	pure tenants[b]	all farms[c]	owner-operators	pure tenants	all farms	farms (no.)
wet season[d]							
over 6 ha	33	20	31	14	19	14	26
4 – 6 ha	17	20	18	11	17	14	11
2 – 4 ha	0	5	3	0	2	1	34
under 2 ha	6	3	5	5	5	5	65
all farms	13	7	10	12	9	11	136
dry season[e]							
over 6 ha	71	20	62	53	25	50	26
4 – 6 ha	0	40	22	0	25	14	9
2 – 4 ha	33	36	35	29	28	28	23
under 2 ha	33	29	31	36	28	31	51
all farms	44	31	39	46	26	40	109

[a]76 in wet season and 61 in dry season. [b]60 in wet season and 48 in dry season. [c]Includes only farms of owner-operators and pure tenants. [d]Mashuri accounted for 88% of the area sown to modern varieties. [e]Based on area sown: Jaya, 49%; IR8, 24%; Ratna, 15%; Mashuri, 9%; others (including IR20 and IR22), 3%.

seasons) than on the larger farms (24 percent). There was no marked difference between owners and tenants in this respect. While the larger farmers were more likely to be adoptors than their smaller neighbors, the adoptors among the smaller farmers were more likely to switch completely to modern varieties.

A stable and growing group of adoptors of modern varieties did not exist in the village. Many more farmers had experimented with modern varieties in one or more past seasons than were cultivating them in 1971/72. Farmers regarded modern varieties as more risky than improved local varieties; they did not yet consider them dependable substitutes.

Changes in the use of inputs. Changes in rice farming in Pedapulleru village can be examined from two points of view: (1) change over time as indicated by the position in 1971/72 compared with the position prior to the HYVP, or (2) the new technology associated directly with the HYVP as indicated by the area in modern varieties compared with the area still in local varieties. The second approach obviates the need for historical data and reliance on respondents' memories, but it could underestimate the overall impact of the HYVP on the farm enterprise in its entirety. Both procedures are used below, depending on purpose and the availability of data.

Organic fertilizers had been virtually replaced by inorganic fertilizers in the delta well before 1965/66 when the HYVP got under way. During the 1971/72 wet season, 57 percent of the Pedapulleru farmers applied inorganic fertilizers. A few small farmers were using organic fertilizers.

Although inorganic fertilizers were accepted and widely used where appropriate, farmers differed markedly in the quantities applied and in their use of the three components nitrogen, phosphorus, and potassium. Nitrogen was almost universally applied on improved local and modern varieties in both seasons (Table 6). Most farmers applied phosphorus to both variety types in the dry season and to modern varieties in the wet season. Few farmers used potassium, but those who did used it mainly in the dry season. In general phosphorus and potassium were more commonly applied in the dry season and on modern varieties.

Fertilizer recommendations were based on crop type and soil type (Table 7). On the average, nitrogen recommendations were followed on modern varieties in each season and exceeded on improved local varieties. The recommendations for phosphorus were higher than for nitrogen for both crop types in the wet season and for local varieties in the dry season, but the average use of phosphorus was low in both seasons,

Table 6. Use of inorganic fertilizers 1971/72.

variety	farmers using (%)		
	N	P_2O_5	K_2O
	wet season		
improved local	92	29	5
modern	100	77	5
	dry season		
improved local	100	87	15
modern	100	96	26

particularly in the wet season. The farmers were even less inclined to use potassium except to a limited extent on modern varieties in the dry season.

Farmers were using more fertilizer on modern varieties than on local varieties, however, and in the dry season many farmers exceeded the recommended levels and were able to report a favorable yield response at least up to 150 kg/ha N. Many farmers exceeded the recommended levels for modern varieties in the wet season, too, but reported that the results were not favorable. A large majority of farmers exceeded the recommendations for local varieties in the wet season and they also reported unfavorable results.

Farm size did not influence the level of use of nitrogen on modern varieties, but the use of phosphorus and potassium tended to increase

Table 7. Average quantities of fertilizer used and recommended applications[a] (kg/ha).

variety type	recommended rate[a] (kg/ha)			actual use (kg/ha)		
	N	P_2O_5	K_2O	N	P_2O_5	K_2O
	wet season					
improved local	17-22	34-67	17	37	8	[b]
modern	56-79	67-90	34	64	17	[b]
	dry season					
improved local	45-67	56-90	17	79	32	3
modern	90-135	67-90	34	121	52	12

[a] Specific recommendations are based on soil type. [b] Less than 1 kg/ha.

with farm size. The use of nitrogen did not differ significantly between tenancy groups, but tenants used less phosphorus and potassium than owners. Even after many years of exposure to inorganic fertilizers and new rice varieties, a marked lag in adoption existed between big and small, and owner and tenant farmers.

A marked increase in the proportion of farmers using pesticides since 1965/66 was directly related to the HYVP:

	1965/66	*1971/72*
wet season	15%	19%
dry season	40%	100%

Farmers did not consider pesticides necessary on local varieties in the wet season, but three-fourths of the farmers who grew modern varieties used them in the 1971/72 wet season. In the dry season the use of pesticides was almost universal for both modern and local varieties.

An examination of pesticide use in the dry season shows that small farmers and tenant farmers lag behind in the year of first use of pesticides, and in the quantities used per hectare — on local and modern varieties. While pesticides were used on all rice crops, considerably higher doses were applied to modern varieties as shown by the following values for 1971/72.

	modern varieties	*local varieties*
wet season	Rs 27/ha	Rs 3/ha
dry season	Rs 89/ha	Rs 42/ha

As might be expected the sprayer was a fairly common item of equipment particularly in the dry season. The use of sprayers follows fairly closely the adoption of pesticides. Only about half the farmers who reported using sprayers owned their own equipment, however. The rest relied on hiring and custom service.

The use of the tractor for plowing and threshing began before the HYVP, but the practice increased since 1965/66 and was common in 1971/72. In these 2 years the proportion of farmers plowing by tractor was:

	1965/66	*1971/72*
wet season	58%	84%
dry season	62%	92%

The proportion using tractors for threshing was:

	1965/66	*1971/72*
wet season	67%	92%
dry season	67%	97%

The land mortgage banks provided liberal loans to farmers for purchasing tractors, and several of the bigger farmers in Pedapulleru had bought tractors before 1965/66. But since then more and more farmers from all groups dispensed with bullocks and had their land plowed and their harvest threshed on contract. In 1971/72 tractor plowing was considered to be cheaper than bullock plowing — Rs 75/ha compared with Rs 86/ha; but tractor threshing at Rs 37/ha was more expensive than the Rs 30/ha needed for threshing by bullock and human labor.

Because of the increased use of the tractor, fewer farmers owned plow cattle and bullock carts. In 1971/72 only 42 percent of the Pedapulleru farmers owned plow cattle. Even among the landowners the number owning plow cattle had halved since 1965/66, and among tenant farmers it had fallen by three quarters. Tractors were used increasingly to cart manure to the fields and produce to the village. Only 10 percent of the farmers still owned bullock carts in 1971/72. These changes in the structure of farm assets have made an increasing proportion of farmers dependent on the tractor hire market.

The Archmedian screw is a metal cylinder with a rotating iron rod used to lift water from field irrigation channels onto rice fields. The equipment is hand operated. It was widely used in 1965/66 and by 1971/72 nearly all farmers used it in both seasons. As with sprayers and tractors, not all users owned their own equipment. About half the users were also owners of Archmedian screws, and this group included about 20 percent of the pure tenants. Hiring of equipment and custom service was common in this practice, too.

Studies conducted in the delta region in 1968/69 by the Agroeconomic Research Centre, Andhra University, Waltair show that the cultivation of modern varieties requires about one-fifth more man-days of labor per hectare than the cultivation of local varieties:

	modern varieties	*local varieties*
wet season	164	136
dry season	220	191

The Pedapulleru farmers were asked if they had used more hired labor per hectare in the cultivation of modern varieties compared with local varieties. Most reported that they did (Table 8). Half the farmers also reported increases in hired labor for local varieties in the dry season where they were using fertilizers and pesticides. For modern varieties, the main increases were in the application of fertilizers and pesticides, and in harvesting, carting, and threshing. Some farmers reported a decrease in the use of hired labor in plowing operations (for both local and modern varieties). This reflects the increased use of tractors and custom plowing in recent years. These results were confirmed by interviews conducted with a sample of 15 landless laborers.

Although modern varieties require more labor, the impact on employment depends on the area planted to modern varieties. In Pedapulleru less than a quarter of the aggregate rice area in the wet and dry seasons was planted to modern varieties in 1971/72. Increased demand for laborers' services is confined to this area. No more than a 4-percent increase in overall employment can be attributed to the shift to modern varieties in this village.

The shift to modern varieties required an increase in the use of purchased inputs — fertilizers, pesticides, and labor. For many farmers

Table 8. Change in the use of hired labor.

| | farmers (%) reporting increase | | | |
| farm operation | modern variety area | | local variety area | |
	wet season	dry season	wet season	dry season
nursery	14	2	0	0
plowing	−9[a]	−13	−5	−5
transplanting	32	19	0	0
weeding	9	7	0	0
fertilizer application	96	87	25	49
pesticide application	91	87	7	48
harvesting	73	63	0	2
threshing	64	44	−1	−1
transporting	68	44	0	3

[a] The minus indicates a reported decrease by that proportion of farmers.

this increased the need for credit. In the dry season, when nearly half the farmers grew modern varieties, the percentage of borrowers from this group was substantially higher than the proportion of borrowers from the group that grew only local varieties − 81 and 56 percent, respectively.

Small farmers borrowed more per hectare than larger farmers, and tenants more than owners. Tenants borrowed 1.5 times the general average per hectare. Most of the borrowing was for agricultural purposes, although it was not possible to clearly separate production and domestic credit for small farmers and many tenants.

Among farmers with less than 4 hectares who grew modern varieties in the dry season, those who grew only modern varieties borrowed Rs 442 while those who grew both local and modern varieties borrowed Rs 356. This and other evidence suggest that credit needs rise as farmers move into modern varieties and as the proportion of rice area sown to modern varieties increases. The level of credit (average for all farms) for farmers growing only modern varieties or only local varieties was:

	modern varieties	*local varieties*	*difference*
wet season	Rs 425/ha	Rs 182/ha	Rs 243/ha
dry season	328/ha	231/ha	97/ha

CHANGES IN PRODUCTION, PRODUCTIVITY, AND INCOME

Modern varieties outyielded local varieties by about 33 percent in the wet season and 83 percent in the dry season of 1971/72. In terms of value (quantity times price) the gains were 41 percent in the wet season and 63 percent in the dry season.

Comparing owners and tenants (Table 9), tenant farmers obtained higher yields with modern varieties (Jaya) in the dry season. The extraordinarily high yields of the small farmers are striking. Small tenant farmers have certain advantages, compared with small owner-operators, in the cultivation of modern varieties − they are usually financed by the landowners who make the main production decisions and share the risks involved. Since the landowners are less interested in local varieties this advantage is limited to the cultivation of modern varieties. Owners tend to outyield tenants with local varieties.

Farmers who grew modern varieties had better results with local varieties than those who grew only local varieties (Table 10), thus

Table 9. Yields of local varieties (SLO 13 and SLO 19) and modern varieties (Jaya and IR 8), 1971/72.

farm size	yield (t/ha)							
	wet season		dry season					
	SLO 13		SLO 19		Jaya		IR 8	
	owners	tenants	owners	tenants	owners	tenants	owners	tenants
below 2 ha	3.1	3.0	2.9	2.5	4.4	6.9	5.7	[a]
2 – 4 ha	3.1	3.1	3.1	3.0	5.7	5.7	5.7	[a]
over 4 ha	3.1	2.8	3.1	2.8	5.5	5.5	5.6	[a]
all farms	3.1	3.0	3.1	2.7	5.3	6.3	5.6	[a]

[a] Less than three observations.

suggesting somewhat superior managerial skills. Yields from modern varieties did not vary significantly with the proportion of the crop sown to them.

The most important variable affecting change in rice production per farm is the area planted to modern varieties. In the delta, the intensity of cropping depends on the water available in the canals in the dry season, a variable of practical importance to the farmers, certainly, but not one over which they have any control.

Table 10. Mean yields, by type of rice enterprise.

tenure group	yields (t/ha) of farmers growing			
	modern varieties only	modern & local varieties		local variety only
		modern	local	
	wet season			
owners	3.7	4.0	3.1	3.0
tenants	4.2	3.9	3.5	3.0
all farmers	4.2	4.0	3.1	3.0
	dry season			
owners	5.2	5.5	3.2	2.9
tenants	5.9	4.8	3.2	2.7
all farmers	5.4	5.5	3.2	2.8

Table 11. Increase in costs and returns from shifting to modern varieties.

increase in	wet season (Rs/ha)	dry season (Rs/ha)
gross returns	768	1274
costs	220	290
fertilizers	87	146
pesticides	25	47
wages	84	87
interest on credit	24	10
residual due to land ownership, management, and capital	548	984

As a consequence of the shift to modern varieties, the total rice output of the village in 1971/72 was about 15 percent higher than it would have been if only local varieties had been planted. In fact the overall gain was probably higher than this because the spill-over effect of the HYVP encouraged application of fertilizers and pesticides to local varieties. But the total gain is not likely to have exceeded 20 percent.

With this level of gain in harvested grain the shift to modern varieties was a profitable shift, although the income gained was not equivalent because of the increased purchase of inputs (Table 11). In addition, 1971/72 was a particularly favorable year, and in the long run the greater variability of modern variety yields could wipe out the differential noted for the wet season and reduce it for the dry season.

The proportion of total rice production marketed is associated with the pattern of control over rice land. In Pedapulleru, control was concentrated in the hands of a few large farmers. This was reflected in a large proportion of the aggregate village output going to market. At least two-thirds of the rice had been marketed at the time of the survey (3 months after the dry-season harvest), and it was known that several large farmers retained stocks that they would sell during the period of high prices just before the following wet-season harvest.

Most of the grain from modern varieties had been sold (94 percent of the wet-season crop and 87 percent of the larger dry-season crop), and so had most of the dry-season crop of local varieties (82 percent). But because consumption needs were retained from the wet-season crop (and mostly from local variety grain), only 44 percent of the wet-season crop had reached the market.

Since the shift to modern varieties increased rice production by about 15 percent above 1965/66 production, and since it is reasonable to assume that in Pedapulleru the marginal propensity to market approaches 100 percent, the increase in the quantity of rice reaching the market from Pedapulleru therefore can be estimated at about 25 percent over this period.

Rice was not the sole source of income in Pedapulleru. Of the 437 households only 185 were those of farmers. Most others were the households of landless agricultural laborers. In addition 74 farm households reported agricultural labor as an occupation of at least one member of the family. Included in this latter group of cultivators and laborers were 60 percent of the farms smaller than 2 hectares, and 84 percent of all pure-tenant farms. There was a somewhat greater dependence on labor as a source of income among the farms that did not grow modern varieties than among the farms that did. That suggests that the shift to modern varieties is associated with reduced dependence of small cultivators on off-farm work. This association is conceivable because farmers who shifted to modern varieties reported increased employment of family labor on their farms. But, at the same time, those who shifted to modern varieties were from upper caste groups among whom the participation of women in hired labor is uncommon. So, the differences in use of hired labor between small cultivators who adopted modern varieties and those who did not are partly due to differences in the caste compositions.

A fifth of all farm households also reported having members with nonfarm occupations in the village and neighboring towns. The diversity was great, ranging from the professions to semi-skilled workers. About a third of these people took up their jobs after 1965. While most of the nonfarm businesses in Pedapulleru started before 1965, it was reported that business activity had spurted since then. Part of the general prosperity of the village and its surroundings is explained by the emergence of dairying as a source of income for farm and landless households, a development which was not related to the HYVP, but rather to the improved communications between the village and the neighboring towns.

CONSTRAINTS TO GROWTH

Important changes in rice farming have occurred in Pedapulleru since 1965, yet the HYVP has hardly affected the main rice season and even in the dry season modern varieties are not fully accepted as dependable.

Why has the HYVP had such a limited impact? Why are the results no better?

The chief explanation for the slow spread of modern varieties and their limited impact is growing season. Modern varieties so far available are not well suited to wet-season cultivation given the rainfall pattern of the delta. In the dry season the area that can be planted to rice is determined by availability of canal water. But to go further in the explanation, three other questions must be asked: (1) what are the characteristics of the farmers who have not participated in the HYVP, (2) who are the past dropouts from the program, and why did they cease to participate, and (3) why do so many farmers who grow modern varieties continue to grow local varieties as well.

Nearly a third of the Pedapulleru farmers had never grown modern varieties. Most of these were small farmers (with less than 4 hectares). More tenants (46 percent) were unwilling to experiment than owners (31 percent).

The nonparticipants belonged to the social group which had less access to the *kshatriya*-dominated village *panchayat* and cooperative. Only 21 percent of the *kshatriya* farmers had never participated in the HYVP compared with 53 percent of farmers of other castes. In more backward communities the proportion of nonexperimenters was higher. Caste did not make much difference among farmers with more than 4 hectares, but among the smaller farmers the *kshatriyas* were most prominent as experimenters. The same relationship holds for owner-operators and tenants. Clearly, the small owners and the tenant farmers who were not aligned to the dominant power group by caste association tended to be by-passed by the program.

An additional disadvantage of the farmers who had not experimented was a high rate of illiteracy: 27 out of 58 were literate, and only six had attended school beyond the elementary level.

Thus the conjunction of adverse circumstances – small size, tenancy, illiteracy, and dependence on others for credit and crucial farm assets – prevented a large group from experimenting with the HYVP package of inputs. This group was by-passed almost completely by the changes in farm technology taking place in the village around them. And, the public institutions did not help to reduce the force of these adverse circumstances. These farmers had essentially no access to cheap institutional credit from the *kshatriya*-dominated cooperative, and when there were shortages of inputs they were the farmers who missed out.

Since the introduction of modern varieties, 127 Pedapulleru farmers had experimented with them, but in 1971/72 only two-thirds were still growing them. The dropouts came from all size and tenure groups in fairly equal proportions. The main reasons for dropping out seemed to be bad experiences with modern varieties in adverse seasons, the feeling that the varieties were not profitable, and difficulties in obtaining sufficient capital. Tenants had the additional problem of higher rents to landlords.

In 1969/70 when the largest group of first-adoptors entered the program a cyclone caused heavy losses. Those who adopted early in the program, when Taichung Native 1 was the main variety, started out with failure due to the variety. There were many other reasons why individual farmers dropped out, but the main ones seemed to come down to high year-to-year variability in yields, and a higher risk of losses from pests.

On large farms, in particular, local varieties continued to be grown along with modern varieties. Smaller farmers were slower to enter the program (to take the risks of experimenting), but once they did enter, they planted a larger proportion of their rice lands to modern varieties than the bigger farmers. Tenants exhibited much the same tendencies as the small owners, but the influence of the landlord might be felt, and tenancy might be regarded merely as an appendage to big landlordism.

Most farmers reported the incidence of pests and diseases as a barrier to the adoption of modern varieties in both seasons. This problem affected local varieties mainly in the dry season. Poor drainage was a fairly common problem in the wet season, but not in the dry season (Table 12).

The main constraints on the use of modern varieties in the wet season were reported to be water management, pests and diseases, and shortages of fertilizers, while in the dry season problems of water management, pests and diseases, water shortage, fertilizer delivery times, fertilizer prices, and the availability of tractor services were most important.

There were also differences between the farm groups. Small farmers and tenants were most concerned with the tractor service, and small owner-operators complained much about credit, particularly in the dry season when they cultivated modern varieties.

In summary, the main reasons for the persisting small proportion of rice lands planted to modern varieties in Pedapulleru were (1) the small area planted to modern varieties in the wet season, (2) the shortage of irrigation water in the dry season, (3) the large group of dissatisfied experimenters who have discontinued using modern varieties for one reason or another, (4) the existence of a group of "underpriveleged farmers" who never joined the HYVP, (5) the exclusion of small owners

Table 12. Constraints reported by farmers.[a]

constraint	farmers (%)			
	wet season		dry season	
	modern varieties	older varieties	modern varieties	older varieties
pests and diseases	86	20	99	99
fertilizer availability	50	53	50	56
water supply for the field	55	43	54	50
drainage	36	31	0	3
tractor service	27	51	43	52
sprayers	5	8	25	33
credit	9	11	18	19
water for nurseries	9	10	10	11

[a]No farmer reported harvesting, threshing, drying, marketing, storage, or availability of seed as a constraint.

and tenants from the supply of cheap institutional credit, and (6) the risk associated with modern varieties particularly for small owner-operators.

ECONOMIC AND SOCIAL EFFECTS OF THE NEW TECHNOLOGY

Agrarian structure. The distribution of ownership and control over land in this rice village profoundly influence the distribution of income. Since the most important change that has taken place in the village in recent years is the adoption of the inputs and technology of the HYVP it may be asked whether this has had any significant effect on the land situation and hence on income distribution.

We begin by comparing two groups of households − cultivators and noncultivators. Noncultivators are all households that do not have land for farming. The proportion of resident households in each category hardly changed between 1964/65 and 1971/72 although some change occurred in the composition of each group − mainly due to switches between tenants and the landless, with some tenants becoming landless and some landless becoming tenants. Only one former tenant became a landowner.

More change occurred in the distribution of land use between farm households. About 40 percent of all farmers reported upward or downward change in the area they farmed. Most of these were tenants, which suggests insecurity of tenancy.

The distribution of land ownership was more stable. Between 1964/65 and 1971/72 only 10 hectares changed hands (involving 8 buyers and 12 sellers), and half of this was between farmers with over 6 hectares. Little evidence exists that small farmers have been able to increase their holdings through the land market. The threat of land ceilings seems only to have frozen the distribution of ownership of land at the 1964/65 position.

The land-lease market shifted land use from big to small farmers to some extent and the distribution of land use was more even than the distribution of land ownership. Nevertheless, the owners who leased out all their lands were more likely to be small landowners; the big landowners operated all or most of their lands. But even with some land leased to nonowners, farmers still formed a minority (42 percent) of all Pedapulleru households.

Caste was important in the village. Ownership and control of land by a caste group which does not allow intermarriage with other caste groups, even between families from the same economic strata, superimposes an economic inequality over social inequality, making the inequalities less tolerable. The distribution of land between caste groups is thus important. The dominant caste in Pedapulleru was *kshatriya* since it controlled a substantial proportion of village land. Even the bigger tenants were from this caste.

The price of leased land. There were two types of rental payments in Pedapulleru: a fixed *amount* in kind, and a contracted share of the gross product. Under the first, all cultivation expenses are borne by the tenant while under the second the landlord contributes to the costs of fertilizers and pesticides in proportion to his share of the harvest. The first type was the common practice during the wet season, while the second was used for the dry season.

Since the introduction of modern varieties important changes have occurred in this system. When a tenant cultivates modern varieties the landlord usually demands a *share* of the gross product regardless of season. Landlords have continued to contribute to the costs of purchased inputs according to the contracted share, but the landlord's share has generally increased up to about two-thirds. In addition, the landlords have taken more responsibilities for production decisions such as the level of fertilizer use and the varieties to be grown. The tenants have become more like permanent farm servants than independent farmers, and the tenancy system has become a convenient arrangement for landowners who relieve themselves from the burdens of labor management while still performing the main entrepreneurial functions. The rents paid by share tenants in the dry season (when they cultivate modern varieties) have more than doubled, and rents paid under share arrangements have exceeded those fixed in kind.

The pure tenants in 1971/72 dry season who grew local varieties obtained an average yield of 2.7 t/ha and paid a rent of 1.4 t/ha. Those who grew modern varieties obtained 5.7 t/ha and paid 3.7 t/ha. By switching to modern varieties, the average tenant increased his product by 3.0 t/ha, but paid 2.3 t/ha more to the landlord and gained only 0.7 t/ha himself. When the relative shares are examined only about one quarter of the additional product resulting from the switch to modern varieties goes to the tenant (Table 13).

The credit market. In a land-scarce, labor-surplus economy, the lease market will not operate in favor of tenants. Institutional credit agencies, however, have been set up to cater to the interests of the weaker sections

Table 13. Shares of landlord and tenant in the product: modern and local varieties.

item	amount (kg/ha)		increase of modern over local (%)
	modern varieties	local varieties	
yield	5727	2720	111
share of landlord[a]	3818	1360	181
share of tenant	1909	1360	40
grain equivalent of cost of			
fertilizers and pesticides	993	384	159
share of landlord[a]	662	192	245
share of tenant	331	192	72
net share of landlord	3156	1168	170
net share of tenant	1578	1168	35
net share of tenant in gross product (%)	28	43	

[a]For modern varieties landlord contributes two-thirds of the costs of fertilizers and pesticides and gets a two-thirds share of the harvest, for local varieties the landlord contributes half the cost of fertilizers and pesticides and gets half the harvest.

of the farming community so the credit market should operate in their favor.

Pedapulleru had a credit society which was financially sound and had increased its business considerably since 1965/66. But the pure tenants, who accounted for 34 percent of the cultivators and 17 percent of the area operated, got almost no credit from this source. The dominant caste group and the bigger farmers of this caste controlled the credit cooperative. The same group also controlled the *panchayat* (village government). They argued that it was poor business management to lend to tenants who could not offer security, but the landowners could borrow and relend to their tenants at their own risk. The small owners were also considered poor risks. The small owners and tenants got credit, but at rates about double those charged by the credit cooperative. While tenants often got interest-free loans from their landlords, this practice weakened their position in the rental market when bargaining on share arrangements. The small owner-cultivators lost out in another way — the high cost of credit to them reduced the profitability of the new technology.

The inputs and produce markets. Inputs were often in short supply. When this occurred, it was the tenants and small farmers who went short.

In the product market all farmers should be on equal ground. All received about the same prices for their grain when it was taken to market. But tenants and small farmers usually sold immediately, or shortly after harvest when prices were down, while the bigger farmers held some of their harvest for sale later in 'the season when prices rose to their peak.

The rental market, the market for loan funds, and the product and input markets all worked in favor of the bigger landowners and against the tenants and small owners. In a rural structure marked by inequalities, these markets did nothing to redress the balance, they merely accentuated the inequality. The new technology based on the use of modern varieties also tended to accentuate the inequality since it was more readily applicable to farmers who had an investable surplus.

The labor market. The new technology could help redress the inequalities of power and wealth if it enabled labor to earn a higher real wage per day worked or to get more employment. It appears that real wages fell from 1958 to 1965, but after 1965 this trend halted and may have been reversed. From 1958 to 1972, real wages per day worked did not change significantly, but there were small increases in the number of days worked. The new technology could increase employment by increasing the intensity of cropping (since the modern varieties mature faster), and by requiring more labor at different stages of cropping. Intensity of cropping is mainly a function of the availability of water in the dry season rather than of the variety grown. Thus it is beyond the control of the farmers. Increased employment is, therefore, related to the labor requirements of modern varieties compared with those of local varieties. In the wet season this effect was negligible since little rice land was planted to modern varieties. There was some increase in the dry season as discussed earlier.

In the future these relatively minor gains by the landless laborers might be eroded by mechanization. There were eight four-wheeled tractors in the village (seven of them owned before the HYVP). These sharply affected the number of draft animals owned and the number of permanent farm servants, but not the use of hired casual labor. As tractors become more reliable through the establishment of repair services and dependable stocks of spare parts, however, the casual laborers may also feel the pinch unless cropping intensity (dry-season water supplies) increases or more labor-intensive crops (wet-season varieties) are grown or nonfarm occupations expand.

Rice profits and levels of living. Only a third of the Pedapulleru farmers reported that their rice profits had increased since 1965/66. The proportion was higher among owners than among tenants and among large farmers than among small farmers (Table 14). Few farmers re-reported a decline in rice profits.

Not many farmers thought that their level of living had increased, but the variation between groups was similar to that based on rice profits. Most farmers reported fairly constant levels of consumption of food items like fish, chicken, eggs, mutton, milk, coffee and tea, and cooking oil, but the consumption of rice and vegetables appears to have gone up somewhat, particularly on tenant farms. Tenants and small owner-operators appear to have been catching up in the consumption of basic foodstuffs.

Most farmers reported little or no change in the consumption of durable goods and expenditure on education, but those who reported an increase were mainly owner-operators. No tenant reported an increase in expenditure on these items.

Only 5 percent of the farmers reported an increase in savings, but no farmer reported a decrease.

Income distribution. Based on indirect evidence, the distribution of income of Pedapulleru farm households was becoming increasingly

Table 14. Increase in rice income and standard of living since 1964/65 by tenure and size.

growers of	tenure			farm size[a]		
	owners	tenants	all farms	less than 4 ha	4 ha and over	all farms
increase in rice profits						
modern varieties only	59	33	50	50	75	59
some modern varieties	82	33	78	50	87	82
combined[b]	73	33	65	50	84	73
local varieties only	20	1	12	17	28	20
all farms	44	10	32	26	66	44
increase in standard of living						
modern varieties only	27	42	32	21	38	27
some modern varieties	44	33	43	25	47	44
combined[b]	38	40	38	22	45	38
local varieties only	6	6	6	2	17	6
all farms	21	14	18	8	36	21

[a] Of landholding farmers. [b] Value for all farmers who grew any modern varieties.

unequal. The evidence is based on data on changes in the distribution of owned land, changes in the distribution of gross product, changes in factor rewards, and changes in levels of living. The distribution of owned land is virtually unchanged. Hence no change occurred in the distribution of income on this account. The distribution of gross product became more unequal partly because tenants and small owner-cultivators were slow to adopt modern varieties. Data on factor rewards show that out of the excess attributable to modern varieties, owners gained much more than tenants (Table 13) and landless laborers. Qualitative evidence of changes in levels of living suggest some catching-up by tenants and small owners, but this does not indicate the observed changes in the style of living of the bigger farmers who had adopted modern varieties. Taking all things together, it is reasonable to infer that the already existing inequalities of the rural structure were increased rather than decreased by lags in rates of adoption between big and small owner-operators, the bias of the new technology in favor of owners, and the unfavorable position of the small tenants and owners in the credit, inputs, and produce markets. In this context effective implementation of land reforms becomes meaningful and urgent.

SUMMARY

The shift to modern varieties was neither dramatic nor universal, though changes in cultural practices created a favorable atmosphere for their acceptance. Modern varieties were not considered dependable substitutes for improved local varieties particularly in the wet season. Both seasons considered, modern varieties accounted for only 25 percent of the area, and many farmers had not shifted to modern varieties. The most severe constraints to shifting were the difficulties in water management in the wet season and the widespread fear of risk due to pests. Yet modern varieties had a significant impact on production and marketed surplus, the former rising by 15 percent and the latter by 25 percent. The impact on input structure, monetization, and integration with urban markets was much more significant. The overall employment effects of modern varieties were negligible. The bias of the new technology in favor of owners, and the unfavorable position of the small owners and tenants in the input, credit, and factor markets increased the existing inequalities of income. Improvements in the living conditions of weaker sections were not perceptible. Given a persisting inegalitarian land structure, modern varieties contributed little to reduction of rural inequalities, though with an egalitarian land structure they would have the potential for contributing toward rapid growth consistent with equity.

North Arcot, Tamil Nadu

V. Rajagopalan

Concerted effort on the part of the state government has led to rapid acceptance of modern varieties and related inputs among a considerable section of the rice-growing community. The yield and level of fertilizer input on modern varieties was very high. However, by 1971/72 less than half of the rice farmers in the three villages studied had experimented with modern varieties, and only a fifth had been growing them continuously over the past three years, these being principally the larger farmers with adequate irrigation facilities. Ways must be found to spread the impact of the program by providing irrigation and other inputs to the remaining farmers.

INDIAN FARMERS have given a mixed response to the modern varieties released since 1965 through the High Yielding Varieties Program (HYVP). This has not been surprising considering the climatic geographic, and cultural diversity of India, and the relatively small number of modern varieties available. Tamil Nadu was no exception. The area planted to rice varieties included under the HYVP was large, with several improved local varieties and a number of modern varieties all being included. The state government was at first reluctant to encourage the planting of "exotic" varieties such as IR8. But convinced of the high yield potential of IR8, particularly in the dry season, the state government mounted a *crash* program in 1969/70 to promote its production. As a result the area in IR8 rose from 690,000 hectares in that year to 1,820,000 hectares in 1970/71.

V. Rajagopalan is professor of agricultural economics at the Tamil Nadu Agricultural University, Coimbatore, Tamil Nadu.

The author wishes to acknowledge the assistance extended by the staff members of the Department of Agricultural Economics, Tamil Nadu Agricultural University, particularly P. K. Aiyasamy and R. Sundaresan and the extension personnel of the Department of Agriculture assigned in the study areas.

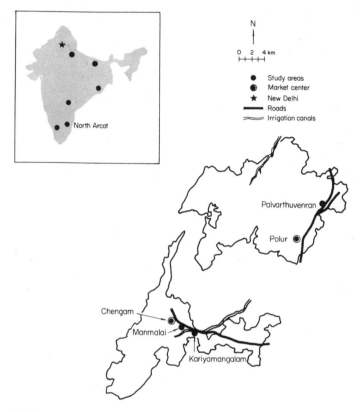

North Arcot District, Tamil Nadu State.

North Arcot District. The two development blocks in the North Arcot District (Chengam and Polur) which received state government prizes for their significant response to the crash program, seemed appropriate areas in which to observe changes in rice farming technology. Two villages in the Chengam block (Manmalai and Kariyamangalam) and one in the Polur block (Palvarthuvenran) were selected as study sites.

Rice farming in North Arcot has been adapted to the two monsoons: the southwest monsoon brings heavy rainfall from June to September, and the northeast monsoon continues the wet season to December. A dry and cooler period occurs during January and February followed by the hot dry months of March through May. There are three growing seasons, although farmers in the area grow only one or two rice crops a year, depending on their available water supply. The main (*Samba*) cropping season begins with the southwest monsoon and continues to November or December. This Samba season is followed by a

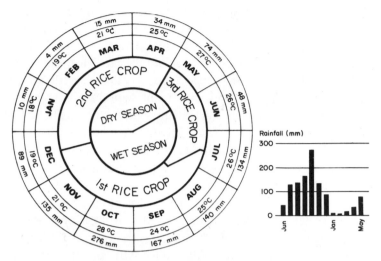

Average monthly rainfall (Chengam Block Recording Stations, 1967-1971) and minimum temperature (Vellore Recording Station, 1961-1971), North Arcot, Tamil Nadu.

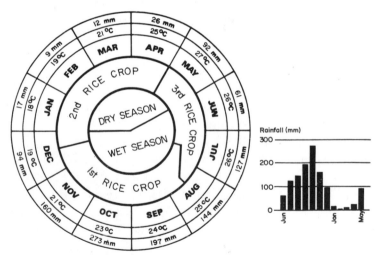

Average monthly rainfall (Polur Block Recording Station, 1967-1971) and minimum temperature (Vellore Recording Station, 1967-1971), North Arcot, Tamil Nadu.

dry season *(Navarai)* which extends to March or April. A second dry season *(Kar)* completes the cycle. Farmers have a good selection of improved local varieties developed in the state rice breeding program which are well adapted to the seasonal pattern. Modern varieties such as the IR series have been considered inferior, particularly in the wet season.

This area is adequately serviced by government extension, input supplies, and credit agencies. The four agricultural divisions of North Arcot each have a divisional agricultural officer who plans the various development activities at the Panchayat Union level. Each of the 36 Panchayat Unions in North Arcot is staffed with a deputy agricultural officer, 10 village level extension workers, one agricultural assistant trained in vocational agriculture, and two skilled field workers. The deputy agricultural officer is responsible for the implementation of agricultural plans developed before each season and for programs including the supply of major agricultural inputs.

Seeds are multiplied in state-owned seed farms and distributed to farmers from depots located in each block. Seeds of new varieties are also available at the National Seed Corporation sales centers and from the private seed growers. Fertilizers are distributed through cooperatives and private firms. The State Department of Agriculture handles the supply of plant protection chemicals, most of which are sold to farmers at 15 percent subsidy. Government, cooperative, and private firms manufacture and service agricultural implements.

The villages. The three villages were selected as study sites because their irrigation facilities were considered to be adequate for the production of modern varieties. In the wet season, rice fields were irrigated from surface-fed tanks supplemented by water from gravity wells. In the dry season, only well water was available and less area was sown to rice, especially in the study site in Manmalai village (Chengam Block) where the springs feeding the wells often dried up. In Kariyamangalam village (Chengam Block) two rainfed tanks supplied water to 300 hectares and 270 wells irrigated an additional 150 hectares in the wet season, while in the dry season only about 160 hectares were irrigated from the wells. In Manmalai there were no tanks and 54 open wells irrigated about 80 hectares in the wet season and a smaller area in the dry season. Palvarthuvenran village (Polur Block) had three tanks which irrigated 70 hectares and 129 wells which supplied water to another 53 hectares in the wet season, but in the dry season only well water was available. In Manmalai and Palvarthuvenran about 90 percent of the wet season rice area was double cropped in 1971/72, while in Kariyamanga-lam only about 60 percent received a second crop.

IR8 had been used in each village since 1967/68 and its use increased significantly under the crash program of 1969/70. Kariyamangalam was the largest village with 385 farms and about 450 hectares of wet-season rice; there were 266 farms in Manmalai with 80 hectares of wet-season rice; Palvarthuvenran was smaller with 96 farms but about 123 hectares

Table 1. Characteristics of the sample farms.

village	farms (no.) in		persons in household (no.)	farm size (ha)
	village	sample		
Kariyamangalam	385	52	6.3	4.1
Manmalai	266	66	6.4	1.8
Palvarthuvenran	96	33	6.5	2.0

	rice area				
	per farm (ha)		double cropped (%)	irrigated (%)	principal form of irrigation
	wet season	dry season			
Kariyamangalam	1.4	0.8	61	100	canal and pump[a]
Manmalai	0.7	0.6	89	100	pump
Palvarthuvenran	1.3	1.2	91	100	canal[a] and pump

	modern varieties				
	farmers planting (%)		area planted (%)		year of greatest adoption
	wet season	dry season	wet season	dry season	
Kariyamangalam	100	100	50	98	1969
Manmalai	100	100	70	86	1969
Palvarthuvenran	100	100	49	41	1969

[a] From tanks.

were sown to rice in the wet season (Table 1). Kariyamangalam supported two rice mills (12 tons a day hulling capacity); there was one mill in Manmalai (10 tons a day capacity), and Palvarthuvenran farmers took their rice to mills in neighboring villages.

Rice-drying facilities were not well organized. Palvarthuvenran had a common threshing floor but in the other villages threshing and drying were carried out in improvised patches in the fields and along the roads.

Irrigation pumps were powered by electricity in all three villages: 90 percent of the wells in Manmalai were electrically powered in 1971/72 as were 60 percent in Kariyamangalam and 40 percent in Palvarthuvenran. Water was lifted from the remaining wells with cattle powered *mhotes*.

Table 2. Distribution of all farms and sample farms by size of farm,[a] 1971/72.

farm size range (ha)	Kariyamangalam		Manmalai		Palvarthuvenran	
	all farms (no.)	sample farms (no.)	all farms (no.)	sample farms (no.)	all farms (no.)	sample farms (no.)
up to 1	214	7	200	37	44	6
1 – 2	106	8	37	9	21	16
over 2	65	37	29	20	13	11

[a]All farms is a total enumeration for each village. Sample farms include only those holdings on which IRRI varieties were grown continuously during the 1969/70 dry season and the 1970/71 dry and wet seasons.

The villages were located on all-weather roads with good public transport facilities between each of them and the nearby market towns with their centers of agricultural administration, credit institutions, and supplies of farm inputs. Rice marketing was orderly and the farmers in each village had a number of outlets for their product including regulated markets in the towns and weekly roadside markets. Farmers did not always sell at the nearest market; Polur and Arani, 8 and 14 km away, respectively, were the nearest market centers for Palvarthuvenran farmers. Arani was generally preferred because it was a regulated market.

Farmers obtained agricultural credit through government agencies, cooperatives, private banks, and moneylenders. While there was no cooperative located in the three villages studied, Kariyamangalam and Manmalai farmers belonged to a cooperative marketing society at Nachipet (4 and 2 km away, respectively) and had access to the Bank of India at Chengam. Palvarthuvenran farmers had access to a cooperative credit society at Kelur, 2 km away, and the State Bank of India and the Land Development Bank had branches at Polur. The government also provided production credit through its block development agencies. As an example of the latter, the government loaned up to Rs 864/ha of modern variety rice and Rs 618/ha of other rice varieties under its Intensive Manuring Scheme, and charged 8.5 percent interest compared with the usual 25 to 30 percent charged by private money lenders.

The radio was an important means for communicating extension and market information. Many farmers owned radios and the village Panchayats maintained community radios. Newspapers and occasional

Department of Agriculture bulletins are available, but the literacy rate ranged between 16 and 30 percent in the study sites. This may improve in time since there were four primary schools in Kariyamangalam, two in Manmalai and one in Palvarthuvenran, and there were secondary schools in Chengam and Kelur towns.

The sample. Farm censuses carried out in the three villages at the beginning of the wet season in July 1971 revealed the following:

	Kariyamangalam	*Manmalai*	*Palvarthuvenran*
farmers (no.)	385	266	96
farmers (no.) who had ever grown modern varieties*	113	169	60
farmers (no.) who had grown modern varieties* in the previous three seasons continuously	52	66	33

*IR varieties such as IR8. Local improved varieties classified as high yielding for purposes of the HYVP are not included.

In order to study the changes in rice farming due to the adoption of high-yielding rice varieties only those farmers who had grown IRRI varieties (other modern varieties were not popular in this area), continuously for the previous three seasons were selected for study. The total sample consisted of 151 farms. This'method of selecting farmers gave samples which were biased towards the larger farms in each village (Table 2).

The study was carried out in three stages. First, the district and *taluk*-level officers of the Department of Agriculture and the Department of Revenue were contacted for assistance in selecting the area to be studied; second, block development officers helped to select the village study sites; and third, the three villages were visited during the wet season (July 1971 to January 1972) and the following dry season (January to May 1972).

ADOPTION OF MODERN RICE VARIETIES

Under the Tamil Nadu HYVP the three villages studied must be regarded as successes — the entire rice area in both the 1971/72 wet and dry seasons was planted to varieties classified as "high yielding." In the

Table 3. Proportion of holdings planted to rice on sample farms.

farm size range (ha)	rice area (%)		
	Kariyamangalam	Manmalai	Palvarthuvenran
wet season			
up to 1.3	55	66	76
1.3 to 2.6	47	46	56
over 2.6	30	29	73
all farms	33	39	68
dry season			
up to 1.3	44	76	71
1.3 to 2.6	38	39	52
over 2.6	17	23	65
all farms	21	35	61

wet season the local improved variety GEB 24 was important in each village and in the dry season the local improved varieties CO 29, Kullakar and TKM 6 were important in Palvarthuvenran.

The area sown to rice in each of the three villages was limited by the availability of irrigation water, nevertheless other irrigated crops like sugarcane, groundnut, and chilli were also grown. The proportion of farmland holdings planted to rice in Kariyamangalam and Manmalai tended to decrease with increasing farm size (Table 3).

The preference for different rice varieties varied among the three study villages, not only between local improved and modern varieties, but also among the modern varieties themselves (Tables 4 and 5). Manmalai farmers made the greatest switch to modern varieties in the wet season — only 30 percent of their wet-season rice area was planted to local improved varieties (GEB 24), and only 30 percent of the sample farmers sowed GEB 24. In contrast, about half the area was under GEB 24 in Kariyamangalam and Palvarthuvenran and over 80 percent of the farmers from these villages sowed all or some of their land with this local improved rice variety.

A preference for GEB 24 over IR 20 in the wet season did not imply conservatism or reflect on the farmer's ability. While GEB 24 yielded only about 3 t/ha to IR 20's 5 t/ha, GEB 24 is a fine-grain variety worth Rs 900/t of rough rice compared with Rs 650/t for IR 20. Moreover, GEB 24 costs less to produce per hectare (Table 6). The net return per

Table 4. Rice varieties planted in the 1971 wet season on sample farms.

village	area planted (%)			farmers planting (%)		
	IR20	GEB24	others[a]	IR20	GEB24	others
Kariyamangalam	44	50	6	83	81	18
Manmalai	47	30	23	73	30	37
Palvarthuvenran	37	51	12	91	85	27

[a]IR8, IR5, IR22, CO_{33}.

Table 5. Rice varieties planted in the 1972 dry season on sample farms.

village	area planted (%)			farmers planting (%)		
	IR8	IR20	local improved varieties	IR8	IR20	local improved varieties
Kariyamangalam	80	18	2	83	21	a
Manmalai	67	18	15	86	15	22
Palvarthuvenran	0	42	58	0	100	85

[a]Only two farmers planted local varieties in Kariyamangalam in the dry season.

hectare was slightly greater for IR 20 than for GEB 24 and since it is a shorter duration crop, its net return per day the crop was in the ground was significantly higher than that of GEB 24 (Rs 15 and Rs 11, respectively). Nevertheless, GEB 24 has certain advantages which might well be more important to many farmers. Farmers had many years of experience with GEB 24. The production cost per hectare was lower than that of the high-yielding varieties and at market time traders could not use the claim of "new variety" to lower prices to the less well-informed farmers. For many farmers IR 20 involved more risk on several fronts with only marginal potential gains. Most farmers, particularly in Kariyamangalam and Palvarthuvenran, planted both IR 20 and GEB 24; only in Manmalai was there a fairly clear preference for IR 20 and other modern varieties (Table 4).

In the dry season, 85 and 98 percent of their total rice-growing area was planted to the modern varieties in Manmalai and Kariyamangalam, respectively (Table 5). IR 8 was the most important modern variety but in each village IR 20 was grown on 18 percent of the total area. IR 8 was not planted at all in Palvarthuvenran — 42 percent of its rice area was in IR 20 and the rest was planted to local improved varieties.

Table 6. Attributed costs for GEB 24 and IR20.

operation	costs (Rs/ha)		difference
	GEB24	IR20	
preparatory cultivation	100	140	40
fertilizer and application	354	553	199
seeds and sowing	115	125	10
irrigation	138	109	−29
after cultivation	54	70	16
plant protection	30	37	7
harvesting and post-harvest activities	140	278	138
cost/ha	931	1312	381
cost/ton	310	262	48

Small farmers tended to plant a larger proportion of their rice crop to modern varieties once they decided to adopt them. This was particularly evident in the wet season in all three villages (Table 7).

RICE FARMING PRACTICES

North Arcot is one of the more progressive rice farming areas of Tamil Nadu and its farmers have been exposed to extension activities related to modern farming methods for many years. Before the introduction of modern rice varieties in 1966, over 90 percent of the farmers in Manmalai and Kariyamangalam were using chemical fertilizers. The significant changes that have taken place since 1966 apart from the use of the modern rice varieties were in the quantity of fertilizer used and an increased sophistication of management techniques in fertilizer use and other farm practices.

Chemical fertilizers. The forms of inorganic fertilizer most commonly used in 1971/72 were complete fertilizers (15-15-15 and 17-17-17) and urea. The use of straight fertilizers, such as ammonium sulfate, superphosphate, and muriate of potash, declined after 1966, partly due to shortages, and there was a switch to complete fertilizer as a basal before transplanting and to urea for topdressing at tillering and panicle initiation stages of growth.

Table 7. Proportion of total rice crop planted to modern varieties by size of holding, sample farms.

farm size range (ha)	rice area in modern varieties (%)		
	Kariyamangalam	Manmalai	Palvarthuvenran
	wet season		
up to 1.3	62	98	58
1.3 to 2.6	61	69	47
over 2.6	47	54	45
	dry season		
up to 1.3	100	87	47
1.3 to 2.6	87	85	42
over 2.6	94	84	46

Table 8. Quantities of fertilizers used on modern and improved local varieties, sample farms.

village	amount (kg/ha) used on					
	improved local varieties			modern varieties		
	N	P_2O_5	K_2O	N	P_2O_5	K_2O
	wet season					
Kariyamangalam	52	5	5	127	52	48
Manmalai	74	16	16	154	64	53
Palvarthuvenran	48	7	7	116	31	31
	dry season					
Kariyamangalam	58	0	0	110	60	61
Manmalai	59	20	20	133	61	54
Palvarthuvenran	38	8	8	76	37	34

In 1971/72 all sample farmers applied fertilizer in the wet and dry seasons to both the modern and improved local varieties. Average applications differed among the villages, but about twice as much fertilizer was applied to the modern varieties as to the improved local varieties (Table 8). In contrast to most rice-growing areas, in these villages, somewhat more nitrogen per hectare was used in the wet season than in the dry season in two of the villages. Yields were about the same in the dry season despite the lower application of nitrogen (Table 9); abundant sunshine and regulated irrigation from wells contributed to the higher yields. A shortage of fertilizer and consequent high prices demanded by traders led many farmers to cut back on the amounts of fertilizer applied.

While the quantities of fertilizer used per hectare varied considerably between farms in each village, in general, the rates were higher on the small and medium farms than on the large farms.

Plant protection chemicals. Many farmers were using plant protection chemicals as early as 1962 in this region, but since the introduction of modern varieties their use has become almost universal. Farmers regarded them as critical inputs especially since high rates of fertilization, particularly the heavy use of nitrogen, increased crop vulnerability to a large variety of pests and diseases at all stages of plant growth. Most farmers followed the crop protection recommendations suggested in the extension literature.

In 1971/72 farmers had difficulty in obtaining the required chemicals at the times needed, and the costs of the chemicals rose steadily throughout the period. Sprayers were also in short supply. However, the use of chemicals increased and public agencies, such as the panchayat unions and cooperatives, began to provide manual and power-operated equipment at nominal charges. Private custom services for plant protection also increased. Estimates of the average cost of plant protection on the sample farms were Rs 77/ha for IR8 and Rs 37/ha for IR20.

Methods of cultivation. Three important changes in production techniques were observed in the survey villages. The most important was the shift from bullocks to electric power to pump water from wells. The

Table 9. Mean yields from improved local and modern varieties, sample farms.

village	yield (t/ha)			
	wet season		dry season	
	improved local	modern	improved local	modern
Kariyamangalam	2.9	4.0	a	5.3
Manmalai	2.9	5.7	2.9	5.6
Palvarthuvenran	3.5	4.8	3.3	4.1

a Only 2 farmers planted improved-local varieties.

Table 10. Extent to which modern varieties used more labor in cultivation and harvesting than improved local varieties in the 1972 dry season.

village	labor increased (man-days/ha)			
	pre-harvest		harvest and post-harvest	
	family labor	hired labor	family labor	hired labor
Kariyamangalam	5	34	12[a]	16
Manmalai	3	44	0	29
Palvarthuvenran	0	13	0	15

[a]Includes 7 man-days/ha exchange labor.

use of electric power for irrigation began before 1969 and was already extensive in Kariyamangalam and Manmalai by 1969, but the shift was more recent in Palvarthuvenran. Before 1969, 96 percent of the farmers in Kariyamangalam used electric power for lift irrigation and the same was true for 88 and 39 percent of the farmers in Manmalai and Palvar thuvenran, respectively. By 1971/72 100 percent of the farmers in Manmalai and 64 percent of the farmers in Palvarthuvenran were using electric power for lift irrigation.

The second change was the hiring of tractors for preparatory tillage and threshing, observed only in Kariyamangalam where the Panchayat Union had purchased tractors that the farmers could hire. The charges in 1971/72 for plowing were Rs 67.50/ha for single plowing and Rs 112.5/ha for two plowings. The third change was in the method of transplanting. Straight-row planting was suggested as an appropriate method for modern varieties. Some farmers tried it, but felt it required too much labor and discontinued the practice in favor of using proper spacing to maintain optimum plant population.

Labor. The cultivation of modern varieties required more labor for weeding, plant protection, and harvesting than did the cultivation of improved local varieties (Table 10).

Heavy fertilization and the dwarf upright stature of the modern varieties contributed to luxuriant weed growth. Improved local varieties usually required one or two weedings but the modern varieties had to be weeded two or three times. Plant protection was also more critical in the cultivation of modern varieties. Improved local varieties were fairly resistant to pests and diseases and were treated with pesticides only occasionally; modern varieties (particularly IR 8), however, required one or two dustings plus three or more sprayings. Finally, at harvest the

Table 11. Number and amounts of cash and kind production loans taken in the wet and dry seasons, 1971/72.

	Kariyamangalam		Palvarthuvenran		Manmalai		all villages	
	wet	dry	wet	dry	wet	dry	wet	dry
	percent of farmers borrowing cash or kind							
	29	33	82	21	68	41	60	32
	number of loans taken							
cash	10	4	24	4	19	9	53	17
kind	13	10	10	0	31	22	54	32
	average amount borrowed (Rs/ha)							
cash	260	495	284	238	192	214	284	290
kind	401	735	290	0	352	338	350	460

dwarf modern varieties, heavy with grain required more effort and more labor than the tall improved local varieties which lodge on maturity and are easier to cut, bundle, and transport. Also, more labor was required for threshing and associated operations with modern varieties compared to local varieties.

In Kariyamangalam local improved varieties used about 175 man-days/ha for all operations; modern varieties used 232 man-days/ha – a difference of 67 man-days/ha. Sixty percent of the additional labor was required during cultivation (weeding and plant protection), and 40 percent at harvest and during subsequent operations. In Manmalai and Palvarthuvenran, 76 and 28 additional man-days/ha respectively were used for modern varieties. Most of the additional labor was hired. The demand for labor increased significantly in the district and the wage rate also increased.

Production credit. During the 1971 wet season, 60 percent of the sample farmers borrowed cash or inputs such as fertilizer and plant protection chemicals. Fifty-three cash loans worth about Rs 284/ha and 54 in-kind loans worth about Rs 350/ha, were taken out. However, in the following dry season, only 32 percent of the sample farmers borrowed, 17 cash loans worth about Rs 290/ha and 32 in-kind loans worth about Rs 460/ha were taken out (Table 11).

In the wet season, 58 percent of the cash loans from private money-lenders accounted for 55 percent of the money borrowed (Table 12).

The private moneylenders were an even more important source of cash in the dry season; they provided 82 percent of the loans and 64 percent of the money borrowed. The cooperatives were the second most important source of cash; they provided 24 percent of the loans in the wet season and 12 percent in the dry season (26 percent and 35 percent of the money borrowed). Cash loans from government agencies and from commercial banks accounted for the balance.

All loans in kind in the wet season and all but two in the dry season were made from cooperatives and government. The government was the major source in the wet season (65 percent of the loans and 57 percent of the value), while in the dry season the cooperatives were more prominent (63 percent of the loans and 72 percent of the value).

While about the same percentage of farmers in the large, medium, and small farm-size groups borrowed (Table 13), the size of the loans per farmer tended to be related to the size of the farm. However, the amount borrowed per hectare tended to decline as farm size increased (in the wet season: Rs 483, 400, and 367/ha for small, medium, and large farms, respectively).

The borrowing patterns differed among the three villages. In the wet season up to 82 percent of the sample farmers from Palvarthuvenran borrowed, compared with 68 and 29 percent in Manmalai and Kariya-

Table 12. Distribution of borrowers and amount borrowed by source of loans, 1971/72 wet and dry seasons.

source	cash		kind	
	wet	dry	wet	dry
percent number of loans taken				
cooperatives	24	12	35	63
government	8	6	65	32
private	58	82	0	5
others	10	0	0	0
amount borrowed as percent of total				
cooperatives	26	35	43	72
government	3	1	57	24
private	55	64	0	4
others	16	0	0	0

Table 13. Credit and farm size of sample farms.

farm size range (ha)	farmers (%) who borrowed				mean amount of loan (Rs/farmer)				mean amount of loan (Rs/ha)		
	wet season		dry season		wet season		dry season		wet season		
	cash	kind	cash	kind	cash	kind	cash	kind	cash	kind	total
up to 1.3	37	39	16	18	164	289	173	302	165	318	483
1.3 to 2.6	37	35	7	24	232	401	250	350	146	254	400
over 2.6	32	34	9	19	469	415	516	766	187	180	367

Table 14. Costs of cultivating IR8 on sample farms in the 1972 dry season.

village	avg cost (Rs/ha)	proportion of costs (%)						
		fertilizer[a]	irrigation	harvesting/ threshing	preparatory cultivation	seeds/ sowing	after cultivation	plant protection
Kariyamangalam	1759	42	17	12	9	10	5	5
Manmalai	1646	44	20	13	9	7	4	3
Palvarthuvenran	1480	33	26	19	9	8	4	1
avg[b]	1628	42	19	14	9	8	4	4

[a]Including application. [b]Simple average of figures presented above.

mangalam, respectively (Table 11). In Kariyamangalam most of the loans went to the larger farms, but in the other two villages the distribution was fairly even.

The sample farmers were in a somewhat privileged position with respect to institutional credit as they had been participants in the HYVP for some time. Generally, credit was available to them if they required it.

Costs of production. The average cost of producing IR8 in the three study villages in the 1972 dry season was about Rs 1,600/ha (Table 14). In each village the purchase and application cost of chemical fertilizers was the largest single expenditure, ranging from 33 percent of the total cost in Palvarthuvenran to 44 percent in Manmalai. The second largest expense was the cost of irrigation. While the average of the three study villages was 19 percent, it varied from 17 percent in Kariyamangalam to 26 percent in Palvarthuvenran. The third major expenditure was the cost of harvesting and threshing.

On the average farmers exceeded the fertilizer application rate recommended for IR8 by the extension service. This appeared to happen because farmers were uncertain about the optimum dose for their area, and about the response of the crop to complex fertilizers with which they had little experience. Some farmers paid more than market rates for straight fertilizers which were in short supply rather than use the complex types which were usually available. Some farmers paid Rs 60 to Rs 70 for a 50-kg bag of urea when the official price was fixed at Rs 49.50.

Disposal of the rice harvest. While there was some variation among the three study villages, about three-fourths of the crop was sold and the rest retained for seed and consumption or paid out as wages (Table 15). Larger farmers retained a substantial share of their harvests for sale a month or more after harvest while smaller farmers tended to sell most of their crop immediately after harvest. Most farmers kept grain of local improved varieties for consumption and for payment as wages rather than grain of modern varieties (Table 16).

CHANGES IN LEVELS OF LIVING

The levels of living of the sample farmers improved since the modern rice varieties were introduced, particularly on the larger farms of Kariyamangalam. Most farmers reported that their net profit from rice growing had increased (Table 17).

Indicators of a higher level of living were improvements in diet, increased spending on consumer durables, household appliances, bi-

Table 15. Disposal of IR8 crop of sample farmers in the 1972 dry season.

village	produc-tion (t/ha)	disposed (%)			sold (%)		
		seed/con-sumption	wages	total	imme-diately	within 1 month	after 1 month
Kariyamangalam	5.3	8	14	78	16	27	35
Manmalai	5.6	17	9	74	40	15	19
Palvarthuvenran	4.1	2	14	84	71	11	2
avg[a]	5.0	10	12	78	41	18	19

[a]Simple average of figures presented above.

cycles, farm implements, and education. Since education was free up to the first year of college, the reported increases in spending was largely on books and clothing and indirectly, was related to the greater cost of sending children to school rather than using their labor on the farms.

Improvements in food consumption were reported in all three villages (Table 17). Increased expenditure on education -was greatest in Kariyamangalam where facilities were more developed. While the level of expenditures on house improvements changed only slightly, expenditures on furniture and household appliances, as well as on bicycle and farm equipment, increased.

Many farmers reduced their debts and attributed this to the higher rice profits earned since the adoption of modern varieties. In Kariyamangalam there was a notable increase in savings.

Some farmers acquired land, particularly in Palvarthuvenran, where much of the reported increase in investment in farm enterprises was on land purchases.

CONSTRAINTS TO FURTHER GROWTH

In 1971/72 less than 50 percent of the rice farmers in the three study villages had experimented with modern varieties, and only 20 percent had grown them continuously over the previous three seasons. The gap in farm efficiency and rice income was marked between the few farmers reported in this study and the majority who, while witnessing the new technology in operation on neighboring farms, remained wedded to older inputs and methods. What were the constraints to a more widespread adoption of modern rice varieties?

The major economic constraints were related to the distribution of land and irrigation water. Most of the participants in the HYVP believed

Table 16. Proportion of local and modern variety harvest retained for consumption/seed on sample farms.[a]

village	rice retained (%)			
	wet season		dry season	
	local	modern	local	modern
Kariyamangalam	45	20	87	9
Manmalai	35	16	30	18
Palvarthuvenran	40	24	24	3
avg[b]	40	20	47	10

[a]The balance being sold or given out as wages. [b]Simple average of figures presented above.

Table 17. Changes in the levels of living of sample farmers since the introduction of modern varieties.

increase in	farmers (%) reporting		
	Kariyamangalam	Manmalai	Palvarthuvenran
rice profits	81	98	100
level of living	79	88	42
food consumption	90	68	97
expenditures for education	71	18	33
expenditures on house improvements	27	26	27

that the existing irrigation facilities were inadequate to sustain continuous cropping of rice throughout the year on the majority of farms. The capacity of the tanks was limited and improvement in water supply could come only from additional wells. Simple dug wells were too shallow to provide water in the dry season, and were expensive: a well costing between Rs 8,000 and Rs 10,000 could irrigate about 2.8 hectares in the wet season, but only 1 hectare in the dry season. The cost of deepening existing wells was beyond the capacity of most farmers. The lack of adequate irrigation prevented many farmers from continuing to plant in the dry season, and thus caused them to withdraw from the HYVP.

The lack of capital for the purchase of inputs was another constraint related to farm size. This was recognized by the authorities, and institutional credit facilities were improved for HYVP participants, but not for nonparticipants.

The most serious bottleneck for further growth was an inadequate supply of modern inputs, such as fertilizers and plant protection chemicals, which were often in short supply and (or) available at the wrong times. Finally, the facilities for drying and storing rice in the study area were poorly developed.

In summary, shortages of capital and inputs, and inadequate irrigation, drying, and storage facilities tended to favor the large landholding farmers.

CONCLUSIONS

Agricultural research, administration, and extension services combined successfully in Tamil Nadu to introduce the modern rice varieties and their associated inputs and practices to the farmers. This study focused on the HYVP and sought to identify the main problems and resource bottlenecks. The response of a considerable section of the rice farming community to the HYVP was found to be positive and productive.

Until 1970 much of the attention of the HYVP had focused on the short-run problem of attracting farmers to the modern varieties. For example, under the crash program for IR8, seed and other inputs were taken to the doors of the participants and liberal credit was made available to them. In terms of area sown to IR8 the results were impressive. However, a long-run strategy is needed to make inputs more readily accessible and easily available to all farmers. Those farmers who wait, or who are not prepared to change, will be the most difficult to contact and include in the HYVP.

Several policy issues also arise. First is the major problem of irrigation. In Tamil Nadu surface water for irrigation has long been fully exploited, and groundwater is being used extensively and productively. But without proper planning this may be counterproductive in the long run. There is probably more need for better water management techniques on the farms than for more wells.

Second, the institutions involved in the purchase, storage, and distribution of seed, fertilizers, and chemicals have encountered many short-run problems. Shortages have revealed serious imperfections in the factor market. The demand for inputs is likely to increase rapidly in the future, and adequate supplies must be guaranteed if the farmers now outside the HVYP are to join the program. The whole question of equity is raised by this issue; the present infrastructure and policies favor the larger farmers. A type of oligopoly has emerged in the input market which can impede equitable economic development.

Third, the proper adoption of modern varieties has generated additional farm income. To the extent that this allows farm families to raise their levels of living and clear past debts it will contribute to better farming and greater freedom for farmers to make production and marketing decisions.

Finally, the output and input price components of farm income require the attention of the public and private sectors working together. In the short run the appropriate price policy should motivate farmers to participate to a greater extent in the HYVP. In the long run the policies dealing with product and input prices should encourage farm diversification along with higher rice output per unit of irrigated land.

INDIA

Nainital and Varanasi, Uttar Pradesh

J. S. Sharma

Modern varieties of both rice and wheat have been widely adopted in the study villages in Western and Eastern Uttar Pradesh. The variation in adoption and the use of production inputs, particularly fertilizer and irrigation appeared to be associated more with farm location and size than with rice or wheat production. The physical and socio-economic environment in Nainital was more suitable for modern technology than in the Varanasi villages where many farmers had problems with irrigation, obtaining credit, and obtaining inputs. These problems were more acute among the small farmers than among the medium and large. Most of the small farmers reported no improvement in their standard of living after the introduction of modern varieties.

MODERN VARIETIES of both rice and wheat have been rapidly introduced into parts of Uttar Pradesh (U.P.), India. The rice and wheat technologies are closely linked in terms of changes in production practices and cropping pattern, and thus the changes occurring as a result of the availability of new technology for both crops — rice in the wet season, and wheat in the dry season — were selected for study. One objective was to determine whether there were significant differences in the use of new technology for these two crops. Because of the marked contrast in environment and farm structure between Western and Eastern U.P., villages in these two regions were selected for study.

J. S. Sharma is professor of economics at the G. B. Pant University of Agriculture and Technology, Pantnagar, Nainital District, Uttar Pradesh.
    The author wishes to acknowledge the assistance of R. K. Verma in conducting the field investigations.

THE DISTRICTS

The two selected regions of U.P. were the "Tarai" part of the Nainital District in northwest U.P. and the Varanasi District in eastern U.P. They differ from each other not only in terms of topography, weather, and other ecological factors, but also in their social and economic situations.

Nainital district. The Tarai portion of Nainital District is a narrow sub-mountainous belt lying just to the south of the foothills of the Himalaya mountains in western U.P. The land was under thick forest before 1943 and was brought under cultivation between 1948 and 1953.

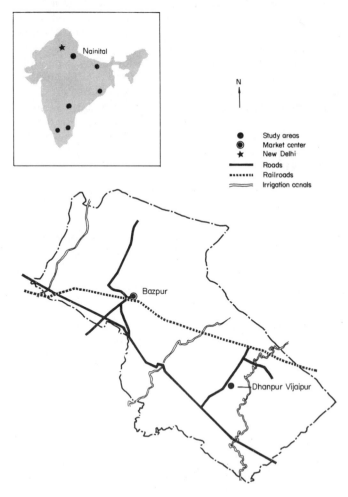

Nainital District, Uttar Pradesh State.

In the early 1950's about 3.0 hectares of cultivable land was allotted to agricultural graduates, 6 hectares to political refugees from Pakistan, and 12 hectares to some of the most progressive farmers in India. The G. B. Pant University of Agriculture and Technology, located in the heart of the Tarai, was instrumental in bringing about considerable progress in the area. A 1969–70 study conducted by the University in this region indicated that large-sized holders adopted new high-yielding varieties of rice and wheat, as did the medium-sized growers. Cash returns per hectare in rice were found to be greater than those in wheat, even though wheat is the staple food in this region.

Rice is grown in the Tarai portion of Nainital during the wet season, from early June to mid-October, while wheat is grown during the dry season, from mid-October to mid-April. The mean annual rainfall is about 1320 mm of which 87 percent is received during the wet season. The amount of precipitation as well as its seasonal distribution varies greatly over the years. Between 1962 and 1971 rainfall varied between 1930 mm and 800 mm giving a range of nearly 1130 mm, equivalent to the average rainfall received during the wet months. Such variations in the precipitation pattern have a major impact on agricultural operations, particularly those used in rice culture.

The soils are rich in organic matter and plant nutrients, are generally 1.0 to 1.5 meters deep, and are underlain with sand and gravel, having developed from calcareous alluvium. Silt loam, loam, silty clay loam,

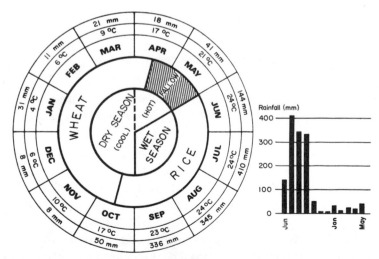

Average monthly rainfall and minimum temperature (Weather Crop Research Station Observatory, Pantnagar, 1967-1971), Nainital District, Uttar Pradesh.

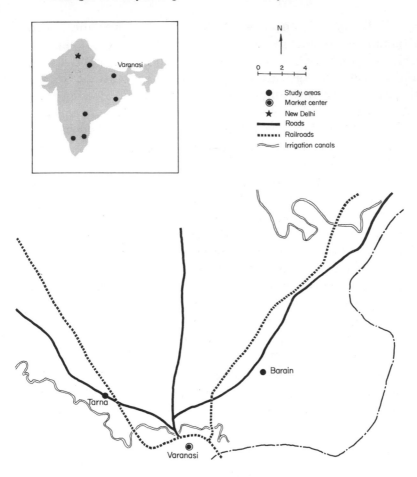

Varanasi District, Uttar Pradesh State.

sandy loam, and clay loam are all present. The water table in the low lying areas, which have the heavier soils, is high and close to the soil surface during the monsoon period. Beginning in October the water table falls until the next May or June; but on the whole, the water table is high and most soils are poorly drained.

Varanasi District. This district is a rice-growing as well as a rice-consuming area. Located in eastern U.P., the district can be divided into two parts: (i) plains tract with both level plains and low-lying plains, and (ii) hills tract. The sampled villages fall in the plains tract, which includes about 75 percent of the Varanasi district. Due to a slight elevation, the western plains of Varanasi are more easily drained than the eastern plains. The watersheds, running at right angles to the Ganges

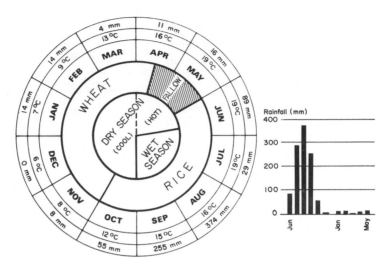

Average monthly rainfall and minimum temperature (UP Rice Research Station, Faizabad, 1967-1971), Varanasi District, Uttar Pradesh.

River, are the main source of drainage in the western region. The eastern part of the plain has a lower elevation and is used extensively for rice cultivation.

The tropical climate of the district is characterized by intense heat and low humidity during the summer. There are three distinct seasons — wet (or rainy season), winter, and summer. The first monsoon showers occur towards the end of the third week of June marking the advent of the wet season which continues through the end of September as in Tarai. Winter lasts from October to March. December and January are the coldest months when the temperature can fall below 0°C or so. Summer starts in April and lasts until about the third week of June, when the first heavy showers begin. Summer is characterized by hot dry winds, with temperatures reaching as high as 39°C.

The average annual rainfall of Varanasi is about 1000 mm (less than that of Tarai region) received over a 55-day period. The distribution of rainfall in the Varanasi district, like that in the Tarai and other parts of the U.P., is uneven; more than 80 percent occurs during the wet season, with the heaviest rainfall occurring during July and August. Rarely is rainfall evenly distributed or available when needed. One month may be extremely dry causing drought conditions followed by flood conditions in ensuing months. Similarly, rainfall in one year may be sparse with a resultant drought causing poor production of rice and other wet season crops. Agriculture in the district is a risky venture.

Table 1. Cropping pattern in percent of operated area.

crop	Dhanpur-Vijaypur	Tarna	Barain
	wet season		
rice-modern	56	33	17
rice-local	17	12	32
maize	7	12	10
sugarcane	13	12	7
millets	7	9	7
pulse	0	5	8
others	0	7	19
	dry season		
wheat-modern	64	48	40
wheat-local	0	8	2
barley and oats	0	0	1
sugarcane	12	12	7
potato	0	9	10
pulse	0	14	5
others	14	9	8
fallow	10	0	27

The soils of the plains are fertile alluvium formed by the Ganges River. While the soils vary widely in texture, they are primarily loams in the plains areas and are deep and well-suited to the cultivation of a wide variety of crops.

THE VILLAGES

The three villages selected for this study were Dhanpur-Vijaypur in the Tarai region of Nainital, and Tarna and Barain in Varanasi District. The Block Development headquarters, which provided technical guidance to the farmers and supplied them with chemicals and other equipment for plant protection, were located close to all three villages. The necessary agricultural inputs, such as fertilizers, pesticides, agricultural machinery, and tools were available either through the Block Development Head-quarters or through private dealers, which in all three villages were located less than 10 km away by good roads.

The interest rate on cooperative loans was about 10 percent per year, but cooperatives provided only a small amount of credit. The private money lender, a major source of credit, particularly for the small farmers, usually charged about 40 percent per year.

All three villages grew a wide range of crops other than rice. Maize, jowar (barley), bajra (millets), and arhar (a pulse) were grown for local consumption, and bringel (eggplant) and other vegetables were grown for the urban market (Table 1). Cropping intensity had increased with the introduction of the modern wheat and rice varieties partly because the practice of keeping land fallow in the wet season to grow wheat in the dry season declined with an increase in the use of improved irrigation facilities and varieties of shorter growth duration. The higher valued wheat and rice crops were gradually replacing the lower valued maize, jowar, and other grains. Rice followed by wheat was the rotation pattern most extensively followed on nearly all farms in the three study villages.

In Varanasi District rice and wheat were mainly subsistence crops and only a small portion of the produce was sold in the market, while in Dhanpur-Vijaypur more than 90 percent was sold. Generally, local merchants bought the products directly from the farmers, but since the roads were good and the villages were near the market center, some farmers went to the market to sell their produce.

Dhanpur-Vijaypur was settled after World War II. Its three hamlets differed in farm size — 12, 6, and 3 hectares, but within each hamlet the land was distributed equally under the land settlement program. The farmers grow wheat, rice, and maize for seed production; the seeds are sold to the Tarai Development Corporation. Sugarcane is also an important crop in the area.

In Barain and Tarna, the environment and the economic conditions are not as favorable as those in Dhanpur-Vijaypur. The major crops are rice in the wet season and wheat in the dry season. Sometimes farmers sell their produce just after harvest to meet credit obligations and later in the season purchase rice and wheat at higher prices for home consumption. While the economy depends principally on farming, farmers often seek employment during the off-season and members of the family look for jobs outside the village to augment the family income.

In Dhanpur-Vijaypur, all the medium and large farms were irrigated, whereas more than one-third of the small farms were not. The main sources of irrigation were canals, tubewells, and artesian wells. Small farmers depended on the canals or on water hired from other farms. Large farmers normally had their own wells to supplement canal irrigation.

Table 2. Basic characteristics of sample farmers.

village	farms (no.) in village	farms (no.) in sample	persons in household (no.)	average farm size (ha)	share tenants (%)	lease holders (%)	owner-operators (%)
Barain	88	57	7	1.2	0	0	100
Tarna	88	43	8	1.2	0	0	100
Dhanpur-Vijaypur	84	51	6	6.0	0	0	100

	area per farm (ha) rice	area per farm (ha) wheat	area irrigated (%) rice	area irrigated (%) wheat	principal form of irrigation
Barain	0.7	0.5	31	100	tube well
Tarna	0.5	0.8	92	100	pumping set
Dhanpur-Vijaypur	3.2	3.8	65	100	canal and pumping set

	modern varieties farmers planting (%) rice	farmers planting (%) wheat	area planted (%) rice	area planted (%) wheat	year of greatest adoption of modern varieties rice	year of greatest adoption of modern varieties wheat
Barain	81	94	50	94	1970	1970
Tarna	100	100	95	85	1969	1970
Dhanpur-Vijaypur	82	100	75	100	1968	1969

In Tarna about 80 percent of the total cultivated land was irrigated. Two-thirds of the farms were irrigated through state tubewells; one-fourth drew water from privately owned pumps. In Barain, which was 90 percent irrigated, about half of the area was served by private tube-wells and half by state tubewells.

The sample. A list of cultivators in each of the three study villages was prepared. Cultivators selected in Barain and Tarna had 30 percent of their total area under rice, while in Dhanpur-Vijaypur the cultivators selected had 60 percent of their cultivated land under rice. The sample consisted of 57 farmers in Barain, 43 in Tarna, and 51 in Dhanpur-Vijaypur (Table 2).

The average family size of the sample farms in Barain and Tarna was larger than in Dhanpur-Vijaypur. Since eastern U.P. (Varanasi) is more densely populated, the average farm size was only slightly over one hectare in Tarna and Barain compared to six hectares in Dhanpur-Vijaypur. The sample farms in all three villages were owner operated.

Rice accounted for 73, 45, and 49 percent of the total cultivated area in Dhanpur-Vijaypur, Tarna, and Barain, respectively. Modern rice varieties were planted on 56, 33, and 17 percent of the total acreage in Dhanpur-Vijaypur, Tarna, and Barain, respectively. The most popular modern high-yielding rice variety was IR 8. Other modern rice varieties grown were Jaya, Padma, and IR 24. The close correlation between the percent of area planted to modern varieties and the percent of area irrigated in each of the three villages are shown in Table 2.

Barain has a large portion of low-lying land where rice is grown without irrigation. Generally only one crop is grown on these low-lying rice lands, as fields are not dry enough to be in condition for the time of sowing of winter wheats.

During the winter, 64 percent of the farm area was planted to wheat in Dhanpur-Vijaypur, 56 percent in Tarna, and 42 percent in Barain. All of the wheat area was irrigated, and almost all of the area planted to modern varieties. Among the several modern varieties of wheat grown in this area, R R-21 was the most widely grown in all three villages during the survey year.

APPLICATION OF NEW TECHNOLOGY

Technological change is associated with the inputs used in modern farming practices and not only with the number of farmers growing modern varieties or the area planted. The use of modern inputs and modern farm practices are necessary to realize the high yield potential of the new varieties. In the survey, farmers were asked about changes in farming practices for both rice and wheat.

The percentage of farmers adopting, specified production practices for rice and wheat prior to and after 1965 is shown in Table 3. The percentage of farmers using these same practices at the time of the survey, 1971/72, is presented in Table 4.

Progress in the use of modern varieties. Taichung Native 1 was the first modern rice variety to be successfully introduced in India in 1966. By 1968, 80 percent of the farmers studied in the Tarai were growing

Table 3. Proportion of farmers adopting specified production practices for rice and wheat before and after 1965 (percent).

production practice	Dhanpur-Vijaypur				Tarna				Barain			
	rice		wheat		rice		wheat		rice		wheat	
	before 1965	after 1965	before 1965	after 1965	before 1965	after 1965	before 1965	after 1965	before 1965	after 1965	before 1965	after 1965
1. HYV seeds	0	100	0	100	0	100	0	100	0	82	0	98
2. irrigation												
a. canal	88	92	88	92	0	0	0	0	0	0	0	0
b. tube well	0	65	0	65	2	98	2	98	2	98	0	98
3. chemical fertilizers	6	100	6	100	23	100	37	100	39	100	42	100
4. insecticides	2	80	16	88	0	33	14	58	0	23	0	25
5. herbicides	0	18	8	24	0	0	0	0	0	4	0	0
6. straight row planting	0	45	39	98	0	100	40	98	0	98	39	100
7. tractors	0	86	0	90	0	2	0	3	2	4	0	4
8. handweeding	100	0	100	100	100	100	100	100	100	100	100	100
9. double cropping	88	100	0	0	51	93	0	0	49	98	0	0

the new varieties. But in the Varanasi village a majority of farmers adopted modern varieties several years later. By 1971–72, 82 percent of the farmers in Barain and all farmers in Tarna were growing modern varieties.

A majority of farmers had adopted the modern wheat varieties by 1967 in Tarai and by 1968 in Varanasi. By 1971–72, 98 percent of the farmers in Barain and all of the farmers in Dhanpur-Vijaypur and Tarna were growing the new wheat varieties. The lower level of adoption in Barain appears to be due to the presence of low-lying poorly drained land that is ill-suited to the new varieties and modern technology.

The pattern of adoption of new rice varieties and technology was influenced by both farm size and location (Fig. 1). Adoption began in 1966 in the Tarai village, progressing more rapidly on the large farms than on the small farms. In eastern U.P. adoption first occurred on the large farms, and did not begin on the small farms until two years later; but by 1971, all farmers had tried the modern varieties.

Trends in farming practices. Fertilizers were used by very few farmers in the study villages before 1966. However, with the expansion of irrigation facilities and the introduction of modern varieties, by 1971–72 essentially all farmers in the three villages were using chemical fertilizers. The use of fertilizers and modern varieties was higher on the irrigated than on the non-irrigated, low-lying water-logged areas. Nevertheless, fertilizer rates were still below the recommended levels.

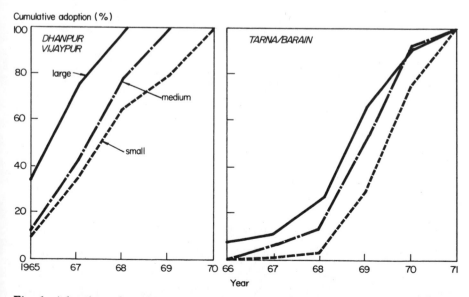

Fig. 1. Adoption of modern varieties by size of farm. Dhanpur Vijaypur: small = 3 ha; medium = 6 ha; large = 12 ha. Tarnal/Barain: small = less than 1 ha; medium = 1 to 1.9 ha; large = 2 ha and over.

Hand weeding was the sole means of weed control for all of the farmers for many years. Some farmers in Dhanpur-Vijaypur experimented with herbicides during the survey year, spraying 2, 4-D about a month after transplanting. There were no mechanical weeders in the study villages.

Insecticides were widely adopted with the introduction of the modern wheat and rice varieties. However, their use was greater in Dhanpur-Vijaypur, where farmers could more easily afford the additional expense, than in Tarna or Barain.

Four-wheel tractors became popular in 1970–71 in the Tarai, and were being used by most of the survey farmers in Dhanpur-Vijaypur (Table 4). The tractors were used principally for land preparation and threshing. On the considerably smaller farms in Tarna and Barain, only one or two farmers were using tractors.

Irrigation facilities differed considerably among the three villages. The introduction of modern varieties greatly increased the demand for irrigation water and pump sets and when water was not available from government canals (Dhanpur-Vijaypur) or state tubewells (Tarna and Barain) farmers purchased private pumpsets. By 1971–72 essentially all farmers in the three villages had access to some form of irrigation, the quality of which varied widely. In Dhanpur-Vijaypur for example, some farmers dissatified with the canal system purchased pumpsets. In Tarna and particularly in Barain, despite the introduction of state tubewells,

Table 4. Farmers' use of improved practices at the time of survey, 1971–72.

practice	farmers (%)					
	Dhanpur-Vijaypur		Tarna		Barain	
	rice	wheat	rice	wheat	rice	wheat
HYV seeds	82	100	100	100	81	94
irrigation						
a. canal	92	92	0	0	0	0
b. tubewells	39	31	100	23	98	98
chemical fertilizers	100	100	100	100	100	100
insecticides	80	41	33	7	14	8
herbicides	18	n.a.	0	n.a.	4	n.a.
straight row planting	41	n.a.	100	n.a.	100	n.a.
tractors	86	82	2	7	3	2
handweeding	100	n.a.	100	n.a.	100	n.a.

inadequate drainage in the low-lying areas prevented the use of new varieties and modern inputs.

Double cropping was practiced on about half of the farms before 1966. However, the introduction of modern varieties and the greater availability of irrigation water not only intensified cropping but also changed the cropping pattern. Prior to 1966 rice and wheat could not be grown in succession on the same farm. Thus, various millets, corn, and sugarcane were more widely grown before 1966 than they were at the time of the survey.

Yield of modern versus local varieties. The yields of modern varieties are compared with those of local varieties in Table 5, where the standard deviation (s_x) indicates a measure of the variability in the yields and the rate at which nitrogen fertilizer was applied.

The yield and level of nitrogen input was greater for the modern varieties than for the local varieties of both rice and wheat. The variability in yield indicates the risk involved in crop production. Ideally, to compare the risk involved in growing rice versus wheat for an individual farmer, the variation in yield over time should be known. However, the standard deviation shown in Table 5 is a measure of the variability in yield during the survey year, and it was greater for rice in Dhanpur-Vijaypur than for any other situation. The comparable levels of nitrogen input for both rice and wheat provided no indication that farmers viewed one crop as being riskier than the other.

Yield comparisons were made by farm size, by source of irrigation (owned versus hired), and by irrigated versus non-irrigated area. For the first two categories, in most cases the yields did not differ significantly. There was a big difference between irrigated and non-irrigated yields (Table 6). However, as the following data show, farmers generally grew modern rice and wheat varieties on irrigated land.

Percent of area irrigated

	Dhanpur-Vijaypur	*Tarna*	*Barain*
Rice – local	75	80	17
Rice – modern	96	99	96
Wheat – modern	100	100	100

Yields tended to be somewhat higher on irrigated paddy when the farmer had his own source of irrigation, because it was a dependable source of water when needed.

Costs and returns. The total cost of production includes expenses for all inputs, actual and imputed, with the exception of land. The average

Table 5. Rice and wheat mean yield, standard deviation S_d, and nitrogen input per hectare.

varietal type	Dhanpur-Vijaypur yield				Tarna yield				Barain yield			
	farm (no.)	mean (t/ha)	S_x[a] (t/ha)	N (kg/ha)	farm (no.)	mean (t/ha)	S_x (t/ha)	N (kg/ha)	farm (no.)	mean (t/ha)	S_x (t/ha)	N (kg/ha)
						rice						
modern	40	4.7	1.0	94	43	3.7	0.8	84	44	3.7	0.4	81
local	29	2.6	0.5	62	14	1.7	0.7	31	53	1.7	0.4	25
						wheat						
modern	46	3.1	0.6	97	43	3.2	0.5	79	53	3.2	0.4	76
local	n.a.[b]	n.a.	n.a.	n.a.	10	2.2	0.6	44	8	2.5	0.4	52

[a] S_x — standard deviation. [b] n.a. — not applicable because it was not planted.

Table 6. Yield of rice under irrigated and non-irrigated conditions.

| | yield (t/ha) | | | | | |
| | Dhanpur-Vijaypur | | Tarna | | Barain | |
	modern	local	modern	local	modern	local
irrigated	4.7	2.6	3.7	1.7	3.7	1.7
unirrigated	3.6	2.4	2.9	1.7	2.4	1.6

cost per hectare was higher for modern than for local wheat and rice varieties in each of the three villages, but the cost per ton was lower (Tables 7 and 8).

The net returns per hectare were higher for modern than for local varieties of both wheat and rice. Although the net returns per hectare were very similar for wheat in all three villages, they were significantly higher for rice in Dhanpur-Vijaypur than in the other two villages.

The factors responsible for differences in costs and returns among villages are yield, costs of inputs, levels of technology, and differences in environmental factors. In Dhanpur-Vijaypur farmers spent more on fertilizers and chemicals than did farmers in the other two villages, accounting for the higher rice yields. At the same time their costs for

Table 7. Costs and return for modern and local varieties of rice, 1971.

| | rupees[a]/ha | | | | | |
| item | modern | | | local | | |
	Dhanpur-Vijaypur	Tarna	Barain	Dhanpur-Vijaypur	Tarna	Barain
fertilizer	456	302	288	197	139	76
plant protection	22	13	8	6	0	1
irrigation	46	163	155	33	56	7
pre-harvest labor[b]	495	710	678	507	617	575
harvesting and threshing	144	137	128	70	122	97
total cost	1163	1325	1257	813	934	749
gross return	2845	2080	2160	1820	1386	1360
net return	1682	755	903	1007	452	611
cost per ton	268	404	393	324	559	446

[a]7.5 rupees = U.S. $1.00 (official rate). [b]Land preparation, planting, weeding, and cultivating.

Table 8. Costs and returns for modern and local varieties of wheat, 1972.

| item | rupees[a]/ha | | | | |
| | modern | | | local | |
	Dhanpur-Vijaypur	Tarna	Barain	Tarna	Barain
fertilizer	302	278	240	187	236
plant protection	17	0	0	0	0
irrigation	190	154	133	146	125
pre-harvest labor[b]	494	624	688	617	621
harvesting and threshing	163	145	141	115	114
total cost	1166	1201	1202	1065	1096
gross return	2356	2400	2356	1760	1888
net return	1190	1199	1154	695	792
cost per ton	376	375	388	484	457

[a] 7.5 rupees = U.S. $1.00 (official rate). [b] Land preparation, planting, weeding, and cultivating.

irrigation were lower, and the land preparation costs were also lower because tractors were used to help prepare the wheat and paddy fields.

AVAILABILITY OF INPUTS AND LABOR USE

New seeds were obtained from several sources. In Varanasi, Block Headquarters was the main source of new rice and wheat seeds, but farmers commonly obtained seeds of the new varieties from their neighbors. In Tarai the major source of seeds was the market. Villagers also obtained seeds from the Tarai Development Corporation at Pantnagar.

Fertilizers and insecticides were purchased principally in the free market. A small amount was distributed through the Block Head-quarters, and an even smaller amount through the cooperatives. In the two villages near Varanasi, small and medium farmers made about 87 percent of their total purchases from the market while large farmers purchased only 48 percent, suggesting that this latter group was able to take advantage of the somewhat lower prices and interest rates offered by the block and the cooperatives.

Growing modern varieties requires additional cash for fertilizer, chemicals, labor, and irrigation. Hence farmers' demands for credit increases to meet these additional cash expenses. While the availability of cash, owned or borrowed, varied among farmers, it was directly dependent on the size of their land holdings. Since small farmers generally had no investible funds from their own savings, credit was important in determining the adoption of improved rice and wheat technology.

Although there was a good network of formal credit institutions in the study area, most farmers depended upon private credit from village traders and merchants, and paid a very high rate of interest. Far more credit was available from cooperatives and banks in Dhanpur-Vijaypur than in Tarna or Barain, where farmers depended upon a wide variety of sources other than banks for credit (Table 9).

Labor requirements. Labor utilization for growing modern rice varieties appeared to be about 15–20 percent greater than for local varieties (Table 10). The difference was less pronounced for wheat. The labor

Table 9. Credit borrowed per farm (rupees[a]) from different agencies.

source	Dhanpur-Vijaypur	Tarna	Barain
money lenders and traders			
cash	.549	14	26
kind	98	1	0
cooperative and sugarcane society			
cash	257	82	18
kind	394	5	16
government			
cash	12	47	38
kind	60	46	31
relatives			
cash	39	116	0
kind	0	0	0
banks			
cash	512	0	0
kind	608	0	0
Total	2529	311	129

[a]7.5 rupees = U.S. $1.00

Table 10. Labor required for modern and local varieties of rice and wheat.

task	labor required (man-days/ha)											
	Dhanpur-Vijaypur				Tarna				Barain			
	modern		local		modern		local		modern		local	
	family	hired	family	hired	family	hired	family	hired	family	hired	family	hired
rice												
land preparation	4	5	6	3	20	4	18	4	25	1	21	0
transplanting	0	33	0	41	29	9	26	14	26	11	27	11
interculture (weeding, etc.)	0	36	0	21	21	11	17	5	25	6	18	2
pre-harvest total	4	74	6	65	70	24	61	23	76	18	66	13
harvesting, threshing, and winnowing	0	44	0	26	37	15	32	14	44	10	32	6
total	4	118	6	91	107	39	93	37	120	28	98	19
grand total	122		97		146		130		148		117	
wheat												
land preparation	6	4	n.a.[a]	n.a.	24	4	16	10	26	4	30	0
sowing	2	0	n.a.	n.a.	7	1	6	3	8	1	9	0
interculture (weeding, etc.)	0	20	n.a.	n.a.	19	9	11	9	25	8	31	4
pre-harvest total	8	24	n.a.	n.a.	50	14	33	22	59	13	70	4
harvesting, threshing, and winnowing	0	35	n.a.	n.a.	29	13	21	16	29	10	43	0
total	8	59	n.a.	n.a.	79	27	54	38	88	23	113	4
grand total	67		n.a.		106		92		111		117	

[a] n.a. = not applicable because it was not included

requirements for land preparation and transplanting for modern rice varieties were similar to those for local varieties. But there were marked differences in the amount of labor used for weeding, application of fertilizer and other culture practices, as well as for harvesting and threshing.

The proportion of hired labor to family labor was much higher in Dhanpur-Vijaypur than in Tarna or Barain. Because the Tarai farms are typically much larger, more hired labor is used. In Varanasi most of the work is done by the farm family with hired labor employed only during peak seasons. The total labor requirements for rice production were lower in the Tarai because of the more widespread use of mechanization.

Hired laborers that worked in the Tarai migrated from other regions, particularly eastern U.P. and Bihar where there was a labor surplus. Large farms maintained a permanent labor force, but during the peak seasons there was frequently a labor shortage. In Tarna and Barain where labor was more plentiful, large farms experienced labor shortages during peak seasons because some laborers left for jobs in the nearby city of Varanasi.

CONSTRAINTS TO INCREASED PRODUCTION

Although there was good progress achieved in the adoption of modern technology by farmers, there were still some farmers who either did not grow modern varieties or who planted these new varieties on only a portion of their land using limited amounts of modern inputs. Problems in growing modern varieties of rice and wheat occurred in four principal areas: (1) irrigation and water control, (2) availability of inputs, (3) obtaining credit, and (4) management. The major constraints to increased rice production identified by farmers surveyed are presented in Table 11.

Irrigation essential for the adoption of modern rice technology, was reported to be one of the major constraints in Varanasi. In Barain, where almost all of the farmers identified irrigation as a problem, there was only one state tubewell serving the village. The area served by the well was over-extended, and the irrigation channels connecting the fields with the tubewell were not completed. In Tarna, some of the smaller farms had irrigation problems because they depended only on canal irrigation.

Availability of inputs, particularly fertilizer, was reported as a problem on about 50 percent of the farms. Black marketing of fertilizer was prevalent in both regions. The problems of obtaining good seed was acute in Tarna and Barain but not serious in Dhanpur-Vijaypur.

Obtaining credit was a more critical problem as a result of the intro-

Table 11. Farmers' perception of requirements needed to expand use of modern rice technology.

need	farmers (%) responding		
	Dhanpur-Vijaypur	Tarna	Barain
adequate quantity and quality of seeds	20	81	82
timely availability of an adequate amount of fertilizer	61	56	49
availability of credit from institutional resources	59	91	91
minimize disease and pests	45	5	19
solution to irrigation problems	51	72	96
reclamation of land	0	0	19
consolidation of land	0	44	28
more knowledge about new rice technology	31	40	28

duction of modern varieties. The problem was more serious on small farms than on large farms, and hence in Varanasi than in Tarai.

Management problems differed between the large and small farms. The large farmer, who had more contact with influential farmers outside the locality, could pay for inputs and obtain credit from institutional sources. He had the time, knowledge, money, power, and influence to bargain and press obligations. On the other hand, the small-sized farmer was economically weak and continually at a disadvantage for buying inputs, selling outputs, and obtaining credit from institutional sources.

CHANGES IN MARKETING, INCOME, AND CONSUMPTION

Marketed surplus. The bulk of the rice and wheat, both modern and local varieties produced in Dhanpur-Vijaypur was sold; in Tarna and Barain less than half was sold and a higher proportion of the local varieties were consumed at home as compared with modern varieties (Table 12). Note however, that only 5 percent of the total rice area in Tarna was planted to local varieties, 25 percent in Dhanpur-Vijaypur, and 50 percent in Barain.

Table 12. Marketing patterns in the three survey villages.

varietal type	Dhanpur-Vijaypur		Tarna		Barain	
	rice	wheat	rice	wheat	rice	wheat
	marketed (%)					
modern	96	85	42	23	56	36
local	82	n.a.	16	0	16	0
	producers selling (%)					
modern	82	90	70	47	51	33
local	59	n.a.[a]	7	0	16	0
	surplus sold in villages (%)					
modern	0	60	59	47	87	95
local	0	n.a.	100	0	80	0
	surplus sold in one month (%)					
	80	76	91	92	95	96

[a]n.a. — not applicable because it was not planted.

In Dhanpur-Vijaypur farmers sold most of their rice and wheat production to the millers in the market. In Tarna and Barain, more than 50 percent of the surplus was sold within the village because landless laborers purchased much of the surplus grain.

About 90 percent of the rice and wheat was sold within a month after the harvest in Tarna and Barain, while in Dhanpur-Vijaypur about 20 percent of the farmers delayed their sales until a later time.

Income. A large percentage of farmers reported an increase in farm income and level of living during the period of adoption of new varieties of wheat and rice (Table 13). Between 20 and 25 percent also reported an increase in nonfarm income. The adoption of the new varieties was accompanied by a number of other changes – improved irrigation, increased use of fertilizer, and an intensification of the cropping pattern – all of which contributed to the higher farm incomes. In all three villages, more growers reported higher incomes than reported an increased standard of living.

Not surprisingly, the percentage reporting improvements in the standard of living was highest in Dhanpur-Vijaypur (82 percent) and lowest in Barain (49 percent). In all three villages the percentage

Table 13. Changes in farm income and standard of living since the introduction of modern varieties.

farm type	farm income (%)			level of living (%)		
	increase	same	decrease	increase	same	decrease
	Dhanpur-Vijaypur					
small[a]	90	10	0	64	36	0
medium	98	2	0	100	0	0
large	90	10	0	83	17	0
all	93	7	0	82	18	0
	Tarna					
small	88	12	0	44	50	6
medium	88	12	0	87	13	0
large	90	10	0	81	19	0
all	88	12	0	70	28	2
	Barain					
small	64	36	0	33	59	8
medium	74	26	0	75	25	0
large	94	6	0	79	21	0
all	76	24	0	49	49	2

[a]In Dhanpur-Vijaypur, small = 3 ha; medium = 6 ha; large = 12 ha. In Tarna and Barain, small = less than 1 ha, medium = less than 2 ha, large = 2 ha or more.

reporting improvements in standard of living was much lower among the small farmers than among the medium and large farmers. For example, in Barain only 33 percent of the small farmers reported an improvement as compared with 75 percent or more of the medium and large farms.

Consumption. Where and how did the farmers spend their incomes? Expenditures increased in a wide range of areas (Table 14). Increased food consumption was reported by a large proportion of the farmers. There was not much improvement in housing, but the majority of farmers in the three villages reported that they constructed farm buildings. Radios and bicycles were the most commonly purchased items. In the Varanasi area many farmers had invested in agriculture; for example, in Tarna 10 new tubewells were installed in the crop year 1971–72, and 10 farmers purchased tractors.

Table 14. Percentage of farmers reporting increase in consumption and investment with the introduction of modern varieties in 1965.

consumption item	Dhanpur-Vijaypur	Tarna	Barain
food	80	60	45
clothing	50	40	30
education	50	30	20
housing	10	5	2
medical	40	45	35
travelling	30	25	22
marriage	3	1	0
motorcycle	1	0	0
bicycles	68	74	35
radio	30	20	15
other household appliances	40	30	20
investment in:			
tubewells	65	96	96
tractors	86	2	2

CONCLUSIONS

A major change has accompanied the introduction of modern varieties of rice and wheat in all three of the study villages. Nearly all the wheat farmers and more than 80 percent of the rice producers were using modern varieties on at least a portion of their farms. However, in all three of the study villages local rice varieties were still being grown particularly in low-lying poorly drained areas. In Dhanpur-Vijaypur and Barain, 25 and 50 percent of the cropped area was planted to local varieties, respectively.

Both the physical and the socio-economic environments in Dhanpur-Vijaypur were more favorable for the production of the new varieties than those in Barain and Tarna. Higher yields in Dhanpur-Vijaypur were accompanied by an increased use of modern inputs such as fertilizer and insecticides. Tractors were also more prevalent. Inputs were generally more difficult to obtain in Tarna and Barain. The lack of institutional credit facilities forced farmers to borrow from village money lenders and traders at interest rates of 30 to 40 percent per annum. However, the major obstacles to the spread of modern technology in Barain were the inadequate irrigation and drainage facilities.

Higher yields resulted in a higher net return for modern rice and wheat varieties as compared with the local varieties. While costs per hectare were higher for modern than for local varieties, costs per ton were lower. The higher cost per hectare for rice was due not only to a higher expenditure for cash input such as fertilizer, but also to an approximately 20 percent greater labor use. The level of nitrogen input for rice was comparable with that for wheat. There was no evidence, on the basis of fertilizer use, that farmers regarded one crop as riskier than the other.

Associated with the adoption of modern varieties of cereal grains, was a reported increase in farm income on the majority of farms. The additional income was spent for a wide range of consumption and production items, with increased food consumption being the most frequently mentioned item among farmers in all three villages. The percentage of farmers reporting an increase in the standard of living is somewhat smaller than the percentage reporting higher incomes in each of the three villages.

The benefits of the new technology were fairly widespread; they were associated not only with location but also with farm size. Nearly all of the medium and large farms and 64 percent of the small farms in Dhanpur-Vijaypur reported higher incomes and standard of living. But in Barain where the physical and socio-economic environment were less favorable 64 percent of the small farms reported a higher income, and only 33 percent reported an increase in the standard of living.

In summary, there was considerable margin for increasing farm production, particularly in the Varanasi villages, and for providing a more equitable distribution of benefits. There are signs that the small farms were losing ground relative to the large farms even though they were able to maintain comparable yield levels using the modern technology.

INDIA

Shimoga, Mysore

A. N. Krishna Murthy

Modern varieties have been widely adopted, and the yield is generally high. The yield and the level of fertilizer input vary by farm size, being greatest on the large farms. The relationship between farm size and use of credit is even more striking, with large farms borrowing more credit in total and borrowing a larger share of their credit from cooperatives and banks as opposed to private sources. Most farmers have made major changes in their production methods, and there is a healthy climate for further extension of modern methods of rice farming.

MYSORE IS NOT ONE OF INDIA'S major rice producing states. It ranks only ninth out of 16 in area planted to rice. Nor is it a state in which the High Yielding Varieties Program (HYVP) for rice has been particularly well received by farmers. In 1971/72 modern varieties covered only 15 percent of the total area under rice (Mysore is the twelfth-ranking state in proportion of rice land planted to modern varieties). But there are pockets in Mysore where modern varieties have been well received. The district of Shimoga is one of them.

Shimoga produces more rice than any other Mysore district although it has the second largest rice area, and rice accounts for only about 6 percent of the district's cultivated area of 303,000 hectares. Just under half of the cultivated area is irrigated in the wet season, mainly from canals and tanks. With the development of canal irrigation and the establishment of several large industrial operations such as iron and steel works, paper mills, a cement factory, a sugar mill, and a hydroelectric station, Shimoga has become one of Mysore's more prosperous districts.

A. N. Krishna Murthy is assistant professor of economics at the University of Agricultural Sciences, Bangalore, Mysore.

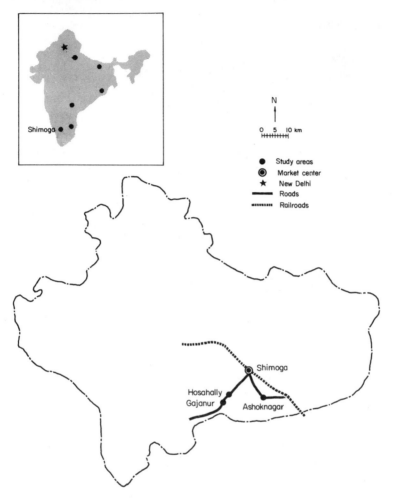

Shimoga District, Mysore State.

The villages. Two sites in Shimoga district were selected for study. The first site includes two villages, Gajanur and Hosahally. The villages' fields adjoin and their farmers share the irrigation system and grow the same crops. Because of these similarities the two villages were treated as one study site.

Gajanur-Hosahally lies along a state highway about 10 kilometers from Shimoga Town, the center of the district administration. Irrigation water comes by canal from a 20-meter-high dam across the Tunga River only a few kilometers from the villages. Constructed in 1954, this dam supplies water to 75 villages and irrigates 21,500 hectares.

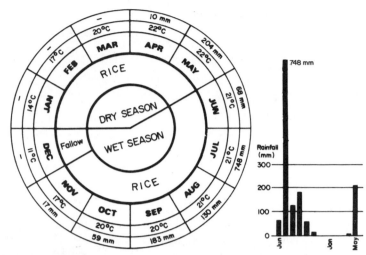

Average monthly rainfall and minimum temperature (1970-71), Shimoga, Mysore.

The second study site, Ashoknagar village, lies about 15 kilometers west of Gajanur-Hosahally. Shimoga Town and the industrial center of Bhadravathi are less than 20 kilometers away. Irrigation water comes from the Bhadra Dam which was completed in 1964 just before the HYVP introduced modern rice varieties to the village.

Rice is the main crop in both sites, although other crops take up almost half the area cultivated in the wet season in Gajanur-Hosahally and nearly a quarter in Ashoknagar (Table 1).

Rice is much more important in Gajanur-Hosahally than these figures indicate, at least for the majority of farmers. On farms under 3 hectares, rice accounted for 84 percent of area cropped in the wet season. On the relatively few large farms it took up only about 40 percent. This difference in cropping patterns between large and small farms, with the large farms producing most of the sugarcane and arecanut (a relative of betelnut), does not occur in Ashoknagar. In both study sites, however, dependence on rice in the wet season is related inversely to farm size:

Farm size	Gajanur-Hosahally	Ashoknagar
Under 1 ha	90%	83%
1 to 1.9 ha	81	92
2 to 2.9 ha	84	70
over 3 ha	40	63

The rice area in the dry season at each site from year to year depends on how much water is available in the canals and how the water is distrib-

Table 1. Main wet-season crops.

site	crop area (%)					
	rice	sugarcane	arecanut	finger millet	chillies	other crops
Gajanur-Hosahally	54	16	8	2	2	18
Ashoknagar	74	5	2	8	–	11

uted. The crop year 1971/72 was considered reasonably good and rice was planted on a third of the operated area in Gajanur-Hosahally and on two-thirds in Ashoknagar. Rice is not grown without irrigation in either site in either season.

The population of Gajanur-Hosahally in 1971 was 3,316 and the villagers farmed 757 hectares. Ashoknagar had a population of 1,330 and its cultivated area was 415 hectares. There were 243 farms in Gajanur-Hosahally (median area: 3.3 hectares) and about half the population were members of farm households. Ashoknagar had 140 farms (median area: 2.8 hectares) and nearly 90 percent of its population were members of farm households. Ashoknagar is a settlement of farmers whose original lands were irrigated in the 1950's under the Lakkavalli Dam project; it forms a subvillage of the old village of Yedihally.

Being close to Shimoga Town, and on good roads, both sites have easy access to agricultural and administration offices, input supply depots, markets, and banks. Gajanur and Hosahally each has its own multi-purpose cooperative society, and Gajanur is the home of the village level worker and a fertilizer depot. Ashoknagar has no such institutions and facilities, but like Gajanur-Hosahally it has its own elementary school and intermediate and secondary schools are nearby. All three villages have electricity.

The cycle of agricultural operations in the area is geared to the marked wet season and dry season. The highest monthly precipitation normally occurs in July (748 mm during the survey year), and the highest temperatures are usually recorded in April at the beginning of the monsoon. The lowest temperatures coincide with the peak of the wet season in June, July, and August.

Work on seed nurseries, and land preparation for the main (wet season) rice crop takes up most of June, normally a relatively dry month. The crop is harvested in November at the end of the rainy season. In January, nursery work and land preparation begin again for the dry season rice crop and this is harvested in May, often during the first heavy rains of the monsoon. The farmers in the study sites have experienced several major changes in production methods and the use of inputs in the last decade. The first, and probably the greatest, was the coming of canal water: 1954 for Gajanur-Hosahally, and 10 years later for Ashoknagar. The most recent was the coming of modern rice varieties through the HYVP. This was in 1966/67. The HYVP promised the farmers substantially higher rice yields and profits if they used the new seeds with high rates of fertilizers, chemical control of pests and diseases, and careful water management. For many farmers it was to prove no idle promise.

The sample. In selecting a sample of farmers, the three villages were treated separately, but the same selection method was used in each. After conducting village surveys three groups of farmers were identified: (1) those who, in the wet season, planted their entire rice area to modern varieties, (2) those who planted 30 to 60 percent to modern varieties, and (3) those who planted only local varieties. The sample of 142 farmers (from a population of 383) was drawn from these three groups.

The farmers were interviewed during the 1971 wet season and again during the following season (1972 dry season). All farmers selected from the third group were found to plant modern varieties in the dry season. Characteristics of the sample farms are summarized in Tables 2 and 3.

ADOPTION OF MODERN VARIETIES

Modern varieties of rice were introduced in Shimoga district in 1966/67 through the HYVP. Taichung Native 1 was the first variety to be released, but in 1967/68 the main emphasis of the program switched to IR8. During the next 2 years, IR8 and the Indian variety Jaya were released, and by 1971/72 these varieties were beginning to challenge IR8 for supremacy in the preferences of many farmers.

In 1971/72 most farmers in Gajanur-Hosahally and Ashoknagar were heavily committed to modern varieties in both seasons, although local varieties continued to be important in Ashoknagar in the wet season.

More rice is planted in the wet season. In the 1972 dry season the rice area was 30 percent less than the area sown in the previous wet season. The drop was not large in Ashoknagar (16%), but it was severe in Gajanur-Hosahally (40%). Although a breach in the wall of the canal serving some farmers in Gajanur aggravated this situation in 1972, the dry-season irrigated area normally fluctuates from year to year and 1972 was not considered a particularly poor year even in Gajanur

Table 2. Characteristics of the sample farms.

site	farms (no.) in		persons in household (no.)	farm size (ha)
	village	sample		
Gajanur-Hosahally	243	91	7.1	3.3
Ashoknagar	140	51	7.5	2.8

	rice area				principal form of irrigation
	per farm (ha)		double cropped (%)	irrigated (%)	
	wet season	dry season			
Gajanur-Hosahally	1.8	1.3	60	100	canal
Ashoknagar	2.2	1.9	84	100	canal

	modern varieties				year of greatest adoption
	farms planting (%)		rice area planted (%)		
	wet season	dry season	wet season	dry season	
Gajanur-Hosahally	90	99	88	99	1967
Ashoknagar	72	100	62	100	1968

(except perhaps by the farmers affected by the canal breach).

As a consequence of this area reduction, while the proportion of rice area planted to modern varieties in Gajanur-Hosahally increased from 85 to 95 percent, the area itself fell by a third. In Ashoknagar, on the other hand, the proportion increased from 62 to 100 percent and the area planted to modern varieties rose by a third.

It is worth repeating that the distinction between 100%, 30–60%, and 0% adoptors of modern varieties (on which the farm sample was based) referred to the wet-season plantings. In the dry season almost all farmers in Gajanur-Hosahally and all farmers in Ashoknagar planted modern varieties exclusively and the distinction therefore ceased to exist.

The villages differed in their preferences for varieties. Ashoknagar farmers planted most of their land to Jaya in both seasons:

season	*IR 8/IR 20*	*Jaya*
wet	28%	72%
dry	36	74

Table 3. Adoption of modern varieties in the 1971 wet season in relation to farm size.

farm size	farms (no.) adopting			
	100%	30–60%	0%	Total
	Gajanur-Hosahally			
Over 3 ha	28	9	2	39
2 to 2.9 ha	17	3	2	22
1 to 1.9 ha	10	3	2	15
Under 1 ha	12	0	3	15
Total	67	15	9	91
	Ashoknagar			
Over 3 ha	10	4	4	18
2 to 2.9 ha	7	2	7	16
1 to 1.9 ha	5	2	2	9
Under 1 ha	5	2	1	8
Total	27	10	14	51

But in Gajanur-Hosahally, the two IRRI varieties (IR 8 and IR 20) held a slight edge over Jaya in the wet season, but the pattern was reversed in the dry season:

season	*IR 8/IR 20*	*Jaya*
wet	53%	47%
dry	42	58

In both study sites most farmers planted more than one variety in each season. This, they said, was mainly a precaution against possible diseases and also changes in relative market prices between varieties.

CHANGES IN RICE FARMING PRACTICES

Several changes in farming technology are associated with the adoption of seeds of modern varieties such as IR 8, IR 20, and Jaya. For high yields, modern varieties require increased purchases of inputs such as chemical fertilizers, herbicides and insecticides, and labor, and for many farmers much of this increased expenditure must be financed by short- and medium-term borrowing.

Chemical fertilizers. Chemical fertilizers are certainly not new in the district but with the spread of modern varieties of rice there has been a substantial increase in the area on which fertilizers have been applied (associated closely with the increase in the area planted to modern rice varieties), and a large increase in the quantities applied per hectare (on modern varieties compared with local varieties).

Some farmers used chemical fertilizers on local varieties before 1967 but this could not be quantified for the study sites. In 1972 wet season the one "non-adoptor" farmer who used chemical fertilizer on a local variety applied 43–21–21 kg/ha ($N-P_2O_5-K_2O$). In the following dry season he doubled this rate on the modern variety he planted. All the other wet-season "non-adoptors" switched to modern varieties in the dry season and switched from no fertilizer use to heavy fertilizer use at the same time. This indicates the sort of change that has taken place in the use of fertilizer in the villages since about 1967. Over the same period, the supply of fertilizers through the agencies of the state's HYVP has improved greatly.

In both seasons of 1971/72 all farmers who grew modern varieties applied chemical fertilizers to them in quantities that far surpassed anything they might earlier have applied to local varieties. The mean rates reported by the sample farmers was 144–60–72 in the wet season and 136–55–78 in the dry season. These averages were only slightly under the general zonal recommendation for IR8 and Jaya of 150–75–75. This recommendation, however, may not have been right for most farmers.

Variation in the levels of fertilizer use were found not only between seasons and between modern and local varieties, but also between farms, and between the mean applications in the two study sites.

There was a much heavier use of nitrogen fertilizer in Ashoknagar in both seasons (Table 4). The seasonal variation is clear from these figures and occurred in both study sites. The differences between the study sites in the use of nitrogen is reflected, broadly, in the mean yields obtained (Table 4). It can be seen here that the output per kilogram of fertilizer was higher in the dry season, particularly in Ashoknagar. While higher rates of fertilizer were used in the wet season, the highest yields were obtained in the dry season. Since fertilizer represents the largest single cost component of production, the dry-season crop has become particularly important in terms of the profitability of rice production over the agricultural year. This may help explain the complete switch to modern varieties in the dry season, while in the wet season many farmers continue to grow local varieties. Another reason, and perhaps the main one, is that the farm households retain their domestic needs from the wet-season crop and they prefer to eat the local varieties.

In both study sites there was a direct relationship between farm size and rates of fertilizer applied on modern varieties. This relationship was stronger in Ashoknagar than in Gajanur-Hosahally. The difference could be a result of different credit facilities in the two sites (discussed below) but to an extent the average yields of the different farm size groups reflect the differences in average fertilizer applications (Table 4). These data suggest that rice output could be increased, particularly in Ashoknagar, if fertilizer use could be raised on the medium and small farms. We do not have the data to make an economic assessment of this, however. Perhaps the medium and small farmers are applying the more economically rational levels, and since the smaller the farm, the smaller the proportion of the crop that can be marketed (in general), small farmers could find it somewhat difficult to pay for large fertilizer applications.

One further point relating to fertilizer use and yields may be noted. "Partial-adoptors" in the wet season (those growing from 40 to 70% local varieties) used more fertilizer, and achieved higher yields with modern varieties on average than did the farmers who grew only modern varieties (Table 5). This same group of farmers also used more

Table 4. Rough rice yield and fertilizer use in relation to farm size, 1971/72.

farm size	variety type	wet season			dry season		
		farms (no.)	rice yield (t/ha)	$N-P_2O_5-K_2O$ (kg/ha)	farms (no.)	rice yield (t/ha)	$N-P_2O_5-K_2O$ (kg/ha)
				Gajanur-Hosahally			
over 3 ha	modern	34	5.7	146−69−69	35	5.8	135−63−78
1 to 2.9 ha	modern	35	4.6	132−53−87	42[a]	4.7	126−45−87
under 1 ha	modern	13	4.7	140−39−60	13[b]	4.4	120−47−78
all farms	modern	82	5.1	138−60−75	90	5.2	129−53−81
all farms	local	27	2.8	55−34−25	[c]	−	−
				Ashoknagar			
over 3 ha	modern	17	5.8	172−64−69	21	6.5	168−61−80
1 to 2.9 ha	modern	16	4.9	150−62−63	25	5.4	135−59−68
under 1 ha	modern	4	4.9	125−61−64	5	5.8	121−49−58
all farms	modern	37	5.3	157−61−64	51	5.9	149−60−72
all farms	local	24	2.7	50−32−20	[d]	−	−

[a]Only 30 of the farms had yield data. [b]Only 12 of the farms had yield data. [c]Only four farmers planted local varieties. [d]Only one farmer planted local varieties.

Table 5. Fertilizer use and yields of modern varieties on farms
of partial and full adopters, 1971 wet season.

adoption class	farms (no.)	yield (t/ha)	$N-P_2O_5-K_2O$ (kg/ha)
	Gajanur-Hosahally		
partial	18	6.0	185−83−90
full	64	5.0	125−55−71
all farms	82	5.1	138−60−75
	Ashoknagar		
partial	10[a]	5.7	170−69−69
full	27	5.3	154−58−62
all farms	37	5.3	157−61−64

[a] Only three of the 10 partial adoptors have yield data.

fertilizer and obtained higher yields in the dry season when they joined the others as "full adoptors."

Other new inputs and practices. The use of insecticides is one of the important components of the HYVP rice package, but this practice was not new to either study site (Table 6). In Ashoknagar all the sample farmers said that they used insecticides before the introduction of modern varieties, and have continued to do so since, while in Gajanur-Hosahally there has been a significant change, from two-thirds to almost all farmers. All farmers in Ashoknagar owned sprayers before the HYVP. In Gajanur-Hosahally ownership has almost paralleled the increased use of the chemicals.

Herbicides were not as commonly used. Data were not obtained from Ashoknagar but in Gajanur-Hosahally the use of herbicides had extended to about a tenth of the farmers by 1971 (Table 6).

Straight-row transplanting started as a new practice before the HYVP, but few farmers had adopted it. A small increase in both sites has occurred since then. Farmers said that this practice is more expensive (for hired labor) and the laborers are not skilled in the method.

Mechanization has gone further in Gajanur-Hosahally than in Ashoknagar, particularly the use of four-wheeled tractors. In 1971 44 percent of the farmers in Gajanur-Hosahally used tractors for land preparation, while only 41 percent did so in Ashoknagar. Other forms of mechanization, including threshers and pumps, are still rare in both sites (Table 6).

The most common problem farmers encountered in the cultivation of modern varieties was attacks of diseases and insects. This was reported

Table 6. Farming practices wet seasons, 1967 and 1971.

| use of | farmers using (%) | | | |
| | Gajanur-Hosahally | | Ashoknagar | |
	1967	1971	1967	1971
chemical fertilizer	74	98	100	100
organic fertilizer	382	3	36	48
insecticide	65	87	100	100
sprayer	59	80	100	100
herbicide	2	11	n.a.	0
straight row planting	14	22	6	13
mechanical weeder	10	2	2	4
two-wheel tractor	10	16	6	8
four-wheel tractor	7	36	4	6
mechanical harvester	0	2	2	2
mechanical thresher	0	1	2	2
canal irrigation	90	91	100	100
pump irrigation	5	14	0	0

as a major problem by 70 percent of the Gajanur-Hosahally farmers and, despite the widespread use of insecticides, by 60 percent of the Ashoknagar farmers. Few other problems were reported up to the harvest. There was some trouble in obtaining good certified seed in Gajanur-Hosahally (reported by 18% of the farmers) and about 30 percent of the Ashoknagar farmers said that they had trouble obtaining credit. Irrigation and drainage and obtaining fertilizers were not problems, at least in the wet season.

Farm labor. Most farmers in the two study sites felt that growing modern varieties required more labor than local varieties. There was also general agreement about the farm operations for which this additional labor was needed.

Each farmer was asked to say whether, since he started growing modern varieties, he used more, the same, or less labor in land preparation (plowing, transporting manure or fertilizers, puddling, leveling, bunding, green leaf manuring, drainage); pre-harvest (straight-row transplanting, fertilizer application, spraying, weeding); and post-harvest (harvesting, transporting produce to the threshing yard, threshing).

Almost no farmers reported an increase in the use of family labor in any operation, but many said that they had to hire more labor for straight-row transplanting, weeding, harvesting, and threshing. Straight-row transplanting is not related necessarily to the cultivation of modern varieties, but the other operations are. The need for weeding increases with the higher rates of fertilizers applied to modern varieties. Harvesting and threshing are both affected by the higher yields and short height of the modern varieties.

There was some variation in response between locations and considerable variation between seasons. For example, few Hosahally farmers thought that they had hired more hours of labor in the wet season, and in the dry season less than a third reported increases in straight-row transplanting, weeding, and harvesting. By way of contrast, over two thirds of the farmers of neighboring Gajanur said that in the wet season they had hired more labor for straight-row transplanting, weeding, and harvesting. In the dry season over three quarters reported this plus an increase in the labor needed for threshing. Ashoknagar farmers responded similarly to those in Gajanur, except that in the wet season a smaller proportion reported increases, and in the dry season almost all reported increases in the four operations. The increases which were fairly general in the dry season may reflect an increase in the area planted to the modern varieties, rather than, or in addition to, increased needs per hectare of modern varieties in comparison with local varieties.

No attempt was made in the survey to quantify labor inputs but some increase in hired labor seems to have occurred in recent years which seems associated with the switch from local to modern varieties. This impression was reinforced by interviews with 48 agricultural laborers from Gajanur-Hosahally. Almost all of those from Gajanur, and two thirds of those from Hosahally said that they have been employed more days a year since the HYVP was introduced — the average increase was from 234 to 264 days a year.

Credit. During the 1972 dry season, 70 percent of the sample farmers in Ashoknagar and 64 percent in Gajanur-Hosahally reported borrowing. All loans reported were taken in cash rather than in kind. Only a few farmers in Ashoknagar reported having trouble getting loans for production purposes.

Production credit was available from cooperatives, commercial banks, and private lenders. Cooperatives operated in Gajanur and Hosahally villages but not in Ashoknagar. A few large farmers in Ashoknagar, however, were members of cooperatives elsewhere, probably in neighboring village of Yedihally. There were commercial banks in Shimoga town, and most of the private lenders were merchants in that town.

The cooperatives were the main source of credit for the Gajanur-Hosahally farmers. Forty of the 55 farmers who borrowed used this source (Table 7) and the cooperative loans accounted for two thirds of all money borrowed (Table 8). By contrast, in Ashoknagar, banks and

Table 7. Sources of loans taken during the 1972 dry season

	farms (no.)		farms (no.) reporting loans from					
farm size	borrowing	not borrowing	coop only	bank only	private only	coop. plus bank	coop. plus private.	bank plus private
Gajanur-Hosahally								
over 3 ha	23	15	15	1	1	4	1	1
1 to 2.9 ha	23	11	12	0	7	1	2	1
under 1 ha	9	5	5	0	4	0	0	0
all farms	55	31	32	1	12	5	3	2
Ashoknagar								
over 3 ha	16	7	1	8	3	0	1	3
1 to 2.9 ha	19	9	3	3	10	0	0	3
under 1 ha	4	1	0	1	3	0	0	0
all farms	39	17	4	12	16	0	0	6

Table 8. Proportion of loans by source during the 1972 dry season in relation to farm size.

farm size	loans (%)		
	coop.	bank	private
Gajanur-Hosahally			
over 3 ha	66	30	4
1 to 2.9 ha	73	4	23
under 1 ha	72	0	28
all farms	68	22	10
Ashoknagar			
over 3 ha	5	72	23
1 to 2.9 ha	10	33	57
under 1 ha	0	6	94
all farms	7	52	41

private lending provided most of the credit. Only four out of 39 farmers dealt with a cooperative, and cooperatives accounted for only 7 percent of the money borrowed.

The source of credit was related to farm size (Tables 7 and 8). In Gajanur-Hosahally the cooperatives were the major source of credit for all size groups. But small farmers relied more heavily on private sources and borrowed much less than large farmers. The reported annual average rates of interest in 1972 was 9 percent for cooperatives, 12 percent for commercial banks, and 25 percent for private lenders. Given the breakdown of loans shown in Tables 7 and 8, larger farmers clearly take more advantage of the cheaper loan money while the small farmers have to depend to a greater extent on high interest loans from private sources.

Since most of the borrowing in Ashoknagar is from private sources who charge high interest rates, it is somewhat surprising that a larger proportion of farmers took out loans in Ashoknagar than in Gajanur-Hosahally. The average amount borrowed per farm was not significantly different (Rs. 3,160 vs. Rs. 2,960). The proportion of farmers borrowing may be a result of the better irrigation facilities in Ashoknagar.

In summary, the sources of credit in Gajanur-Hosahally and Ashoknagar make an interesting contrast. When the cooperative works well, as in Gajanur-Hosahally, the importance of the private moneylender declines dramatically, although the private moneylender continues to be an important source for many small farmers even in Gajanur-Hosahally.

CHANGES IN LEVELS OF LIVING

Without doubt, yields from modern varieties are considerably higher than those from local varieties in the villages studied, and consequently the switch to modern varieties has substantially increased the physical product of the farm. The extent of this increase depends on the size of the rice area and the proportion planted to modern varieties, the quantity of fertilizers applied, the quality of irrigation, the incidence of pests and diseases and the measures the farmer takes to prevent or combat these, the weather, and so on. But whatever the increase may be it does not show *per se* that the farmer and his family are better off. For such a judgment the profitability of the farm operation must be assessed. This is particularly important when dealing with modern varieties because they involve considerable cash outlays for production which must be recovered through the sale of that part of the crop not retained for consumption. It is this factor perhaps which makes the switch to modern varieties more difficult for the small farmer who retains a large proportion of his crop to eat himself.

All farmers in the two study sites were fully aware that the cash costs of production had increased with the switch to modern varieties and only about a third thought that their rice "profits" had increased as a result of the switch. Most claimed that the higher costs ate up the extra money earned through increased sales. But most farmers also reported that they had been able to increase their consumption of rice since switching to modern varieties. And while they obviously did not see it as such, this increase in consumption is a form of increased "profits." A larger proportion of "full adoptors" reported increased rice consumption than "partial adoptors" and "non-adoptors" (three-quarters, a half, and a third, respectively).

This subjective evidence suggests that farm incomes and levels of living of farm families have increased as a result of the adoption of modern varieties. The rapid rate of adoption itself, with little if any reversion to local varieties, is further (indirect) evidence that the farmers have found themselves and their families better off as a result.

Farm laborers also have apparently become somewhat better off as a result of the switch to modern varieties. It appears that more work is available and where laborers are paid by the day, and the number of days work increases, this is an important change. Income data were collected from the laborers interviewed, for 1967 and 1971/72, and these were deflated by the consumer price index in an attempt to approximate real income levels. On average there had been an increase in real incomes equivalent to about 200 kilograms of rice per year. Nearly 70 percent of the laborers interviewed in Gajanur and 90 percent of those interviewed in Hosahally thought that their living conditions had improved since the introduction of modern varieties in their villages.

THE FUTURE

Most farmers showed a lively interest in the new varieties which went further than the acceptance of the seeds. They were interested in improving the productivity and incomes of their farms. They wanted to know more about the technical side of growing modern varieties. Many were not satisfied with their current yields and profits. Some wanted better arrangements for the supply of certified seeds, and periodic soil testing so that specific recommendations on fertilizer rates could be made. They found little value in the broad zonal recommendations. They were concerned about the water situation of course, but also wanted sound advice on the timing of irrigation and associated farm operations. Many felt that research findings on methods of raising seedlings, transplanting, application of fertilizers were not reaching them quickly, or, in many cases, accurately. Some farmers felt that such technical advice as was available was passed on to a small group of farmers and that most were by-passed by the officials responsible for extension.

There appeared to be a healthy climate in both study sites for the further extension of modern methods of rice farming. Most farmers had made major changes in their production methods and already were anxious for more. Both the mental and the physical environment were favorable and the villages seemed poised for further moves towards a modern agriculture.

Cuttack, Orissa

T. K. Pal

The study villages are located within a 15-minute bus ride of India's Central Rice Research Institute. Three-quarters of the owners, tenants, and owner-tenants accepted modern varieties within 3 years of their release. There was no difference in the level of use of fertilizer or pesticides by tenure groups. In the dry season, farmers had replaced their former dry season pulses and vegetables with modern rice varieties and produced a marketed surplus of rice for the first time. About 25 percent more labor is used to produce the modern varieties than is required for improved local types.

CUTTACK IS AN IMPORTANT rice-producing district and the home of India's Central Rice Research Institute (CRRI). This study was carried out in two Mahanadi Delta villages only 15 km from CRRI. The area has rich alluvial clay loam soils and year-round canal irrigation. Farms are very small. Weather conditions are nearly cyclonic around September and October of almost every year.

May is the hottest month of the year with mean maximum temperature of 38°C and mean minimum temperature of 26°C. January is the coldest month when mean temperature falls to 28°C maximum and 14°C minimum; this month is the sunniest month, however, with some 285 hours of sunlight. The monsoon season starts in June and continues until October. Rainfall reaches its peak in July, averaging about 332 mm that month.

Before the introduction of modern varieties in 1966, only one crop of rice was grown during the wet season (May to December). In the dry season, vegetables (such as potato and cauliflower) and pulses were the

T. K. Pal is agricultural economist at the Central Rice Research Institute (CRRI), Cuttack, Orissa.
The author wishes to acknowledge the help extended by M. M. Dash, Statistics Section, CRRI, in the compilation and tabulation of the data.

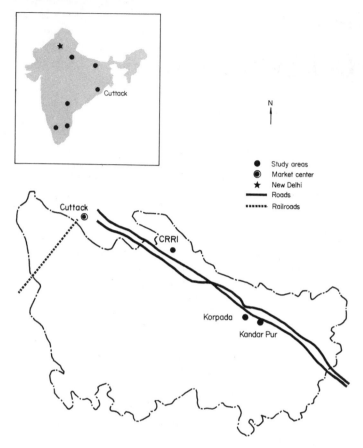

Cuttack District, Mysore State.

main crops. Since 1966 there has been a steady shift to rice in the dry season and rice now grows throughout the year in most of the district.

The villages. The villages Kandarpur and Korpada were selected for several reasons, including their proximity to the Central Rice Research Institute, availability of irrigation water, and an all-weather road which connects them to the urban market center of Cuttack. They are adjacent to one another and are quite similar.

The study area receives assured irrigation water from a distributory canal of the Mahanadi Delta Irrigation System. At the time of the survey neither village had field channels. Instead, the water flowed from field to field, keeping plots constantly submerged. The availability of irrigation water is somewhat uncertain during the dry months of April and May.

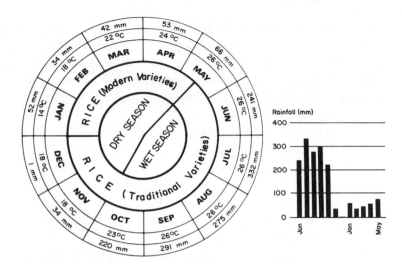

Average monthly rainfall and minimum temperature (Central Rice Research Institute, 1967-1971), Cuttack, Orissa.

A roadside village market in Kandarpur is the main marketing outlet for most of the farmers in both villages. Agents from Malgodown, a trading center of Cuttack, come to the village to buy rice. There are no large rice mills in the vicinity of the villages; the paddy is dehulled by small electric hullers or by the traditional method of pounding with heavy wooden devices called *dhenki*. The number of electrical hullers has increased from one in 1966 to eight in 1972, and the use of the *dhenki* has declined.

Six-month crop loans at 10 percent annual interest are available to members of the cooperative service society of Kandarpur. Three-year loans are also available at 9.5 percent for the purchase of cattle and agricultural implements. A member can obtain a maximum of Rs 2,000 by mortgaging his land to the society. The Marginal Farmer and Agricultural Labor Agency also operates in the area. Farmers with less than 1 hectare can receive a 33-percent subsidy on agricultural loans. For larger loans, farmers have the facilities of a modern banking system in Cuttack.

The villages are served by the national extension service. The block headquarters and the district agricultural office are only 15 minutes away by bus.

The villages are small with only 169 farm families living in both. Farms are also small. The largest is 2.4 ha, and the average size is 0.6 ha. Fifty-seven percent of the farm families own the land they farm, 36 percent add to their own land by leasing, and 7 percent are pure tenants. All tenants are share-croppers who pay their rent in kind. Twelve families are landlords. Eleven families are agricultural laborers, 7 are non-agricultural laborers, 21 are businessmen, and 7 are engaged in other occupations. Altogether, the two villages support 227 families, of whom 75 percent are farmers.

Rice dominates the economy in both seasons, but it is not the only crop in the villages. A few farmers grow vegetables in the dry season and grow betel nut on small areas.

The populations of the two villages increased by 16 percent between 1966 and 1972 (2.6 percent per year). Male population increased at a faster rate than did the female population which, in the 10–50 year age group, actually fell by 12 percent.

With the average household of six persons cultivating only 0.6 ha, the need for hired farm labor might be slight except that female family members take little part in agricultural operations. Most farmers hire supplemental labor for transplanting, harvesting, and threshing.

The sample. Because the total number of farmers in the two villages was small, all were included in the survey. Because all farms were small, no attempt was made to classify them by farm size. They were classified by tenure, however, to determine if this influenced the adoption of of modern rice varieties and accompanying new technology.

As the socio-economic and agro-climatic characteristics of the two villages were virtually identical, the data are pooled to form a single sample (Table 1). Rice varieties are classified into three groups, modern varieties, improved local varieties and traditional varieties. Modern varieties are non-photosensitive, semidwarf types, which respond to fertilizer and resist lodging at high fertilizer levels. Improved local varieties were developed by single plant selection or by crossing *indica* and *japonica* varieties; they are tall but respond better to fertilizer and yield higher than do traditional varieties. The traditional varieties are tall photosensitive *indicas* which respond poorly to chemical fertilizer and have a tendency to lodge at high fertilizer levels.

The survey began in the 1972 dry season (from January to May) and continued into the following wet season (from May to December).

ADOPTION OF MODERN VARIETIES

In 1966 three farmers obtained small quantities of seed of Taichung Native 1 (TN 1), a modern variety from Taiwan, from the Central Rice Research Institute and sowed them in the wet season. The results so

Table 1. Characteristics of the sample farms.

tenure class	farms in villages[a] (no.)	persons in household (no.)	farm size (ha)
owners	97	6	0.5
tenants	11	7	0.7
owner-tenants	61	7	0.9
all	169	6	0.6

	rice area				principal form of irrigation
	per farm (ha)		double cropped (%)	irrigated (%)	
	wet season	dry season			
owners	0.5	0.4	80	99	
tenants	0.6	0.5	83	100	
owner-tenants	0.7	0.6	86	98	
all	0.6	0.5	83	99	canal

	modern varieties				year of greatest adoption
	farms planting (%)		rice area planted (%)		
	wet season	dry season	wet season	dry season	
owners	45	98	14	89	1967
tenants	64	91	11	95	1967
owner-tenants	80	100	17	93	1967
all	60	98	15	91	1967

[a]Kandarpur, 57; Korpada, 112. All farms in the villages were included in the study.

impressed one of these farmers that he wrote an article in *Samaj,* a local daily, proclaiming that Orissa farmers could harvest gold from their soil. The following year, 94 farmers grew TN 1. By 1972, only three farmers had not tried any of the modern varieties then available (Table 2). The fast pace of initial adoption or experimentation (80 percent of all farmers in 3 years) could indicate that these farmers are less con- servative and less afraid to try new varieties than was generally believed. Data on the areas planted each year would be needed to substantiate

Table 2. Year of first adoption of modern varieties by tenure classes.

year	percentage first adopting			
	owners	tenants	owner-tenants	all farms
1966	2	0	2	2
1967	53	64	58	56
1968	25	9	25	24
1969	8	9	8	8
1970	9	0	2	6
1971	1	9	3	2
1972	0	0	2	0
adopting by 1972	98	91	100	98

such a generalization, however, and those were not available.

By 1972 the number of modern varieties available to the farmers had increased, and they had become firmly associated with the dry season. In 1972, 91 percent of the rice area was under modern varieties during the dry season, but only 15 percent during the wet season (Table 1). Modern-variety rice had virtually replaced vegetables in the dry-season cropping pattern.

This emphasis on the dry season is explained by two facts that soon became obvious to the farmers. Modern varieties gave higher yields under the sunny dry-season skies, and the incidence of diseases and insect pests was much lower. The latter factor may be more important because it reduces the risk of growing modern varieties, when farmers invest considerable amounts in fertilizer, the probability of loss is a major consideration.

Tables 1 and 2 clearly indicate that tenure had no effect on the timing and extent of adoption of modern varieties in the two villages.

CHANGES IN FARMING PRACTICES

An important objective was to study the impact of the new rice technology on farm practices and the use of inputs. One approach might be to compare the use of inputs per hectare before and after the introduction of modern varieties. Another might be to compare the use of inputs per hectare on modern and on traditional and local improved varieties at the present time. We used the second approach. To indicate the possible effects of the introduction of modern varieties, we looked at the sequence of adoption of both inputs and modern varieties and at varietal differences in input use.

Chemical fertilizers. Organic fertilizers have long been commonly used in the area; only chemical fertilizers are associated with the adoption of modern varieties. Only 14 percent of the farmers used any chemical fertilizer on their rice lands before they adopted modern varieties; by the 1972 dry season, all used chemical fertilizers (Table 3).

In 1972 considerably higher rates of fertilizer were used on modern varieties than on other varieties (Table 4). In the dry season, half as much nitrogen was applied to improved local varieties as to modern varieties; 40 percent as much P_2O_5; and one-fourth as much K_2O. In the wet season, the level of fertilizer applied was reduced to half of its dry-season level or less; fertilizer applied to improved local varieties was between 75 and 50 percent of its dry-season level.

No difference was observed in the use of nitrogen on the modern varieties by tenure group during the dry season. But on the improved-local varieties, owner-tenants used slightly more than the pure owners and pure tenants. In the wet season, the pure tenants applied lower rates of nitrogen than did the other farmers. Similar differences were noted in the use of P_2O_5 and K_2O, although they were relatively minor.

Other new inputs and practices. Farmers adopted insecticides along with the modern varieties. Only 8 percent of the farmers reported using insecticides before the introduction of modern varieties, but about 80 percent used them in 1972. The insecticides are used on traditional, improved local, and modern varieties, and in both seasons, although more is used on modern varieties. Again, tenure groups differed little in the adoption of this practice.

There was little mechanization of farm operations in the study area. No farmers used tractors for land preparation before 1966, and only

Table 3. Percentage of farmers using chemical fertilizers before and at the time of adoption of modern varieties.

tenure	before adoption	year of adoption	in 1972
owners	13	81	100
tenants	27	73	100
owner-tenants	11	70	100
all farms	14	77	100

Table 4. Fertilizer use (kg/ha) on the three types. of varieties, 1972.

fertilizer, variety type	owners	tenants	owner-tenants	all
		dry season		
nitrogen				
modern	99	98	100	99
improved local	54	52	67	59
traditional[a]	47	n.a.	n.a.	47
phosphorus				
modern	46	46	42	45
improved local	10	13	28	17
traditional	0	n.a.	n.a.	0
potash				
modern	56	47	41	48
improved local	9	0	18	12
traditional	0	n.a.	n.a.	0
		wet season		
nitrogen				
modern	54	42	57	55
improved local	42	26	42	41
traditional	31	35	43	36
phosphorus				
modern	19	16	22	20
improved local	12	9	13	12
traditional	7	13	13	10
potash				
modern	18	2	7	12
improved local	7	5	4	6
traditional	6	11	5	6

[a]Not grown by tenants and owner tenants in the dry season.

two used tractors in 1972. Similarly, the mechanical thresher was almost unknown and was used by only one farmer in 1972. The reasons for the lack of interest in mechanization are obvious — farms are very small and highly fragmented, and labor is cheap. Plowing with tractors was 50 percent more expensive than plowing with animals. Even when the Department of Agriculture made tractors available a few years after the introduction of modern varieties, farmers showed so little interest in hiring them that the service was withdrawn.

Farm labor. Family labor use increased on 90 percent of the farms after the introduction of modern varieties, particularly labor for applying fertilizers and insecticides in the wet season (there was no dry season rice crop before 1966). Half of the farmers thought that family labor use had increased in transporting the rice produced, and between 20 and 40 percent thought that family labor use had increased in other rice farming operations.

There was general consensus about the increased use of hired labor. The percentages of farmers who reported hiring more labor for given operations in the wet season follow:

plant protection	95
fertilizer application	91
threshing	84
harvesting	82
weeding	80
pulling and transplanting	78
land preparation	55
transporting	30

Because rice is a new dry-season crop, both family and hired labor use have obviously increased during the dry season in all rice farming operations since 1966.

The total man-days (md) of labor utilized for production of modern and improved-local varieties in 1972 was:

	modern	*improved-local*
dry season	219 md	174 md
wet season	169 md	145 md

These data show that 25 percent more labor was used on modern varieties than on improved-local varieties in the dry season and 17 percent more in the wet season.

Credit. No farmer reported borrowing for agricultural purposes before 1966, although appalling debt existed (as was well documented in studies such as the All India Rural Credit Survey). In this study, however, we were concerned with production credit. Since most farmers in this area started using the two inputs, which required cash expenditures, chemical fertilizers and pesticides, only with the adoption of modern varieties after 1966, the claim may be true.

In the 1972 dry season 49 farmers (29 percent) took out production loans, and in the following wet season 31 farmers (18 percent) borrowed. These borrowers included 22 farmers who took loans in both seasons, making a total of only 58 farmers (34 percent) borrowing during the year for production purposes.

Cash loans predominated in the dry season; 48 cash loans were taken out compared with only 4 loans in kind. Three farmers took out both cash and kind loans. In the wet season 29 (17 percent) took cash loans and 17 (10 percent) took loans in kind; of these, 14 farmers had both types. A total of 32 farmers (19 percent) were borrowers in this season.

Cash loans in the dry season averaged Rs 189/ha, and in the wet season, only Rs 58/ha. Loans in kind were small in the dry season (Rs 12/ha) and almost equal to cash loans in the wet season (Rs 51/ha). The dry season borrowers were predominantly owners and owner-tenants while considerably more wet-season borrowers were tenants (Table 5).

CHANGES IN PRODUCTION, PRODUCTIVITY, MARKETING, AND OFF-FARM INCOME

Area and productivity changes. No rice crop was grown in the dry season before the adoption of modern varieties, so any change in dry-season production and productivity is caused by direct and indirect effects of this change in cropping pattern. Dry-season rice production in 1972 accounted for 59 percent of the total 1972 rice output. Sixty-one percent of the rice output came from the modern varieties (Table 6), which clearly indicates their dominant role in current rice production.

Table 5. Production credit used (Rs/ha) by borrowing farmers, 1972.

tenure	dry season		wet season	
	cash	kind	cash	kind
owners	233	7	59	63
tenants	30	0	84	23
owner-tenants	163	19	53	42
all	189	12	58	51

Table 6. Rice production by type, 1972.

type	percent of total crop		
	dry season	wet season	both seasons
modern	56	5	61
improved local	3	23	26
traditional	0	13	13
all types	59	41	100

The benefits from this change were not evenly distributed among tenure groups. Curiously, the lowest yields from both modern and local varieties were obtained on tenant farms in the dry season, but the same farmers obtained the highest average yields in the wet season (Table 7). The yield level from modern varieties in the 1972 wet season was lower than usual because of an attack of stem borers and gall midge. Despite the greater disease and insect problems reported on modern varieties and in the wet season (Table 8), in most years the wet-season yields of modern varieties were slightly higher than those of the improved-local varieties.

Changes in marketing patterns. Before 1966 almost all of the rice crop was retained for family consumption and rice was not a market commodity in these villages. Rice became a marketed commodity only after 1966 when it began to be produced in both seasons and surpluses (over family needs) were harvested. Even in 1972, most rice production was retained for family consumption, particularly the improved local and traditional varieties, which most households prefer to modern varieties. Ten percent of the dry-season crop of modern rice varieties was sold at harvest; 6 percent was sold 1 month after harvest; and another 6 percent was sold more than 1 month after harvest. Sales of wet-season modern varieties were negligible. Only 3 percent of the 1972 harvest of improved local and traditional varieties was marketed. Since the adoption of modern varieties it appears that the area is being slowly transformed from a subsistence into a market-oriented economy.

Changes in-off-farm income. Fifty-four percent of the farm families reported no changes in their off-farm earnings; 46 percent reported higher off-farm incomes. The families which reported no changes in their off-farm incomes had never earned income outside of agriculture, either before or after the introduction of the modern varieties. In a sense this situation reflects an acute village unemployment problem.

Table 7. Average yields (t/ha) by variety type, 1972.

	owners	tenants	owner-tenants	all
dry season				
modern	4.2	3.6	4.2	4.1
improved local	2.3	1.9	3.0	2.9
traditional[a]	2.2	n.a.	n.a.	2.2
wet season				
modern[b]	1.5	2.1	1.8	1.6
improved local	2.6	2.5	2.5	2.5
traditional	2.1	2.2	2.0	2.0

[a]Not grown by tenants or owner-tenants in the dry season. [b]Affected by stem borer and gall midge.

CONSTRAINTS TO GROWTH

Two significant changes have taken place in the study area: rice has emerged as the single major crop in the dry season, and the use of new inputs, such as chemical fertilizers and pesticides, has become an accepted practice. Are the farmers happy with the results of these changes?

Forty percent of the farmers were satisfied with the yields they obtained in the dry season, and 35 percent were satisfied with their wet-season rice yields. Therefore, we see that most of the rice farmers were not satisfied with their 1972 rice crops, a finding that needs explanation.

The main constraints to yields are related to difficulties in obtaining seeds, chemical fertilizers, and production credit; inadequate irrigation water; and attacks of insects, diseases, and other pests (Table 8).

Even before 1966 a third of the farmers claimed to have experienced some difficulties in getting quality seeds. In the 1972 dry season, 47 percent reported difficulties obtaining seeds of modern varieties in the wet season, about 30 percent reported the same problem. Only a few farmers reported difficulty getting seeds of other rice types. Considering that the High Yielding Varieties Program has been operating since 1966, the farmers clearly have a valid complaint — the program can hardly succeed unless high quality seeds are readily available.

Thirty-four percent of the farmers reported difficulty obtaining fertilizer before 1966; almost the same percentage claimed that this was

Table 8. Problems encountered by farmers in rice production before and after modern varieties were introduced.

problem		farmers (%) reporting			
		1972 dry season		1972 wet season	
	pre-MV	MV	LV's	MV	LV's
obtaining seeds	31	47	6	32	6
obtaining fertilizer and other chemicals	34	31	31	27	27
obtaining credit	24	16	16	25	25
irrigation	32	28	28	21	21
disease, insect and pests	29	43	14	64	37

a problem in 1972. They said that the cooperative service at Kandarpur had distributed fertilizer until 1972, and had met fertilizer requirements of its members and other village farmers. But in 1972 the state government reversed its decision to distribute fertilizer through cooperatives. Fertilizer became acutely scarce and prices rose.

The institutional credit situation in the area has improved greatly since 1966 for land owners, but tenants and owner-tenants reported that production credit is more difficult to obtain.

The overall irrigation situation has improved somewhat since 1966 according to many farmers, but 28 percent claimed that a lack of adequate irrigation hampered farming operations in the dry season and 21 percent claimed this in the wet season.

Since the introduction of the modern varieties farmers are more aware of disease and pest problems in the study area.

The problems associated with rice farming in the study area do not seem very serious. Assuming that resistance to the common rice diseases and insects will soon be incorporated into modern varieties, and that the supply of seeds and chemical fertilizers will be improved, most farmers can expect much higher levels of rice production in the coming years.

CHANGES IN ECONOMIC AND SOCIAL STRUCTURE

Adoption and socio-economic changes. Social scientists, almost without exception, feel that technological shifts are somehow responsible for inducing changes in the socio-economic relationships among different classes of people in the community. Reactions to changes vary among and within groups of people; established relationships break down and new relationships evolve. In the end new social and economic orders emerge. Evidence of such processes is hard to find in the study area. A distinctive feature of the two villages is that an overwhelming majority of farmers operate small holdings — nearly 75 percent of the resident families. The rest are non-cultivating land owners, landless agricultural and non-agricultural laborers, and petty businessmen. There is virtually no interdependence between the farmers and the non-farmers, which may explain the continuation of the old social structure even after wide-scale adoption of the new rice technology. This may be a common characteristic of many other communities dominated by subsistence agriculture.

This does not imply that no change has taken place. It only shows that there is little reason to include non-farmers in the discussion. The changes in cropping intensity, input use and types of varieties are of an economic — not a social — nature.

Changes in size of holdings and land prices. Changes in the size of holdings reflect, to a certain extent, changes in the economic conditions of the farmers. Since 1966, 9 percent of the farmers have bought new rice land while 13 percent have sold rice land. Tenants neither bought nor sold rice land. Owner-tenants increased their previous holdings through purchasing, sharing, and leasing more rice land. Owners sold more land than they bought, resulting in a net decrease in farm size for this group since 1966. The pure tenants increased their rice areas by new sharing agreements.

Government acquisition of land for the construction of a railway between Cuttack and the Paradeep sea port accounts for most of the sales. Changes in the area of rice land are therefore, largely of fortuitous nature. The control of land has shifted slightly, however, in favor of the non-owning groups.

Since 1966 land prices have increased by about 30 percent. The 1972 price of land is in the range of Rs 18,750/ha to Rs 25,000/ha. Most farmers ascribe the increase in land prices to the increased double-cropping of rice.

Changes in rental arrangements. Crop sharing is the only method of rental payment in this area, except for leases of government land where fixed cash payments are required. Before the introduction of modern varieties, when rice was grown only in the wet season, sharing arrangements between tenants and owners were in the ratio of 1:1. This is still the sharing arrangement for the wet-season rice crop. In the dry season, however, only pulses and vegetables were grown before 1966, and the

Table 9. Farmers' view of their present profits from rice and level of living compared with the period before the introduction of modern varieties.

| | farmers (%) reporting | | | |
	pure owner	pure tenants	owner tenants	all farms
Satisfaction with present yields				
dry season, 1972	41	27	41	40
wet season, 1972	34	45	36	35
Profit from rice				
higher	87	91	80	85
lower	1	0	0	0
same	12	9	20	15
Level of living				
higher	54	73	38	50
lower	1	0	0	0
same	45	27	62	50

produce was shared at a tenant-to-owner ratio of 3:2. Since 1966 modern varieties have almost entirely replaced pulses and vegetables, but the old dry-season sharing arrangement of 3:2 continues to hold. The tenants meet all expenses and make all farming decisions. The situation reflects inertia more than conscious bargaining between the tenants and the owners.

Changes in rice profits and levels of living. Use of modern variety rice seeds, chemical fertilizers, and pesticides seem to have increased profits from rice cultivation. Eighty-five percent of the farmers reported higher rice profits than in 1966. Changes in the levels of living may also indicate more rice profits, though the relationships between levels of living and rice profits than in 1966 (Table 9). Changes in the levels of living may also indicate more rice profits, though the relationships between levels of living and rice profits may be somewhat tenuous because opportunities to earn off-farm incomes are increasing. Half of the farmers reported that their standards of living had improved since 1966 and half thought that there had been no change.

More farmers reported higher rice profits than reported improvements in standards of living. This may be because increases in the cost of living have taken away some of the benefits of higher rice profits. Besides, the amount of rice land operated per farm is very small and the absolute increases in rice profits might not show in terms of observably higher standards of living on most farms. A higher proportion of tenants reported both higher rice profits and higher levels of living than did the other two groups of farmers, a finding that is difficult to logically explain.

Changes in daily consumption emphasize the general poverty of the people of this area. Rice consumption increased among all classes of farmers; this is due to the new dry-season crop. Higher tea consumption is also reported by a majority of farmers in each class, which indicates urban habit formation among rural people. Practically no change is observed in the consumption of fish, eggs, mutton, and chicken. Adoption of the new rice has hardly affected the deficiency of protein in the diets of farm families.

Changes in durable consumption items and farm implements. Even though diets are poor, purchases of status symbols in the form of consumer durables have proceeded (32 farmers had purchased radios since 1966 and 78 had purchased bicycles). One farmer had bought a sewing machine, another had bought a motorcycle, and seven had invested in sprayers. Four farm owners and three owner-tenants had purchased sprayers since 1966.

The impact of the new rice technology on the social and economic life of the village community itself is small. Even though rice profits have increased, individual gains are rather small. The added benefits are not sufficient to bring about significant changes in the levels of living and consumption habits of the farmers in this part of Orissa.

Klaten, Central Java

John Ihalauw and Widya Utami

A favorable environment coupled with government policies to encourage rice production have broadened acceptance of modern varieties in this area. The cropping pattern has been intensified to increase the frequency of harvests; landlords and tenants have benefited, but landless laborers, who are increasing in number, report no income benefits as a result of the introduction of modern varieties. Furthermore, certain problems have arisen particularly in employment and in relationships among various groups in the society, which if ignored may well become the seeds of future tension and conflict.

RESEARCH ON CHANGES in rice farming in Central Java was carried out in the Regency of Klaten. Particular attention was given to the question of who is benefiting from the new technology. How are the gains being used or spent? To what degree are profits being capitalized into rising rents and land values? How have the relationships between landowners, tenants, and landless laborers changed?

The Regency of Klaten was chosen for several reasons. The Klaten area has achieved impressive progress in rice production as a result of the introduction of the new rice technology. For 3 years prior to the study it was the site of a pilot rice intensification project, the Progressive Farmers Project *(Tani Makmur),* carried out, as a joint venture between

John Ihalauw and Widya Utami are researchers at the Research Institute in Social Sciences, Satya Wacana Christian University, Salatiga, Java.

The authors wish to acknowledge the help extended by the District Head of Klaten, Sutiyoso, and his assistants, sub-district heads of Polanharjo and Kabonarum, the other respective village leaders of the 3 villages studied, the Tani Makmur Project at Klaten which provided the secondary data needed, and particularly the following persons who participated in the work: Dr. Buger and Dr. N. Daldjoeni who assisted in preparing the part of the report relating to the physical and geographical aspects; Paul Stange and Dr. D. King who made the translations; village team members T. Suharto, Suharno, Suharsono, Aris Kristianto, S. R. Mutapea, Sugiardjo; and Dr. N. G. S. Nordholt, who served as technical expert.

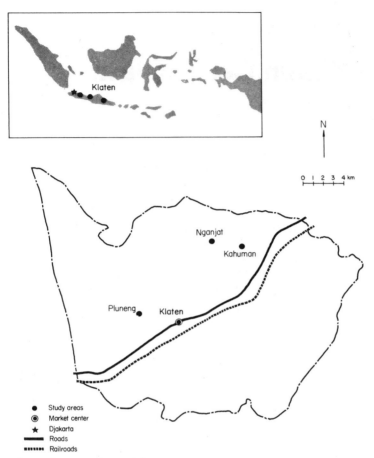

Klaten District, Central Java.

the governments of West Germany and Indonesia. Moreover, several publications that deal with agricultural problems in Central Java focus on the area of Klaten. These publications provide valuable data as a basis for research and for comparative studies.

Two villages, Kahuman and Nganjat, in the subdistrict of Polanharjo and one village, Pluneng, in the subdistrict of Kebonarum were selected for the study. Polanharjo had been the site of the Progressive Farmers Project. Kebonarum had been influenced only by the rice intensification project of the Indonesian government (the so-called *Bimas* or mass guidance in rice intensification). The selection was also based upon the distance from Klaten, the capital town of the regency.

Kahuman's land is fertile and tobacco growing is carried on by the State Tobacco Plantation Enterprise. Nganjat's land is not so fertile and

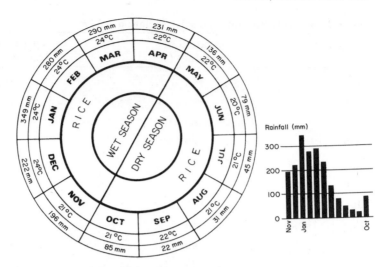

Average monthly rainfall (1931-1960) and minimum temperature (1958-1960), Central Java, Indonesia.

no tobacco is grown. The village of Pluneng, like Kahuman, has fertile land and tobacco is grown there for the State Tobacco Plantation Enterprise.

The research area. The Regency of Klaten covers about 660 square kilometers, including 355 square kilometers of rice fields, and 71 square kilometers of dry fields. The population of the regency in 1971 was 958,000 persons, living in 23 subdistricts which were divided into 401 villages.

The area includes land ranging in altitude from 100 meters to 2,900 meters at the peak of Mount Merapi. The land above 200 meters consists of volcanic rock; below 200 meters, of deposits of ancient marine and river clays. The productivity of the area is based partly on the fertile volcanic soil, but is also influenced by the area's plentiful supply of water, which comes from sources on the slopes of Mount Merapi between the altitudes of 250 and 1,000 meters.

Eighty percent of the annual precipitation falls between November and April. During this period over 200 mm of rain falls each month. In July, August, and September, the monthly averages are less than 60 mm. The average monthly temperature is about 27°C for the hottest month, October, and 25°C for the coolest month, July. The average relative humidity is between 80 percent and 90 percent in the rainy season and between 70 percent and 80 percent in the dry season. The amount of sunshine is more favorable for the dry season crop than for the wet season crop (Table 1). From July to November, the dominant

Table 1. Monthly sunshine and solar radiation.

month	duration of sunshine[a] (%)	solar radiation[b] (cal·cm^{-2} ·day^{-1}
Jan	55	410
Feb	58	426
Mar	62	427
Apr	69	433
May	74	404
Jun	74	399
Jul	78	419
Aug	84	465
Sep	82	492
Oct	77	495
Nov	71	465
Dec	64	430

[a]F.H. Schmidt, *On the Distribution of the Duration of Sunshine in Java* (Jakarta: Jawatan Meteorologi dan Geofisika, 1950), Verhandelingen No. 40, maps. No. VI and III. [b]Sir M. Macdonald and Partners, Consulting Engineers, *Kali Progo Basin Study, Main Report,* October 1971, p. 2. These data were based on the area of Yogyakarta, 30 kilometers to the west of Klaten, where climatic conditions are almost the same as those of Klaten.

wind is the southeast trade wind. In the wet season the southwest wind is dominant and the weather is humid and unstable.

The soil in the Regency of Klaten is generally volcanic ash, defined as including loose silt, sand, gravel, and stones which have been deposited by rivers from the upper slopes. Because of the imperfect stage of weathering, it contains little clay. The amount of clay does increase, however, in cultivated soil which receives continual irrigation.[1] The soil in the Polanharjo subdistrict is brownish-gray sand to sandy loam containing clay and small amounts of iron-manganese concretions. This soil is good for the growing of rice. In the sub-district of Kebonarum the soil is an easily friable gray sandy loam. It is one of the best soils in Java, very good for rice and sugarcane, and the best soil for growing tobacco.[2]

[1]R.W. van Bemmelen, *De Geologische Geschiedenis van Indonesie.* (Den Haag: Stockum en Zoon, 1952), pp. 67–69.

[2]F.W.G. Dames, *The Soils of East Central Java* (Bogor: 1955). pp. 26–36.

The cropping patterns differed somewhat between villages (see diagram), but in all three villages there was an increasing tendency to harvest five crops in 2 years. This cropping pattern was made possible by the adoption of the *petukan* method of cultivation in which seedlings for a new crop are prepared before the old crop is harvested. The *petukan* method permits a considerable shortening of the period between harvest and transplanting.

The population of the three villages was growing at 2.2 to 2.4 percent per year. The geographical density ranged between 1673 and 1995 persons per square kilometer, while the agricultural density (in relation to rice fields alone) was between 1953 and 2297.

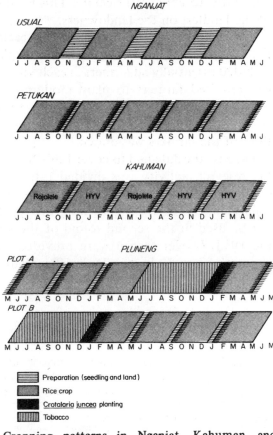

Cropping patterns in Nganjat, Kahuman, and Pluneng.

Most of the inhabitants were Moslems, but there were many Hindus, Catholics, and Protestants.

Although rice was the major crop in the villages, it was controlled by a small number of persons within each of the villages, along with the village officials and the village as a whole (Tables 2 and 3). Only 41 percent of the households had their own rice fields in Nganjat, only 46 percent in Kahuman, and only 25 percent in Pluneng. In Nganjat, about 9 hectares of village rice fields were used by seven village officials; in Kahuman, 10 hectares by eight officials; and in Pluneng, 9 hectares by seven officials (Table 3).

Ordinarily villagers within the sample villages owned an average of 0.5 hectare of rice fields, while the average official controlled 1.2 hectares. At the same time, population growth had reduced the man-land ratio to about 0.1 hectare. This means an evergrowing dependency of the landless on the landowners.

The sample. The sample farms in each village were drawn from a population of all farmers who had ever planted a modern variety. This included essentially all farmers in each village because the *Bimas* program had required farmers to plant modern varieties. Names in each village were provided by the village official responsible for agricultural extension work *(Pamong Tani Desa)*. A random sample of approximately one third of the farmers was drawn.

Because the data had to cover both the dry season and the wet season, the research activity was divided into two rounds. For the 1971 dry season, the total sample was 186 persons (60 from Nganjat, 60 from Kahuman, and 66 from Pluneng). As expected, part of the sample could not be used in the second round of the study — the data gathered for the 1971/72 wet season were provided by a sample of 54 farmers in Nganjat, 53 in Kahuman, and 59 in Pluneng. In each village 10 farm

Table 2. Distribution of land ownership, 1972.

village	persons (no.) owning					
	rice fields and home lot	home lot only	rice fields only	house on other's land	no land or house	rice field given by *Kasunanan*
Nganjat	129	51	7	49	74	0
Kahuman	231	145	54	218	0	4
Pluneng	150	133	10	115	105	0

Table 3. Pattern of land use and control.

item	area (ha)		
	Nganjat	Kahuman	Pluneng
land use			
rice fields	64.4	167.0	99.2
dry fields	0.3	0.8	0.1
home lots	8.3	22.7	24.4
others	1.9	4.5	0.2
distribution of rice fields			
village treasury	2.5	23.7	9.8
village officials' salaries	8.6	10.1	9.2
given by *Kasunanan*	2.6	3.4	0.0
owned by villagers	50.7	129.8	80.2
average owned			
rice fields	0.4	0.6	0.6
home lot	0.1	0.1	0.1

laborers were also interviewed. Laborers were selected to include those who were working for each of the tenure groups — owners, tenants, or sharecroppers. Field researchers used a questionnaire to gather data in each village. The first round of interviews was carried on from February 7 until March 2, 1972. The second round began on July 24 and ended on August 5, 1972.

The major difficulty encountered in this study was the inability of many people to remember conditions before modern varieties were introduced. Thus much of the data collected was not based on precise recollections or reliable records.

The cultivated rice fields in Nganjat consisted of three plots located in separate blocks; the rice fields in Kahuman and Pluneng each consisted of two separate plots. In all three villages the land received sufficient irrigation throughout the year (Table 4).

Most farms were owned by those who worked the land. These landowners were also the ones who most often leased or sharecropped land (Table 5). The raising of tobacco, carried on by the State Tobacco Enterprise, influenced the patterns of farming in the villages of Pluneng and Kahuman.

Table 4. Characteristics of the sample farms.

village	farms (no.) in village	sample wet season	sample dry season	persons in household (no.)	farm size (ha)
Nganjat	129	60	54	5.1	0.5
Kahuman	231	60	53	5.8	0.6
Pluneng	150	66	59	5.9	0.5

	rice area per farm (ha) wet season	dry season	double cropped (%)	irrigated (%)	principal form of irrigation
Nganjat	0.5	0.5	100	100	canal
Kahuman	0.6	0.6	100	100	canal
Pluneng	0.5	0.5	100	100	canal

	modern varieties farms planting (%) wet season	dry season	rice area planted (%) wet season	dry season	year of greatest adoption
Nganjat	57	90	39	63	1968
Kahuman	87	20	66	12	1968
Pluneng	98	100	91	86	1969

ADOPTION OF MODERN VARIETIES

In the three villages, the modern varieties were introduced by the *Bimas* program. In the beginning, farmers were required to plant modern varieties, but they now use them voluntarily. The variety PB5 (IR5) was the most widely planted modern variety during the survey year. A handful of farmers in Pluneng were planting C4–63 from the University of the Philippines, College of Agriculture. During the 1971/72 wet season, two farmers in Nganjat and four in Kahuman planted a newly released Indonesian variety, Pelita.

In Nganjat the changes in the number of farmers planting modern varieties and the area planted to them were influenced by attacks

Table 5. Tenure characteristics.

village	season	owned	owned and sharecropped	owned and leased	owned, leased, and sharecropped	farms (%) sharecropped	leased	sharecropped and leased	not farming-leased out
Nganjat	dry	80	3	5	3	4	0	5	0
	wet	78	2	2	9	1	2	6	0
Kahuman	dry	67	3	15	2	2	8	0	3
	wet	55	0	24	0	4	17	0	0
Pluneng	dry	71	10	12	1	2	0	1	3
	wet	70	14	10	5	0	1	0	0

Table 6. Comparison of fertilizer use and yields between modern and local varieties.

village	local[a]			modern			difference[b] (%)		
	N (kg/ha)	P$_2$O$_5$ (kg/ha)	yield (t/ha)	N (kg/ha)	P$_2$O$_5$ (kg/ha)	yield (t/ha)	N	P$_2$O$_5$	yield
1971 dry season									
Nganjat	57	9	5.3	91	27	5.9	60	200	11
Kahuman	94	34	6.5	121	41	6.5	29	21	0
Pluneng	61	0	4.0	128	0	6.1	110	0	52
1971/72 wet season									
Nganjat	72	9	3.9	89	24	3.6	24	167	-8
Kahuman	101	21	6.6	114	28	6.9	13	33	5
Pluneng	87	0	4.4	126	0	5.6	145	0	27

[a] Average of *improved local* and traditional varieties. [b] Difference between modern and local varieties divided by value for local varieties.

of rats and stem borers and by difficulties in obtaining seeds and credit, and also by the fact that despite heavier applications of fertilizer the modern varieties did not give significantly greater yields. In Kahuman, the significant changes in the number of farmers planting modern varieties were influenced by the desire to get five crops within 2 years. Changes in Pluneng were influenced by tobacco planting and the effort to obtain four crops within 2 years.

Farmers generally used less fertilizer for local varieties in the dry season. The farmers said that the need for fertilizer was less because they plowed the land and let it dry for a few weeks before planting for the dry season. Nevertheless, on the modern varieties, farmers applied more fertilizer in the dry season than in the wet season (Table 6).

Although farmers used more fertilizer on modern varieties they did not get consistently impressive difference in yields (Table 6). On the other hand the price of the local variety, Rojolele, was higher than that of PB5 (Table 7), and the peak of rice prices was usually reached either in November or December. It is not hard to understand why many farmers plant Rojolele along with modern varieties in dry season.

CHANGES RELATED TO THE INTRODUCTION OF MODERN VARIETIES

Introduction of modern varieties did not in any sense revolutionize the practices of rice farming among the sample farmers. Nevertheless, it has been accompanied by a continued increase in adoption of other new practices (Table 8).

Data concerning the fertilizer rates in 1968 are not available for comparison. But the *average* rice field in 1971 in the three villages received more fertilizer than the *best* plot in each village did in 1968 (1968: Nganjat, 41 kg/ha N and 7 kg/ha P_2O_5; Kahuman, 57 kg/ha N and 37 kg/ha P_2O_5; Pluneng, 58 kg/ha N). In Pluneng, the number of farmers using nitrogen fertilizers has also increased (Phosphate fertilizer

Table 7. Price of rough rice by variety, 1971 dry season.

| village | modern | | local | | | | | |
| | | | price (Rp/100 kg) | | | | | |
	PB5	C4	Rojolele	Gendruwo	Gondomono	Gembira	Mujahir	Ketan
Nganjat	2700	–	3100	–	–	–	–	3400
Kahuman	2500	–	3100	3100	3100	3100	–	–
Pluneng	2200	2475	2600	–	–	2400	2500	–

Table 8. Changes in farming practices.

village	year	farmers (%) using						irrigated farms (%)
		chemical fertilizer	organic fertilizer	insecticide	sprayer	rotary weeder	straight-row planting	
Nganjat	1968[a]	100	42	95	98	95	100	100
	1971[b]	100	33	100	98	95	100	100
Kahuman	1968	100	70	98	93	100	100	100
	1971[b]	100	38	98	93	98	100	100
Pluneng	1968	75	55	36	56	79	88	100
	1971[b]	100	38	86	90	90	100	100

[a] The year modern varieties were introduced to the village. [b] Dry season.

is not needed in this village because the Mount Merapi soils provide enough of this nutrient). The use of organic fertilizer in all three villages has decreased. Farmers prefer using chemical fertilizer which require less labor and time.

The sharp increase in use of insecticide in Pluneng was connected with the rise in pests and diseases reported by many sample farms in 1970/71. All three villages reported a probably irreversible trend toward heavy use of insecticides, although undesirable side effects were reported by 91 percent of the sample in Nganjat, 15 percent in Kahuman, and 76 percent in Pluneng. These effects included the death of fish, eels, and other small creatures which live in the rice fields and the fact that cattle and fowl became sick after coming to the rice fields.

Few farmers had sprayers because they were expensive, but they could be hired from the village office at a very low charge. Even before the introduction of modern varieties in 1968, sprayers were used by 57 percent of the sample in Nganjat, 82 percent in Kahuman, and 53 percent in Pluneng. By the 1971 dry season nearly all farmers in the three villages used sprayers.

Straight-row planting and the rotary weeder had been used since 1942 (the Japanese Occupation), but these practices have been improved and intensified since the introduction of modern varieties.

Two-wheel tractors were used in Kahuman and Pluneng in 1970 as part of the Village Modernization program. Eighteen percent of the sample farmers in Kahuman and 55 percent in Pluneng had used them at some point. At the time of the study, the tractors were no longer used because they were out of order.

Harvesting was mostly done with the *ani-ani* or hand knife, but under certain conditions the sickle was used.

All rice fields in the three villages were irrigated. Water reaches the rice fields by gravity flow from springs within the villages of Nganjat and Pluneng and from outside the village of Kahuman. Virtually all farmers said their irrigation facilities met their needs.

Animals played an important role in cultivation. In all three villages some cattle had to be hired from outside for plowing and harrowing. Draft animals plus driver cost between Rp 200 and Rp 250 for a capacity of one-tenth of a hectare in 1 working day (3 hours).

Government programs to extend the use of new farming practices were conducted through the Progressive Farmers Project and the regional offices of the Department of Agriculture, in cooperation with the village officials responsible for agricultural extension. Also, "village broadcasts" were produced over the provincial radio station, and listeners' groups

Table 9. Labor use in 1971 dry season and 1971/72 wet season compared with 1968.

village	labor source	farmers (%) using									
		before-harvest labor					harvest and post-harvest labor				
		more	less	no change	not used	no answer	more	less	no change	not used	no answer
		1971 dry season									
Nganjat	family	57	0	43	0	0	12	3	82	3	0
	exchange	3	0	42	55	0	0	2	53	45	0
	hired in village	37	0	63	0	0	15	3	80	2	0
	hired outside village	2	0	50	48	0	5	0	57	38	0
Kahuman	family	37	2	56	5	0	15	0	75	10	0
	exchange	2	0	37	61	0	0	0	35	65	0
	hired in village	35	3	57	5	0	37	0	52	11	0
	hired outside village	20	2	67	11	0	25	0	58	17	0
Pluneng	family	20	3	74	3	0	18	0	77	5	0
	exchange	8	6	51	35	0	12	0	14	74	0
	hired in village	12	53	29	6	0	95	0	3	2	0
	hired outside village	11	18	6	65	0	47	0	2	51	0
		1971/72 wet season									
Nganjat	family	48	2	48	2	0	0	4	81	15	0
	exchange	0	0	0	100	0	0	0	0	100	0
	hired in village	43	0	50	7	0	60	2	38	0	0
	hired outside village	4	13	0	83	0	2	2	31	65	0

(Table 9 continued)

village	labor source	farmers (%) using									
		before-harvest labor					harvest and post-harvest labor				
		more	less	no change	not used	no answer	more	less	no change	not used	no answer
Kahuman	family	17	9	74	0	0	13	6	79	0	0
	exchange	0	0	0	100	0	0	0	0	100	0
	hired in village	34	3	62	0	0	2	7	83	8	0
	hired outside village	19	0	81	0	0	52	2	46	0	0
Pluneng	family	22	0	64	2	12	15	0	71	2	12
	exchange	2	2	23	61	12	0	0	20	68	12
	hired in village	19	0	64	5	12	44	0	44	2	12
	hired outside village	2	2	24	61	11	15	0	17	56	12

had been formed in the villages. "Extension seeds." were supplied by breeding centers at Huma, Jokopuring, and Tegalgondo, at Rp 35/kg.

Labor requirements. The use of modern varieties increased the frequency of certain activities in the three villages. A large percentage of the sample reported that the planting of modern varieties increased the labor required for pre-harvest activities (Table 9). These needs were met mainly with family labor, possibly because hired labor for these activities cost between Rp 66 and Rp 136 a day (8 hours).

Farmers who experienced an increase in labor requirement for harvest and after-harvest activities used mainly hired labor. This practice was influenced partly by the wage paid in harvesting (1/30 to 1/18 of harvest) and the spread of the *tebasan* system[3] under which the standing rice crop is sold not long before it is harvested. Under the tebasan system the buyer is responsible for harvesting the crop. This in effect limits the number of harvesters and encourages the use of sickles rather than *ani-ani* knives for the harvesting. The spread of the *tebasan* system coupled with the replacement of the *ani-ani* may cause labor replacement effects in the rural communities which should be investigated further.

Particularly in Pluneng, labor needs were also influenced by the *glebagan* system,[4] an inheritance from the colonial period which requires that land be made available to the State Tobacco Plantation Enterprise. One effect of this system was that farmers invested labor to save growing time, employing the *petukan* method of cultivation. Thus most farmers in Pluneng were growing four rice crops on their land in 2 years, even though they had to lease the land out for tobacco during part of each year.

Size of farm and land values. In Nganjat, owners leased out more of their land in 1971 than in 1968, while farmers leased in or sharecropped less land in 1971 than in 1968 (Table 10). This change occurred because rents rose sharply due to an increase in taxes beginning in 1969. The rent paid in the 1971 dry season was Rp 75,000/ha per year, an increase of 88 percent over 1968. In Kahuman, leasing and sharecropping decreased from 1968 to 1971, because of the sharp increase in rents. The rent in the 1971 dry season was Rp 90,000/ha per year, an increase of 51 percent compared with 1968. In Pluneng, the area of land leased

[3]Cf. Widya Utami, "Tebasan, Suatu Gejala Sosial Ekonomi," *Cakrawala*. v. 4 (March–April, 1972), pp. 23–33.

[4]Cf. Selosoemardjan, *Social Changes in Jogjakarta* (Ithaca, New York, Cornell University Press, 1962), p. 219.

Table 10. Changes in farm size since 1968 (the year modern varieties were introduced).

village	owners whose land leased out or sharecropped			operators who leased or sharecropped land		
		area (ha)			area (ha)	
	no.[a]	1968	1971	no.[a]	1968	1971
			dry season			
Nganjat	13	0.2	1.5	9	4.6	4.4
Kahuman	7	1.3	1.2	7	4.8	1.0
Pluneng	3	2.2	5.1	7	1.9	4.9
			wet season			
Nganjat	17	0.8	3.4	13	' 5.3	7.0
Kahuman	5	0.9	1.6	27	14.3	12.2
Pluneng	6	0.3	2.4	15	1.2	6.2

[a] Who experienced changes.

out by owners or sharecropped, as well as the amount leased or share-cropped by farmers, increased. This may have resulted from efforts by farmers to make up for the losses they incurred through the required planting of part of their rice fields to tobacco. The rent paid in the dry season 1971 was Rp 53,000/ha per year, an increase of 43 percent compared with 1968.

The changes were also related to different systems of sharecropping. The systems used in these villages are termed *maro, mertelu, mrapat,* and *sromo.* In the *maro* system, the sharecropper bears the cost of all inputs and receives half of the harvest. In the *mertelu* system he pays for all the inputs and receives one-third of the harvest. In the *mrapat* system, the most common in the three villages, he is more like a contracted farm laborer, providing only the labor to cultivate the land and getting one-fourth of the yield at harvest time. In the *sromo* system, the share-cropper pays in advance a certain amount of money in exchange for the right to work the land. The amount of the *sromo* payment depends on when it is paid and how much of the input cost must be borne by the sharecropper.

Changes in the area of cultivated land in all three villages in the 1971/72 wet season may have resulted from *mrapat* sharecropping, awareness of the benefits of modern varieties, and the influence of tobacco planting.

Table 11. Average amounts borrowed for stated reasons.

village	amount borrowed (Rp/ha)						
			in kind[a]				
	cash for cultivation	urea	triple superphosphate	diazinon	zinc phosphide	endrin	BHC granular
1971 dry season							
Nganjat	6600	7660	1700	1900	340	0	0
Kahuman	6150	7550	2190	1600	0	0	0
Pluneng	8020	7720	0	530	0	0	0
1971/72 wet season							
Nganjat	8880	11350	960	0	b	100	0
Kahuman	5220	6640	990	0	b	2000	75
Pluneng	5110	7570	0	0	0	0	0

[a]Calculations based on market price.
[b]Negligible.

Changes in farm size seldom occurred as a result of sale or purchase of land. Only in Kahuman was there any sale of land, and that involved only two members of the sample group. Compared with 1968, the selling price of rice land had increased 52 percent in Kahuman and 95 percent in Pluneng.

Use of production credit. Before the introduction of modern varieties, sources of credit available to the farmers included government-sponsored farmers' cooperatives, moneylenders, village officials, the Farmers' Bank, the government pawn shop, and relatives, friends, or neighbors. Now most credit comes from the People's Bank of Indonesia (Bank Rakyat Indonesia). Other sources included official institutions such as the Village Credit Bank and the government pawn shop.

The People's Bank charged 1 percent per month and extended credit for 7 months. The Village Credit Bank charged 4 percent per month and the government pawn shop rate was 5 percent. Rates for credit from relatives or neighbors were variable. Moneylenders provided credit at interest rates between 10 percent to 40 percent per month.

The granting of production credit was carried on through cooperation among three government bodies. The People's Bank provided cash and a delivery order, while the State Agricultural Enterprise *(Pertani)* provided production means and supplies, and the local Department of

Agriculture office offered assistance. The use of production credit by the sample farmers in 1971 is shown in Table 11.

The Bimas program offered credit at the following maximum amounts per hectare:

	modern varieties (PB5 or PB8)	*other varieties*
fertilizer (urea)	Rp 5320 (200 kg)	3900 (150 kg)
cash	5100	4100
triple superphosphate	1197 (45 kg)	1197 (45 kg)
diazinon	600 (0.5 liter)	600 (0.5 liter)
zinc phosphide	43 (100 g)	43 (100 g)

The maximum credit available under the Bimas was less than farmers were actually using in 1971 so they were obtaining additional credit elsewhere.

Compared with the year in which modern varieties were introduced, farmers taking out loans increased by 32 percent in Nganjat, by 27 percent in Kahuman, and by 21 percent in Pluneng. In Nganjat, many of the sample farmers (40% in Nganjat, 30% in Kahuman, 23% in Pluneng) said that the conditions for credit were better than before the introduction of modern varieties because it seemed easier to repay the loans.

Furthermore, during the 1971 dry season, 20 percent of the sample farmers in Nganjat, 27 percent in Kahuman, and 44 percent in Pluneng hoped to use even more production credit. In the 1971/72 wet season, as many as 79 percent of the 24 borrowers in Nganjat viewed their credit as insufficient. Similarly, 62 percent of the 39 borrowers in Kahuman and 39 percent of the 41 in Pluneng wanted more credit. The majority of those wanting more credit expressed the intention of using it for fertilizer, insecticide, and cultivation costs.

Yield and disposal. Although no large or consistent change in yield per hectare occurred (Table 12), the introduction of modern varieties did bring about changes in cropping patterns, especially in the varieties of rice planted in each season and changes in frequency of harvests through use of the *petukan* system, thus producing up to five harvests in every 2-year period.

Before the use of modern varieties, the bulk of the harvest was used for family consumption and whatever surplus remained was sold. After

Table 12. Average yield of farmers' best rice fields before and after the introduction of modern varieties.

village	variety type	yield (t/ha)			
		dry season		wet season	
		1968[a]	1971	1968[a]	1971/72
Nganjat	modern	0	5.9	0	3.6
	local[b]	5.9	5.3	6.3	3.9
Kahuman	modern	0	6.5	0	6.9
	local[b]	5.6	6.6	5.6	6.6
Pluneng	modern	0	6.1	0	5.6
	local[b]	4.1	4.0	3.7	4.4

[a] The year before modern varieties were introduced to the village. [b] Includes both the traditional and improved local varieties.

the introduction of modern varieties, farmers in Nganjat and Kahuman tended to sell the major part of their harvest, both modern varieties and other varieties. Moreover the selling itself occurred soon after the harvesting (Table 13). Rice was disposed of at or immediately after harvesting because of increasing use of the *tebasan* system and the requirement that production loans be repaid within 1 month after the harvest.

In Pluneng farmers tended to sell their PB5 and use other varieties mostly for family consumption. In this village only one plot (of each farmer's two plots) could be planted with rice. Within the plot, farmers grew two varieties, with modern varieties taking up the major part of the land.

Problems in rice production. Pests (stem borers and rats) were most often mentioned among problems which arose along with the introduction of modern varieties (Table 14). A second major problem was obtaining seed, because of growing demand for better quality seed. The third major problem was obtaining fertilizer, pesticides, and credit, despite the credit package offered through the *Bimas*.

Water problems were encountered by only a few farmers and these problems were related to drainage only. Harvesting and post-harvest handling of grain have become less difficult because of the increasing use of the *tebasan* system.

Farmers have tried to overcome their problems mostly by the extension or intensification of methods they used before. Those methods

Table 13. Disposition of the rice harvest before the introduction of modern varieties (1968) and after.

village	disposition (%)					
	dry season			wet season		
	1968	1971		1968	1971/72	
	local	local	modern	local	local .	modern
	used by family					
Nganjat	51	40	40	51	36	37
Kahuman	49	41	36	56	50	40
Pluneng	63	88	31	61	93	43
	sold within first month after harvest[a]					
Nganjat	47	56	58	42	64	62
Kahuman	51	55	64	44	45	60
Pluneng	37	12	68	39	7	54
	sold more than 1 month after harvest[a]					
Nganjat	0	3	2	0	0	1
Kahuman	0	4	0	0	5	0
Pluneng	0	0	1	0	0	3
	other					
Nganjat	2	1	0	7	0	0
Kahuman	0	0	0	0	0	0
Pluneng	0	0	0	0	0	0

[a]Including standing crops sold under the *tebasan* system.

were improved implementation of *Panca Usaha,*[5] increased cash credit and labor power, the practice of crop rotation, and control of marketing channels.

CHANGES IN INCOME AND EXPENDITURE PATTERNS

In Nganjat, 42 percent of the sample farmers who planted modern varieties reported increased income, while 30 percent of those who did not plant modern varieties reported a higher income (Table 15).

[5]*Panca Usaha* ("the Five Activities") is a statement of the five activities involved in the rice intensification, which include: improvement of land preparation, use of modern varieties, use of chemical fertilizer, improvement of irrigation, improvement of crop maintenance.

Table 14. Difficulties in rice production before the introduction of modern varieties (1968) and after.

season	variety type	farmers reporting (%)										
		before harvest						harvest and after harvest				
		seeds	chemicals[b]	credit	irrigation	insects and diseases	others	harvesting	drying	storage	processing	selling
Nganjat												
1968[a] dry	local	0	3	2	0	94	0	7	2	2	3	2
1971 dry	local	0	5	0	0	93	3	12	3	3	2	2
	modern	7	18	0	0	95	3	18	3	3	2	2
1968[a] wet	local	0	0	0	0	33	0	0	0	0	0	0
1971/72 wet	local	0	9	7	2	87	0	4	4	4	2	13
	modern	3	0	3	0	97	0	3	10	10	3	13
Kahuman												
1968 dry	local	0	10	8	0	48	0	3	0	3	3	0
1971 dry	local	7	8	8	2	45	0	3	2	2	5	0
	modern	2	2	0	2	25	0	3	2	2	5	0
1968 wet	local	4	42	23	2	57	0	0	0	0	0	0
1971/72 wet	local	0	35	12	8	85	0	c	0	0	0	0
	modern	4	46	24	9	76	0	c	0	0	0	0
Pluneng												
1968 dry	local	0	44	21	0	79	0	0	0	0	0	0
1971 dry	local	0	2	0	0	17	0	c	0	0	0	0

			higher	lower	no change	no answer		higher	lower	no change	no answer		higher	lower	no change	no answer
1968 wet	local	local	0	59	0	49	0	7	76	0	0	0	0	0	0	0
1971/72 wet	local		0	0	0	0	5	0	9	85	c	c	0	0	0	0
	modern									85						

a Before modern varieties were introduced. b Fertilizer and pesticides. c Data not available.

Table 15. Tenure status, adoption of modern varieties, and changes in farm income, 1968–72.

	Nganjat					Kahuman					Pluneng				
tenure	families (no.)	income higher (%)	income lower (%)	no change (%)	no answer (%)	families (no.)	income higher (%)	income lower (%)	no change (%)	no answer (%)	families (no.)	income higher (%)	income lower (%)	no change (%)	no answer (%)
						modern varieties planted									
owners	21	33	57	10	0	25	85	13	2	0	40	94	0	0	6
owner-tenants	6	70	15	15	0	12	65	26	9	0	17	76	0	0	24
tenants	4	40	40	20	0	9	88	12	0	0	1	100	0	0	0
avg	–	42	46	12	0	–	80	16	4	0	–	89	0	0	11
						no modern varieties									
owners	21	28	51	21	0	4	100	0	0	0	1	100	0	0	0
owner-tenants	0	–	–	–	–	1	0	100	0	0	0	–	–	–	–
tenants	2	50	50	0	0	2	50	50	0	0	0	–	–	–	–
avg	–	30	51	19	0	–	77	23	0	0	–	100	0	0	0
farm laborers	10	0	33	56	11	8	60	0	40	0	5	12	38	25	25

In Kahuman, 80 percent of the sample farmers who planted modern varieties received more income, while 77 percent of farmers who did not plant modern varieties experienced an increase in their income. In Pluneng, 89 percent of the sample who used modern varieties said that their income had increased, but the one farmer who did not plant modern varieties also said that his income had increased. Clearly, those using modern varieties were not the only farmers with higher incomes.

Most farm laborers in Nganjat said their income either declined or remained the same. While 60 percent of the sample in Kahuman and 12 percent in Pluneng said their income had increased, it is not clear that this was a real increase, since many related the increase to inflation. None of the farm laborers in any of the villages mentioned modern varieties as a cause of his increased income.

In Nganjat among the landowners (91 percent of the sample), 49 percent had outside sources of income, especially nonfarm work. Most of those with extra jobs were the landowners and families of landowners who cultivated only their own land (Table 16). Among the nonowners (9 percent of the sample), 6 percent had extra jobs, and 4 percent had family members also doing outside work.

In Kahuman 79 percent of the sample were landowners of whom 19 percent had nonfarm work. Again it was the families of landowners who had the highest percentage of members doing off-farm and nonfarm work. Nonowners constituted 21 percent of the sample, and 9 percent of the heads of household had outside sources of income, while 8 percent had family members also engaged in outside work, especially of the nonfarm type.

In Pluneng, only landowners had outside sources of income. Generally these landowners farmed their own land, and generally the outside income was from nonfarm types of work. Again it was the owners who worked only their own land whose family members were most likely to earn outside income.

More than half of the heads of household who were farm laborers had other family members earning some income, usually also as farm laborers. Usual pay rates in the region were Rp 30 to Rp 100 per day for a farm laborer, Rp 50 to Rp 125 per day for other kinds of labor, Rp 400 per day for a plowman, Rp 50 to 200 per day for other craftsmen (stonemason, carpenter, tailor), Rp 50 to Rp 150 per day for a peddler, Rp 3000 to Rp 17,000 per month for a clerk or teacher, Rp 15,000 to Rp 80,000 per year as a rice buyer *(penebas)* and Rp 4000 to Rp 12,000 per month in home industry.

Table 16. Families with off-farm and nonfarm sources of income.

type of work	Nganjat (%)		Kahuman (%)		Pluneng (%)	
	head of household	other household members	head of household	other household members	head of household	other household members
			owners			
off-farm	17	11	0	4	3	5
nonfarm	26	9	17	11	24	5
unclear	0	2	6	2	9	7
			owner-tenants			
off-farm	2	2	0	0	3	2
nonfarm	4	4	2	4	10	2
unclear	0	0	9	0	6	0
			tenants			
off-farm	2	0	0	2	0	0
nonfarm	4	4	9	6	0	0
unclear	0	0	6	0	0	0
			farm laborers			
off-farm	100	44	100	100	100	38
nonfarm	0	11	0	0	0	25
unclear	0	0	0	0	0	0

During the 1971 dry season, 37 percent of the sample farmers in Nganjat, 77 percent in Kahuman, and 92 percent in Pluneng said their standard of living had increased since the introduction of modern varieties.

Food consumption required the largest expenditure among both landowners and nonowners (Table 17). This was followed by education, house improvement, and other expenditures. Farmers in Nganjat and Kahuman felt that expenditures for education had increased most significantly. This was caused by the opening of a new junior high school, about 4 kilometers from Nganjat; Kahuman had a junior high school since 1965. The production expenditures are distorted by difficulties in obtaining production supplies that were needed in the previous wet season.

Table 17 Largest categories of expenditures and largest increases in expenditures.

village	families (no.)	families in each village (%) with largest expenditure for							families in each village (%) reporting largest increase in expenditure for						
		food	cloth-ing	children's education	house improve-ment	produc-tion	other	no answer	food	cloth-ing	children's education	house improve-ment	produc-tion	other	no increase
owners															
Nganjat	42	69	3	14	0	0	14	0	15	8	37	0	0	9	31
Kahuman	29	72	4	20	0	0	4	0	38	20	31	0	0	11	0
Pluneng	41	73	0	0	11	3	10	3	42	4	4	0	6	31	-13
owner-tenants															
Nganjat	6	54	0	15	0	0	31	0	15	15	55	0	15	0	0
Kahuman	13	71	0	29	0	0	0	0	8	8	76	8	0	0	0
Pluneng	17	65	7	7	7	0	0	14	14	10	56	0	0	10	10
tenants															
Nganjat	6	45	0	22	0	0	22	11	0	0	22	0	0	44	34
Kahuman	11	62	0	29	0	0	0	0	19	38	43	0	0	0	0
Pluneng	1	100	0	0	0	0	0	0	0	0	0	0	0	0	100
farm laborers															
Nganjat	10	78	0	0	0	0	22	1	0	33	0	0	0	11	56
Kahuman	8	100	0	0	0	0	0	0	30	30	10	0	0	10	20
Pluneng	5	100	0	0	0	0	0	0	25	0	0	0	0	25	30

Table 18. First choice of uses for additional income.

village	farmers (%) reporting					
	added consumption	production	production and consumption	consumption and savings	savings	undecided
Nganjat	68	18	9	0	0	5
Kahuman	79	9	6	6	0	0
Pluneng	52	25	2	2	2	17

Most farm laborers spent the largest single share of their incomes for food, but most also spent as much as possible for the education of thier children.

Awareness that the use of modern varieties and other types of new technology can increase yields has given higher expectations to the farmers. Most farmers (73% in Nganjat, 57% in Kahuman, and 79% in Pluneng) believed that incomes would continue to increase in the future. The importance of additional food consumption is an indication of how low the standard of living still was in the villages (Table 18).

CONCLUSIONS

From all that has been described above, a number of conclusions can be drawn:

First, favorable physical conditions, satisfactory socio-economic conditions, and government policies to encourage rice production broadened acceptance of modern varieties in the area.

Second, the use of modern varieties on small farms encouraged the use of the *petukan* system, increased the use of family labor, increased the number of landless, made unofficial sources of credit more important, made sale of the standing crop more common, raised the incomes of farmers, and encouraged the landowners to use the income to lease or sharecrop more land.

The *petukan* system was extended as farmers sought to increase the frequency of harvests. Under this system, every operation throughout the agricultural year must be carefully scheduled to provide inputs needed for rice cultivation.

Use of family labor increased to reduce the need for cash and credit. This created employment problems, especially for those who owned no land.

The number of landless increased, leading to increasing dependency on landowners. Landowners, in turn, sought to maximize their benefits from modern varieties by limiting expenses, and the *mrapat* system of sharecropping consequently became the most common pattern.

Because credit was limited, unofficial sources of credit were important in spite of their unfavorable interest rates.

The spread of the *tebasan* system of sale of the standing rice crop freed many farmers from various socio-cultural and socio-economic ties and at the same time farm laborers had less opportunity to get additional income from harvesting.[6]

The incomes of landowners increased since the introduction of modern varieties, but so did incomes of tenants and sharecroppers. Only the farm laborers reported no income benefits as a result of modern varieties or mentioned no connection between modern varieties and any gains they had experienced.

Landowners used their increased incomes to lease or sharecrop additional land. The income was also used to raise their standard of living, especially for consumption of primary necessities, for education, and for house improvements. The introduction of modern varieties apparently strengthened the socio-economic position of landowning farmers too.[7] This permitted them to establish conditions most profitable for themselves in leasing out land (at high rents), in sharecropping (by using the *mrapat* system), and in the sale of their harvest through the *tebasan* system.

Third, for the whole area rice production increased since the introduction of modern varieties. At the local level, certain problems arose particularly in employment and in relationships among various groups in the society. If these effects are ignored they may well become the seeds of future tension and conflict.

Fourth, this study indicates the need for further research into:
● Relationships between physical factors and the cultivation of local varieties (especially Rojolele) in the dry season. The use of Rojolele in the dry season seems to have become a general practice, because in that season it gives the best yield.

[6] Widya Utami & John Ihalauw, "Farm Size: Its Consequences on Production, Land Tenure, Marketing and Social Relationship in Klaten Regency, Central Java," *A Special Report*, pp. 13–17.

[7] In her study in Klaten Regency in 1958 Ina Slamet found that villagers who had no land must lease land from the landowner under unfavorable conditions known as *sromo*. Cf. Ina Slamet, Pokok-Pokok Pembangunan Masyarakat Desa (Jakarta: Bhratava, 1965).

• The problem of dependency on cultivated land, and the various patterns of sharecropping and leasing land. The landless farmers are in such a weak position that they are forced to accept the *mrapat* system. More knowledge is needed about social relations between landowners and sharecroppers.

• The *tebasan* system. This system is important because it involves socio-cultural as well as economic elements. It must be studied in relation to government efforts to develop various marketing institutions on the village level.

• The contract labor system. This system appeared particularly in Pluneng. Study is needed on the background of this system, on the formation of a stable group of contract laborers, and on their social and economic relations with their employers.

• Nonfarm income. Some data have already been gathered, but the extent of nonfarm work and its influence on the income of the village society should be studied.

• Rural employment. The limitation of employment to farm work, combined with the relatively rapid increase in population, creates a number of employment problems. Further research should examine other employment possibilities within the rural society.

INDONESIA

Sidoarjo, East Java and Subang, West Java

Dibyo Prabowo and Sajogyo

The adoption of the new rice technology has been much greater in the East Java than in the West Java village chosen for this study. A major reason has been the serious attack of gall midge in the West Java village. Local varieties proved more resistant. Despite the widespread adoption of modern varieties and increased use of fertilizer in the East Java village, yields of the new rice varieties were not significantly greater than those of local varieties. Part of the reason lies in the already intensive cultivation practices and high yields obtained for local varieties on the extremely small Javanese farms.

THE INDONESIAN GOVERNMENT sees adequate domestic rice production as a major policy objective. Population is growing at 2.3 percent per year, per capita rice consumption is increasing, and rice production is not keeping pace. Rice yields have consistently averaged less than 2 t/ha for several decades. For several years the importation of rice has cost Indonesia 5 to 15 percent of her foreign exchange earnings each year.

The government has been aware that speedy adoption by farmers of the new rice technology requires funds. Various national efforts have been made to raise rice production. The latest, the so-called *Bimas* program, is a coordination of extension and credit. Due to this program, farmers are using better methods of farming and getting better yields. But late disbursement of credit and badly coordinated distribution of agricultural inputs continue to be a major obstacle to such efforts. Consolidation of such activities is proceeding.

Dibyo Prabowo is a member of the Faculty of Economics at the Gadjah Mada University, Yogyakarta; Sajogyo is the head of Agro-Economic Survey, Bogor.

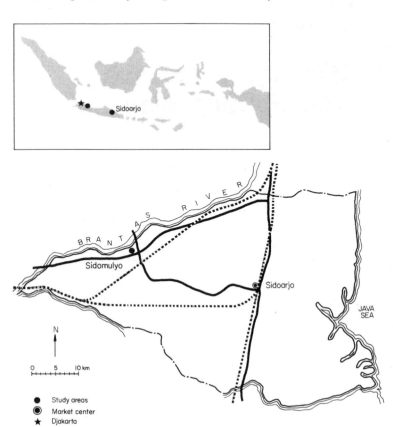

Sidoarjo District, East Java.

It is apparent that the new rice technology is being accepted more rapidly in some areas than others. To study the reasons for this difference, we chose two villages with high potentials for rice production but with very different experiences in the adoption of modern varieties.

THE STUDY VILLAGES

The two sample villages are in East and West Java, two of the three major rice growing areas of Java. In choosing these villages, the first step was to select two districts in regencies with high rice production potentials. The East Java village of Sidomulyo has shown spectacular response to the introduction of modern varieties. The West Java village of Cidahu has shown poor response.

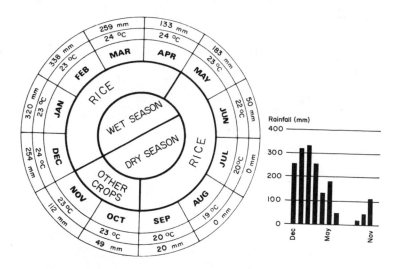

Average monthly rainfall and minimum temperature (Mojosari Experiment Station, 1971-1972), East Java, Indonesia.

Sidomulyo, the "high-response" village, is in the large Brantas river delta of East Java. It is only 9 meters above sea level, with a dry season of 4.5 to 6 months. The village is 40 kilometers south of Surabaya, the provincial capital. Cidahu, the "low-response" village, is in the northern coastal plains of West Java. It is 150 kilometers west of Jakarta, the national capital. It is 90 meters above sea level, on flat and gently sloping terrain, with 3 to 4.5 months of dry season. The rainiest months are December and January.

In the 1971 population census, Sidomulyo had 2,137 persons in 453 households. Of its 170 hectares of farmland, half was wet rice land. The rest was used for trees and vegetables, for other crops, and for the house sites. Of the wet rice land, one third was rented out each year for sugarcane production. Population density on total farm land was 0.08 hectare per capita and on wet rice land, 0.04 hectare. Cidahu had a population of 3,322 persons in 958 households. Of its 480 hectares of farm land a little over half was wet rice land and a fourth was other crops. It had 0.14 hectare of farm land per person, or 1.8 times more than Sidomulyo.

From the provincial capital, Surabaya, it takes about 1 hour to reach Sidomulyo by road. The village is about 1.5 kilometers from Krian town, through which buses pass regularly. Krian is also on the railroad, but only third-class trains stop there. Local transportation is by horse cart (*becak*). Sidomulyo has a road density of 10 kilometers per square kilometer, of which 6 percent is paved. In the dry climate, dirt roads do

Subang District, West Java.

not often present a problem for truck-transport. Cidahu is only 5 kilometers from its district capital of Subang. Its road density is 4 kilometers per square kilometer, of which 27 percent is paved.

Sidomulyo has one elementary school, Cidahu has two. All three are government operated. There is no clinic in either village.

Irrigation and the cropping pattern. In both the wet and dry seasons farms in both study areas usually have enough irrigation water, and all sample farmers were able to double-crop. During the 1972 dry season, a water shortage occurred in Sidomulyo because a new irrigation system (Karangkates dam) was being developed and water distribution throughout the area was being controlled in an effort to give all localities equal

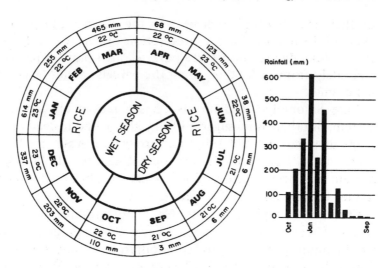

Average monthly rainfall and minimum temperature (Pusaka-negara Experiment Station, 1971-1972), West Java, Indonesia.

access to water. For this reason only 70 percent of the sample farmers in Sidomulyo were able to grow rice during the 1972 dry season.

Both study areas are served by modern canal irrigation facilities drawing water from the river. Water is under the authority of the Ministry of Public Works up to the secondary canal. Its management in the village (tertiary canal) is handled by village officials (*ulu-ulu* in Cidahu, *kuwowo* in Sidomulyo). Each of the 15 officials in Cidahu is responsible for about 17.5 hectares of rice land. In Sidomulyo, each of the four officials is responsible for 20 hectares of wet rice land in one of the four sub-villages.

Strictly speaking, farmers do not pay for water, but they pay an assessment in terms of rough rice or labor service. The amount of each year's contribution depends on how much work is needed on the repair of canals, bridges, etc. In Sidomulyo, sample farmers made an average contribution of 25 kilograms of rough rice in the 1971/72 wet season and 20 kilograms in the 1972 dry season. In Cidahu farmers contributed 42 kilograms in the 1971/72 wet season and 49 kilograms in the 1972 dry season plus two man-days of labor service each season.

The cropping pattern is dictated by the weather. In Sidomulyo, the wet-season rice crop is grown from December to April, the period of heaviest rainfall. The dry-season crop is grown from May to September. The seasonal variation in rainfall is pronounced, but temperatures vary little.

In Sidomulyo, in recent years, multiple cropping has been general. Farmers of Sidomulyo, have been obliged, however, to rent out a third of their irrigated land each year to the nearby sugar mill in a rotating cycle of 18 months for the production of sugarcane. The farmers' rice land is thus divided into three parcels. Most plots or parcels are located separately from each other, so all the parcels cannot be cultivated at the same time.

Like Sidomulyo, Cidahu also has a reasonably intensive irrigation system. But there is no sugar mill in Cidahu, and instead of growing such crops as sugarcane and tobacco, farmers cultivate rice throughout the year. Due to lack of water, a rice-planting intensity of only 100 to 150 percent has been reached. The locally practiced rotation calls for the farmer to leave his land idle during September and October.

Credit and supply of inputs. Generally speaking, farmers had limited credit. Those who participated in the *Bimas* program could borrow a fixed amount per hectare to buy modern farm inputs. Loans matured in 7 months and interest was 12 percent per year. Farmers in the *Bimas* program received necessary agricultural inputs such as fertilizer, pesticides, and insecticides from the government as part of their credit package. For urea fertilizer they were charged Rp 26.60/kg. Urea was available commercially at a price at least 5 percent higher. Farmers outside the program had almost no sources of production credit. In Sidomulyo the paddy bank (*lumbung desa*) lent paddy mainly for consumption. In Cidahu, fellow farmers, neighbors, and relatives were common sources of credit.

The sample. Before the main survey a partial census was made of 150 farm households in each village. The next step was to select samples of 75 farmers in Sidomulyo and 77 farmers in Cidahu. These 152 farmers were interviewed in the 1971 dry season, in the 1971/72 wet season, and in the 1972 dry season.

Sample households were larger in Sidomulyo than in Cidahu, but farms and the rice area were a little smaller (Table 1). Nearly all sample farmers were owner-operators. Tenants and part-owners operated on either a share crop or a leasehold system. When share cropping was practiced, half the crop went to the owner and half to the tenant.

ADOPTION OF MODERN VARIETIES

Varietal recommendations change over time, depending heavily upon the results of rice breeding or evaluation trials at the Central Research Institute of Agriculture at Bogor. Before modern varieties were introduced in Java, several earlier varieties were considered high yielding.

Table 1. Characteristics of the sample farms.

village	farms (no.)		persons in household (no.)	farm size (ha)	farmers (%) by tenure category		
	village	sample			full owner	part owners	tenants
Sidomulyo	n.a.	75	6.0	0.48	86	7	7
Cidahu	n.a.	77	4.1	0.53	90	9	1

	rice area				
	per farm (ha)		double cropped (%)	irrigated (%)	principal form of irrigation
	dry season	wet season			
Sidomulyo	0.29	0.38	98	100	canal
Cidahu	0.48	0.52	100	100	canal

	modern varieties				
	farmers planting (%)		rice area planted (%)		year of greatest adoption
	dry season	wet season	dry season	wet season	
Sidomulyo	95	99	95	95	1968
Cidahu	46	45	45	26	1971

These varieties were mainly the result of the breeding work based on Indonesian traditional local varieties that are medium-responsive to fertilizer and have good flavor. These varieties are commonly known as *bibit unggul nasional* (*ungnas*). They include Syntha, Dara, Sigadis, Ramadja, and Bengawan, and farmers in the *Bimas* program are permitted to plant them. Thus, *ungnas* are improved local varieties.

The modern varieties, first introduced in 1967, were known as *bibit unggul baru.* They included PB8 (IR8), PB5 (IR5), and C4-63, and their use was required for maximum credit from the program. Modern rice varieties have spread with an encouraging speed from the point of view of Indonesia as a whole. They covered 190,000 hectares in the total *Bimas* area in the 1969 dry season and 306,000 hectares in the 1970/71 wet season. By that time the modern varieties accounted for 10 percent of the total rice area in Indonesia, their adoption occurring mainly through the *Bimas* program.

In Sidomulyo the first seeds of modern varieties were obtained in the

1967/68 wet season from the district extension service. Availability of the seeds was limited, and village heads and some village officials took the lead in testing the new technology. More general adoption took place in the 1968 dry season. Under the *Bimas* program of that period, 30 out of 75 farmers had at least a portion of their land planted to IR 8. By the 1971 dry season and the 1972 dry season, 90 percent were full adopters (farmers with all land in modern varieties). Despite a drought in the 1972 dry season, 44 out of 46 rice planters were full adopters. It is apparent that Sidomulyo sample farmers had confidence in these varieties (Table 2).

Farmers in Cidahu also began adopting the modern rice varieties in the 1968 dry season. As in Sidomulyo, the first seeds were obtained from the extension service and were planted by village leaders. Later, marked differences in the pattern of adoption occurred. In the first year of adoption, only three out of the 77 Cidahu sample farmers used the modern varieties exclusively. The number of farmers planting all their rice to modern varieties rose steadily until the 1971/72 wet season. During the 1971/72 wet season, a pest (gall midge) attacked the rice crop and caused especially serious damage to the modern varieties. Apparently this susceptibility moved farmers back to local varieties because in the 1972 dry season, the number of full adopters dropped tremendously, from 20 farmers to one. The proportion of farmers planting any modern varieties dropped from 53 percent in the 1971/72 wet season to 17 percent in the following dry season (Table 2).

Table 2. Adopters and area planted by varietal type.

year	season	adopters (%)			average area (ha)			
		modern only	local only	modern + local	modern only	local only	modern + local	avg
				Sidomulyo				
1971	dry	92	5	3	0.30	0.25	0.22	0.29
1971/72	wet	94	6	0	.38	.00	.48	.38
1972[a]	dry	96	4	0	.24	.30	.00	.24
				Cidahu				
1971	dry	16	61	23	.35	.40	.77	.48
1971/72	wet	27	47	26	.54	.41	.72	.52
1972	dry	1	83	16	.19	.45	.83	.51

[a]Of 70 sample farmers only 46 planted rice due to the lack of water.

Table 3. Reasons farmers gave for planting modern varieties, 1971/72 wet season.

reason	farmers (%) reporting[a]	
	Sidomulyo[b]	Cidahu[c]
higher yield	100	25
resistant to drought	11	0
do not lodge	11	0
grain expands when cooked	9	0
short maturity	6	0
resistant to disease	3	0
birds do not like it	3	0
others	2	10
no response	0	65

[a] Some farmers gave more than one answer. [b] 66 respondents. [c] 20 respondents.

High yield was the reason most often cited in both communities by those using the modern varieties (Table 3). Farmers in Cidahu who experienced pest damage were slower to convince about the superiority in yield, and expressed concern about the flavor of the newer varieties, particularly when the rice is served cold.

YIELD PERFORMANCE AND FARM PRACTICES

Farm yield comparisons of local and modern varieties (Table 4) are not easy to interpret, because conditions differ from farm to farm. To justify such comparison we must assume similar environmental conditions, soils, and water control among sample farms within the village.

In Sidomulyo the modern varieties were at least moderately higher yielding than local varieties in each of the three crop seasons. In Cidahu local varieties outyielded the modern ones except in the 1971 dry season.

The average rice yield was generally lower in Cidahu than in Sidomulyo. There are at least three reasons: in most seasons (except for the special circumstances of the 1972 dry season) Sidomulyo had a better water supply, farmers there used more fertilizer (Table 4), and pests have been less destructive. In the 1971/72 wet season, the attack of the *hama-ganjur* (rice gall midge, *Pachydiplosis oryzae*) was considered the worst since 1968. It destroyed 60 to 70 percent of Cidahu's

Table 4. Yields and fertilizer use.

varieties	1971 dry season			1971/72 wet season			1972 dry season		
	farms (no.)	yield (t/ha)	N-P[a] (kg/ha)	farms (no.)	yield (t/ha)	N-P (kg/ha)	farms[b] (no.)	yield (t/ha)	N-P (kg/ha)
				Sidomulyo					
modern	69	4.8	134−18	66	5.1	144−2	14	4.7	142−0
local	4	4.5	106−0	0	n.a.[c]	n.a.	1	4.4	70−0
both	2	4.8	94−0	4	4.5	117−0	0	n.a.	n.a.
				Cidahu					
modern	12	3.9	107−21	20	2.1	100−2	1	1.6	85−0
local	47	3.0	85−5	34	3.0	82−1	60	3.0	94−1
both	18	3.4	92−8	18	2.4	89−1	11	3.3	97−2

[a]Nitrogen and phosphorus applied. [b]In Sidomulyo, only 15 of the farmers sampled had harvested at the time of survey. [c]n.a. − not applicable.

rice crop. Although *Bimas* farmers had applied insecticide, four applications of Demicron and Basudin, they got poor results. Farmers noticed that attacks were much more severe on such modern varieties as PB5 than on local varieties.

Variation in yield from year to year also affected the willingness of a farmer to accept a variety. In Sidomulyo the modern varieties consistently gave high yields (Table 4). In Cidahu yields tended to decrease over time. This resulted in a decline in adopters (Table 2).

Fertilizer use. A striking increase in use of nitrogen fertilizer seems to have followed introduction of new varieties in Sidomulyo (Table 4). In Cidahu, the difference was not as consistent or striking, and the general level of fertilizer use was lower.

We could not explain why farmers in Sidomulyo continued a higher level of fertilization for modern varieties despite an only slight yield advantage over local varieties, except by pointing to the shorter growth duration of the new varieties. This was important in the extensive cropping system of Sidomulyo, especially because one-third of a farmer's land in any year was rented to the sugar plantation. The recognition of the yield superiority of modern varieties (Table 3) was in comparison with the local varieties that preceded them, that is, traditional local varieties such as Merali, Wrijal, and Jawa which averaged only about 2 t/ha. The initial yield advantage of modern varieties has been narrowed considerably, especially comparing their yields with the performance of improved local varieties (Bengawan, Syntha, Dara, Sigadis) with fertilizer.

Other farm practices. In Cidahu, farmers used rotary weeders. In Sidomulyo, hand weeding was common and the labor used for it increased after introduction of modern varieties. Rotary weeders were not used in Sidomulyo because straight-row planting was not practiced. Some farmers tried the rotary weeder, but switched back to hand weeding.

Insecticides were used more in Cidahu because pests and diseases were considered a more serious danger, especially to the modern varieties.

A third of the sample farmers in Cidahu used sickles to save time and labor in harvesting, but most still used the *ani-ani* hand knife. In Sidomulyo, the sickle was introduced in the 1972 dry season by the village head (*lurah*). Other farmers had not begun using it.

USE OF CREDIT

Farmers in the survey area obtained credit from both government sources (*Bimas*) and from private lending agencies and individuals. Since not all of the sampled farmers were participating in the *Bimas* program, we were able to obtain data on how farmers outside the program obtain credit for farming and other activities.

Credit extended through Bimas scheme. The "new *Bimas*" rice-intensification scheme began operations in the area of this study during the 1970/71 wet season and operated throughout the period of the study. Credit was to come from a State Bank (Bank Rakyat Indonesia), partly in cash but mostly in the form of vouchers for such inputs as fertilizer and pesticides, redeemable either at the village-unit branch or from farm-input shops in the village (Table 5). These loans were repayable in 7 months, i.e. 1 month *after harvest,* at 1 percent interest a month (this interest rate is exceptionally low compared with alternative sources of rural credit). How much was granted depended upon the farmer's actual credit needs: the farmer got more inputs if he planted the modern varieties (in "new *Bimas*") than if he planted local varieties ("ordinary *Bimas*").

In the 1971/72 wet season the actual credit granted under the Bimas program was Rp 13,290/ha in Sidomulyo and Rp 8,335/ha in Cidahu which was below the recommended credit package. Farmers in Sidomulyo received more credit because more of them were planting modern varieties. They were thus entitled to borrow the "new *Bimas*"

Table 5. Recommended Bimas credit package, 1971/72 wet season.

input	"new Bimas"		"ordinary Bimas"	
	amt/ha	Rp/ha	amt/ha	Rp/ha
	in kind			
urea fertilizer	200 kg	5320	100 kg	2660
TSP fertilizer	45 kg	1200	35 kg	990
insecticide	2 liters	2350	2 liters	2350
zinc phosphide	100 kg	50	100 kg	50
total	–	8920	–	6050
	in cash			
sprayer rent[a]	–	600	–	600
seeds	–	1000	–	0
intensification cost[b]	–	3500	–	3500
total	–	5100	–	4100
total credit	–	14020	–	10150

[a] Available only if at least 50% of the insecticide credit is accepted.
[b] Available only if at least 160 kg/ha (80 kg/ha ordinary Bimas) of fertilizer is accepted.

package, which is larger than the "ordinary *Bimas*" package to which most of Cidahu's farmers, planting local varieties, were limited. Many of the sample farmers in both villages expressed dissatisfaction with the amount of credit obtained from the *Bimas* program and would have liked to borrow more.

Repayment of loans in Sidomulyo was 86 percent. The repayment rate in Cidahu was slightly below 50 percent, largely because of serious damage caused by gall midge in the 1971/72 wet season which reduced rice yields sharply from the previous season.

Credit from outside Bimas. Seventy of the 152 sampled farmers obtained loans from the *Bimas* program. Many did not borrow through the *Bimas* program because they still had outstanding credit from a previous season and thus were not allowed to participate. Thus, to finance production and family needs they had to look for outside help.

More farmers borrowed in the wet season than in the dry season (Table 6). Outside the *Bimas* program, the most common source of credit in Sidomulyo was the paddy bank (*lumbung desa*); in Cidahu, it was neighbors or fellow farmers or relatives. Borrowing was both in money and in kind. Rough rice was borrowed in Sidomulyo, mainly for

Table 6. Type and terms of credit from sources outside of Bimas, 1971/72 wet season and 1972 dry season.

village	type of credit	borrowers (no.)	value of credit (Rp/farm)	interest per month (%)	loan period (months)
			wet season		
Sidomulyo	cash	4[a]	3400	0	0.5–6
	in kind	30[b]	1500	0–5	4–6
Cidahu	cash	4[c]	750	0–2.5	1–4
	in kind	38[d]	4700	0–15	1–6
			dry season		
Sidomulyo	cash	3	2300	0	4–6
	in kind	25	1700	0–3	6
Cidahu	cash	0	0	0	0
	in kind	29[e]	5500	0–11	4–6

[a]Three were also in the *Bimas* program. [b]Eight were also in the *Bimas* program. [c]Three were also in the *Bimas* program. [d]Twenty were also in the *Bimas* program. [e]Fourteen were also in the *Bimas* program.

consumption purposes. In Cidahu, loans in kind came from peddlers of cloth, kerosene lamps, etc., who move from village to village.

The small size of farms and the large size of households jointly affected the need to borrow for consumption purposes when production fell short of the food demands of the family. Borrowing in kind usually occurred in the time of scarcity (*paceklik*). Money loans were much less common. Little money was available for borrowing in the village, and moneylenders in town charged up to 5 to 10 percent a month interest.

LABOR USE

In Sidomulyo, the cultivation of modern varieties used 19 man-days/ha more labor than local varieties (Table 7). The difference related to weeding. Heavy fertilization stimulates weed growth. Local varieties, which are less heavily fertilized, required one or two weedings. Modern varieties required two or three.

In Cidahu, modern varieties used 16 man-days/ha less labor than local varieties. Pest infestation was high in Cidahu, and plant protection for modern varieties took extra time. But some farmers in Cidahu began to use the sickle for harvesting the modern varieties, while the hand knife continued to be used for harvesting local varieties. This difference in harvesting method reduced the total labor need.

Hired labor accounted for about 70 percent of total labor use in the sample villages (Table 7). The majority of Java's small farm operators rely on such hired help and in turn hire themselves out to fellow farmers in their village.

Use of labor in Sidomulyo was influenced by the relationship of sugarcane to other crops. When sugarcane was being planted or harvested, labor was in short supply. Laborers hired from as far as 100 kilometers away stayed in the village for 2 or 3 months until the work was finished. Farmers in Sidomulyo also liked to work at the sugar mill, because they were paid as much as Rp 200 (about US$0.50) per day. Male laborers in rice production normally received only about Rp 100 plus one meal worth Rp 25 per day, for a 7-hour day, and female laborers received only Rp 60 without food for a 3- to 4-hour working day.

Rice production in Java is labor intensive, however. Philippine data show 70 to 130 man-days of family and hired labor are used on a hectare of rice. Java's farmers in the study areas used roughly twice as much labor per hectare. The situation is related to the total population and total cultivated land in the two regions. In Java about 70 million persons are concentrated on 5.6 million hectares of cultivated land. The Philippines has the same amount of cultivated land but only about 35 million people. A higher percentage of redundant labor is employed in Java than in the Philippines and there is a lower productivity per unit of labor employed. The high labor input in Java reflects the "share-and-share-alike" philosophy which entitles landless laborers to a share of the crop.

Table 7. Labor use for modern and local varieties, 1971 dry season.

village	varietal type	farmers (no.)	rice area (ha)	labor (man-days/ha)		
				family	hired	total
Sidomulyo	modern	69	0.30	94	121	276
	local	4	.25	62	194	256
	both	2	.22	58	192	250
Cidahu	modern	12	.35	42	112	154
	local	47	.40	43	127	170
	both	18	.77	38	109	147

INCOME, STANDARD OF LIVING, AND CONSUMPTION LEVELS

Income from rice production. We measured rice income as return above variable cost, since only variable costs are important in short-run decision-making once fixed costs have been committed to agricultural production. In the 1971 dry season in Sidomulyo, net return from local varieties was about the same as from modern varieties (Table 8). In Cidahu, modern varieties gave a one-fourth higher net return per hectare than local varieties. The reason for the difference between the two villages is that in Sidomulyo in that season the yields of the local and modern varieties were about the same.

In Cidahu small and medium farms had significantly lower net returns per hectare than large farms (Table 9). These differences appear to be due to differences in yields. There is little sign that small farms are at a disadvantage when it comes to procuring cash inputs other than labor. In Sidomulyo the returns of the small and medium farms were not significantly different, and there was only one "large farm." Its hired labor costs were much higher than those of other farmers.

Income other than rice. In Cidahu two-thirds of the sample farmers earned income from off- and nonfarm activities in the 1971 dry season (Table 10). The smaller the farm, the more likely the farmer was to obtain income from off-farm activities such as farm labor, nonagricultural labor, trading, or transportation services. Farmers who got a smaller net return from rice found it more often necessary to do off-farm work to get additional income. But those from larger farms who did work off the farm tended to have higher incomes from these outside activities.

In Sidomulyo, differences in farm size did not produce differences in propensity to seek additional income. Moreover, farmers from the smaller farms obtained somewhat more income from such activities than large farmers.

Aside from off-farm and nonfarm income, farmers also obtained some additional income from backyard enterprises (*pekarangan*) and livestock. In the backyard, the farmer can raise a variety of crops such as papaya, banana, coconut, and vegetables. He can harvest these almost throughout the year and need not depend upon the season. A third of the sample farmers in Sidomulyo and half of the farmers in Cidahu were engaged in backyard production. Cidahu has more available farm land. Backyard income per farm, however, did not seem to be significantly different for the two villages. Livestock feeding was a source of income for 35 percent of the farmers in Sidomulyo and 21 percent in Cidahu. The difference in livestock income between the two villages was also not significant.

Table 8. Yield and return above variable costs by varietal type, 1971 dry season.

village	variety type	farms (no.)	yield[a] (t/ha)	gross return (thousand Rp/ha)	cost (thousand Rp/ha)						net return (thousand Rp/ha)
					seeds	fertilizer	insecticide	interest[b]	hired labor	total	
Sidomulyo	modern	68	3.8	81.0	1.0	8.9	—	0.6	14.6	25.2	55.8
	local	4	3.6	66.1	1.0	6.5	—	.5	11.2	19.2	46.8
Cidahu	modern	12	3.4	62.2	0.6	7.8	0.8	.6	11.7	21.5	40.8
	local	47	2.6	51.1	0.6	5.5	0.9	.4	11.7	19.1	32.0

[a] In terms of rough rice; harvester's share has been deducted (one-fifth of gross yield in Sidomulyo and one-seventh in Cidahu).
[b] Interest at 1% per month calculated for 6 months.

Table 9. Costs and returns above variable costs, by size of farm, 1971 dry season.

farm type	farms (no.)	farm size (ha)	rice yield[a] (t/ha)	gross return[b] (thousand Rp/ha)	cost (thousand Rp/ha)					net return[c] (thousand Rp/ha)
					seeds	fertilizer	insecticides	hired labor	total	
Sidomulyo										
small	45	0.19	3.9	74.1	0.8	8.2	—	22.4	31.4	42.7
medium	24	0.43	3.8	72.2	.8	9.5	—	23.4	33.7	38.5
large	1	0.80	6.0	114.0	.9	11.4	—	52.8	65.1	48.9
Cidahu										
small	22	0.25	2.5	47.5	.5	5.9	1.0	8.6	16.1	31.4
medium	41	0.43	2.6	49.4	.5	7.5	1.0	11.4	21.4	29.0
large	14	1.20	3.1	58.9	.6	5.5	0.9	11.5	18.4	40.5

Because of higher returns from rice farming (Table 9) and higher off-farm and nonfarm income (Table 10), the average household income of farmers in Sidomulyo in the 1971 dry season was appreciably higher than that in Cidahu. Per caput, Sidomulyo farmers were still a little better off (11 percent higher income) in spite of the smaller households in Cidahu.

Change in levels of consumption during the period in which the modern varieties were being introduced is one criterion of increasing welfare among farmers.

Consumption pattern for staple foods. For most farm households the normal length of the rice shortage is 2 to 3 months each season but for some it runs as much as 4 months. In the wet season it is usually most serious in February, March, and April, and in the dry season, in August, September, and October.

Of 70 farm households in Sidomulyo, 35 percent reported no shortage in the 1968/69 wet season, compared with 33 percent in the 1971/72 wet season. In Cidahu, 33 percent reported no shortage in the 1971/72 wet season. The absence of change in Sidomulyo indicates that two thirds of the farmers were no better off 3 years after general adoption of the modern varieties than before (Table 11).

Although in normal times all families were rice eaters, during the shortage in the 1971/72 wet season the number of rice eaters decreased by one-third in both areas. At the same time, however, the number of corn eaters increased by eight times in Sidomulyo (to 50% of the families in the village). The Cidahu farmers did not use corn as substitute for rice (Table 12). The consumption of most other food and household commodities also decreased during shortage (other commodities include meat, egg, salted fish, salt, cooking oil, kerosene, vegetables, sugar, soap, and cigarettes).

CONSTRAINTS ON FURTHER PRODUCTION INCREASE

Interviews with five groups of six farmers enabled us to identify major problems in growing rice. Although farmers could not enlarge their small land holdings, they could do something about several other problems of rice production. These can be conveniently divided into problems within and outside the *Bimas* program.

Problems in the Bimas program. In both villages, farmers believed that for optimum yields they had to apply heavy doses of the right chemical fertilizer at the proper time. They felt, however, that the *Bimas* program had not always met this requirement. They reported that

Table 10. Income from off-farm and non-farm activities, 1971 dry season.

village	outside labor	large farms		medium-sized farms		small farms	
		no.	income (Rp)	no.	income (Rp)	no.	income (Rp)
Sidomulyo	other farms	0	0	0	0	2	10,500
	non-farm	1	16,800	6	12,500	6	31,200
	trade	0	0	5	25,400	8	18,900
	transport	0	0	1	27,000	7	26,300
	none	0	0	17	0	22	0
	avg	1	16,800	29	7,900	45	12,100
Cidahu	other farms	0	0	8	900	10	2,100
	non-farm	1	1,300	16	1,700	3	800
	trade	0	0	7	800	3	800
	transport	4	13,100	7	3,000	1	1,800
	none	9	0	3	0	5	0
	avg	14	3,800	41	1,500	22	1,500

fertilizer often arrived late, especially the type of fertilizer needed for basal application. Therefore, most farmers, particularly in Sidomulyo, did not apply this type fertilizer (officials of *Bimas* informed us that in 1971 the supply of basal fertilizer was far from adequate). Many farmers also said that they did not receive enough fertilizer from *Bimas*. As a result they either applied less than was needed or, if they had the money, they bought from private stores at 5 percent or more above the authorized selling price.

The farmers in Cidahu complained about the rigid formalities followed in processing loan applications. Because of the resulting delays in obtaining credit, they felt that the credit period of 7 months was too short.

Table 11. Length of family food shortages, Sidomulyo and Cidahu, 1968/69 and 1971/72 wet seasons.

village	year	farmers (no.)	farmers (%) reporting shortages lasting				
			1 month	2 months	3 months	4 months	none[a]
Sidomulyo	1968/69	70	3	20	38	4	35
	1971/72	70	5	20	39	3	33
Cidahu	1971/72	72	11	29	21	6	33

[a]Or less than 1 month.

Table 12. Change in consumption of staple food grains among families experiencing food shortage, Sidomulyo and Cidahu, 1971/72 wet season.

village	period	amount consumed (g/day)	
		rice	corn
Sidomulyo	before shortage	2000	250
	during shortage	1250	500
Cidahu	before shortage	1600	1500
	during shortage	0	0

Sidomulyo farmers did not report difficulties in processing of loan applications. One group stated, however, that the amount of cash credit that could be obtained from *Bimas* to apply to living expenses was too small.

Problems outside the Bimas program. The rice farmers who did not participate in the *Bimas* program were relatively worse off in terms of credit and farm input availability, than participants. Nonparticipants in Sidomulyo reported fewer troubles than those in Cidahu. Farmers in both villages stated that it was difficult to find enough seed conforming to specified standards of purity and germination. Water for irrigation was scarce, especially during the 1972 dry season (which was in fact a drought year), and was a main topic of discussion in these villages as it was with farmers throughout Indonesia.

Farmers in Cidahu regarded plant protection as a serious problem. Modern rice varieties were considered less immune to the attack of pests and diseases. Farmers reported difficulties in getting effective chemicals during the attack of gall midge. Endrin, Dieldrin, Folidol, Demicron, and Aldrin were all expensive, and the results were often disappointing. In addition, Cidahu growers reported much loss from rats, especially in fields that were planted late.

In both villages, farmers have said that the agricultural taxes and other contributions they must pay are too heavy.

CONCLUSIONS

Farmers were surveyed in Sidomulyo, East Java, and Cidahu, West Java, to determine the impact of the new rice technology and changes in rice farming. The two areas were chosen because they are located in Java's main irrigated rice areas. There has been a spectacular response to the introduction of the modern varieties in Sidomulyo, but not in Cidahu.

The adoption of modern varieties began in both villages in the same year, the 1968 dry season. It was not initially an independent decision of the farmers, because participation in the *Bimas* program required farmers to plant modern varieties.

Almost all the sample farmers in Sidomulyo moved quickly to the modern IR5 (PB-5) variety, where the area planted to modern varieties increased year by year.

Adoption of modern varieties in Cidahu was low. Serious attacks of gall midge resulted in low yield from modern varieties, and farmers began switching back to local varieties.

The differences in farm practices between the new and local varieties in Sidomulyo are in the amount of fertilizer used and the additional labor for weeding. In Cidahu, farmers who adopted modern varieties also tended to change their method of harvesting, using the sickle instead of the hand knife. This change required less labor in harvesting. Nearly all other practices were essentially the same.

Although more fertilizer was used on modern varieties in Sidomulyo, there was little effect on yield; modern varieties yielded only slightly more than local varieties there. Possibly, the shorter maturity of the new varieties explains the preference there: Sidomulyo had an intensive double-cropping system (rice, other food crops, and sugarcane). In Cidahu, farmers said modern varieties gave lower yield than local varieties because PB-5 was more susceptible to gall midge than local varieties. However, in both villages, yields of local varieties have risen sharply since the adoption of chemical fertilizer that came with the new varieties in the *Bimas* program.

Farmers in the *Bimas* program reported better ability to get credit and farm inputs. Farmers outside *Bimas* could find farm inputs such as fertilizer in private stores, but still had to locate credit to finance purchases. Private credit available in the village was mostly used for consumption purposes.

In Sidomulyo, the modern varieties brought slightly lower net return per hectare than did the local varieties. Gross returns for modern and local varieties were not significantly different. Production costs for modern varieties were somewhat higher than for local. As a result, the modern varieties gave lower returns than local varieties.

In Cidahu modern varieties brought a higher net return than did the local varieties.

In Cidahu, the smaller the farm, the larger the percentage of farmers who obtained income from off-farm and nonfarm activities. But those from larger farms tended to average more income if they engaged in outside activities. In Sidomulyo, farm size did not have a comparable effect; the smaller the farm, the larger the income obtained from outside activities. Whether or not income from backyard crop and livestock enterprises is included, Sidomulyo's sample farmers received higher total incomes than those of Cidahu as well as higher per caput income.

The regular occurrence of rice-shortage months, comparing 1969 with 1972, does not support the idea that higher yields and production of rice have meant "enough rice to eat for each farmer."

To conclude, although sample farmers have responded well to the introduction of modern varieties wherever the factors that permit the adoption of modern varieties are all present, there is no sign as yet of any "green revolution" in the sample areas.

Kelantan,West Malaysia

Moktar bin Tamin and N. Hashim Mustapha

In the rolling countryside of the study villages one part of a field frequently lacks adequate water while another part of the same field has excess water. This has prevented the use of modern varieties shorter than 120 cm. Farmers get about the same yields from those modern varieties as from their traditional varieties. The short-duration modern varieties were adopted rapidly after irrigation became available. Together these inputs made double-cropped rice a reality. Institutional credit is restricted to just enough to buy the fertilizer recommended for one acre. Tenants with larger farms apply substantially lower rates of fertilizer than small tenants or large owners. Over half the sample farmers said they would not like to use more credit, and despite high prices for rice, economic returns for tenants were negative.

RICE IS THE STAPLE food of Malaysia. Annual per-capita consumption is about 130 kg, but from 20 to 30 percent of consumption needs is normally imported, mainly from Thailand. These substantial imports strongly affect the government's rice policy. During most of the 1960's one of Malaysia's objectives was to achieve self sufficiency; recently this objective has been changed to becoming from 80 to 90 percent self-sufficient.

An important policy instrument has been the maintenance of farm floor prices higher than world prices as an incentive to increase production. This price floor has been achieved by requiring importers to purchase a given quantity of domestic rice from the local market or the government stockpile for every ton imported. Another important policy to encourage the expansion of production is to provide irrigation

Mokhtar bin Tamin is a member of the Faculty of Agriculture at the University of Malaya, Kuala Lumpur; N. Hashim Mustapha is a researcher at the Malaysian Agricultural Research and Development Institute, Serdang.

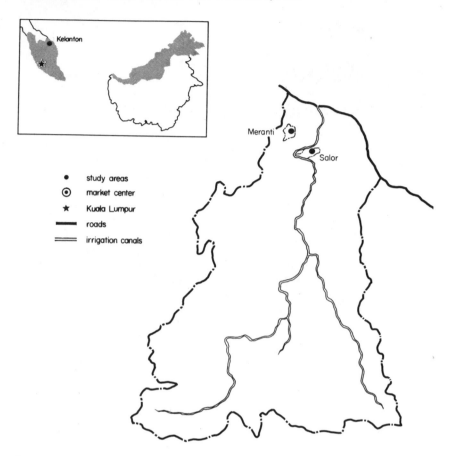

State of Kelantan, West Malaysia.

facilities, which encourages second crop (dry season) rice production. By the end of the 1970/71 crop year, 43 percent of the total wet paddy land was being double-cropped.

THE STUDY AREA

In West Malaysia rice ranks second only to natural rubber in area planted. Seventy percent of the rice area is concentrated in three regions: Kedah and Derlis with 39 percent, Kelantan with 18 percent, and Perah with 13 percent. Kelantan was selected for this study because it has been studied less than other regions, and because its particular set of physical, cultural, and institutional characteristics presents a set of complex and inter-related problems which differ from those of other regions. Because of these problems, the region lags behind the rest of

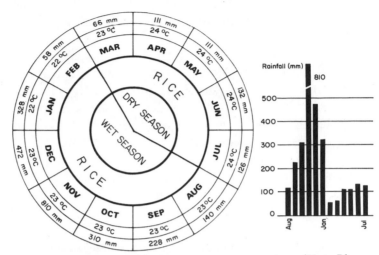

Average monthly rainfall and minimum temperature, (Kota Bharu
Meteorological Station, 1967-1971), Kelantan, Malaysia.

West Malaysia in adoption of new technology. In 1971/72, rice yields
in Kelantan were 18 percent below the national average in the wet
(main) season and 13 percent below in the dry (off) season. Meranti and
Salor, the villages selected for this study, are typical of Kelantan and
provide an opportunity to examine changes in rice production technology in a lagging area.

Physical environment of the area. The northeast monsoon winds from
the South China Sea bring torrential rains to Kelantan, particularly
in October, November, and December. Flooding generally occurs during
these months, sometimes severely damaging crops. The months of
February through June are usually fairly dry. Year-to-year variations in
rainfall are large, as are fluctuations in monthly rainfall among years.
The wet season is from August through February, while the dry season
is from March through July.

The two study villages fall within the main plain soil association
which is made up of a number of soil series with varying drainage and
texture. Both villages are situated on two soil series, the Lundang series
and the Batu Hitam series. Essentially, these soils are poorly drained,
with high water tables and low nutrient and organic matter contents.
Pockets of acid-sulfate soils are also found in Meranti. Both villages lie
within the Kelantan Plain, on the built-up river delta of the Kelantan
River. The delta is characterized by rolling topography. Paddy is
cultivated on the flat land and depressions; homesteads, villages, and
horticultural lands are on the higher ground.

Salor and Meranti are near the mouth of the Kelantan River. Both are prone to flooding in the wet season, but require irrigation during the dry season.

Salor is only about 7 km from the principal town and state capital of Kota Bahru, while Meranti is 20 km away and is served by a poorer road system. Salor is easily accessible from the main trunk roads by a reasonably good network of feeder roads. Some are paved and always passable; the smaller ones are only surfaced with laterite. As a result, carts, lorries, buses, and pedicabs can all be used for transportation to and from the village.

Meranti's road system is somewhat less developed. An all-weather road connects Meranti to the district town of Pasir Mas, but most feeder roads are surfaced only with laterite and are difficult to use during the wet season.

Focal points for each of these villages are small village centers, each serviced by a number of government sub-branches, a row of wooden shops, and an area for a weekly market and fair.

The Salor and the Lemal irrigation systems serve these villages. These large pump systems are operated by the government's Drainage and Irrigation Department. They draw water from the Kelantan River and pump it into secondary and tertiary laterals that supply the water to farmers' fields. The government has invested quite a bit of money to develop the system in Salor. In the newer system, which serves Meranti, only the major laterals were completed while the sub-laterals were left for the farmers to develop. In many cases the farmers have not fully developed the sub-laterals and farm ditches, which presents additional problems in the delivery of water to their fields.

The Salor irrigation system was first opened in 1951 to irrigate 1,100 hectares. It was extended in 1956 to cover about 1,700 hectares. The Lemal irrigation system, which supplies water to Meranti, was also developed in stages. Beginning in 1960, it was expanded in 1963 and again in 1965 to cover a total of 9,300 hectares. The major defect of these systems, particularly the Lemal system, has been the frequent breakdowns of the huge pumps because of annual flooding. In 1967 the costs of repairs on the pumphouse amounted to US$184,000, and an annual budget of US$200,000 is required to keep the system going.

Both villages are characterized by rolling topography, Meranti more so than Salor. As a result, the fields are not completely level, making irrigation water difficult to utilize efficiently. Farmers with fields located on high sloping ground along the canals are often forced to build high bunds to hold the water. In other areas, it takes a number of days for water to reach the fields; when it finally does, some parts of the field are deeply flooded while other parts lack adequate water. This presents problems in land preparation and subsequent operations. The late arrival of water in some fields frequently delays transplanting. These problems of water availability are further compounded by the short period between the main season and the dry season. Three-fourths of the survey area in Meranti and two-thirds in Salor were reported to have inadequate water control.

Rice production practices. Except for a few shopkeepers and government employees, all of the households in the two villages depend on farming for their livelihood. In addition to the main rice crop, rubber, coconut, tobacco, fruit, and vegetables are also grown.

The farms in both villages average about 1 hectare in size, about half are owner operated, about a third are operated by owner-tenants, and the rest by pure-tenants. Tenants usually share-crop, paying 50 percent of the crop as rent. The landowner normally pays the land tax and half the cost of fertilizer.

In these villages, farmers sow their seeds in wet nurseries normally located in the paddy fields or in plots near the homesteads. Nursery land is carefully prepared using hand tools such as the *tajak* or hoe. The nursery is then fenced to keep animals and ducks away. Farmers tend to use about 37 kg/ha of seed, which is more than the recommended rate. The seeds are presoaked for about 48 hours, then broadcasted on the drained seedbed. Fertilizer is commonly used on the seedbed.

Land preparation methods have been undergoing changes since double cropping was started, with tractors replacing more traditional methods. The *tajak* and water buffalo are still being used by some farmers, however, either alone or in combination with tractors. When both are used, the tractor makes one pass with a rotovator followed by water buffalo for harrowing. Both four-wheeled tractors and two-wheeled power tillers are widely used. The four-wheeled machines are normally owned by contractors, while some farmers own tillers. Custom rates for the large tractors average about US$20/ha, and about $15/ha for the two-wheeled tillers. A large tractor normally plows about 4 ha/day while the two-wheeled tillers handle only about half that much.

Transplanting is done by hand; men pull the seedlings and women do the actual transplanting. Although the method used cannot strictly be classified as straight-row planting, it is possible to weed between the somewhat straight rows. Transplanting is very labor intensive, requiring 15 to 25 man-days/ha. Family labor is usually augmented for transplanting by hired or unpaid community *gotong royong* labor.

Farmers have widely used insect control practices to combat small localized attacks; a growing number of farmers own their own sprayers. Crops are almost never weeded, despite the fact that weeds are clearly present. Although fertilizers are widely used, the rate of application is low because adequate credit is difficult to obtain. The Farmers' Association normally extends fertilizer credit to cover only 1 acre (0.40 ha) of paddy land. Often this amount is spread over the entire farm.

Harvesting and threshing are carried out by hand, with communal or hired labor supplementing family labor. Before harvest, the farmer usually selects the best panicles to use as seeds for the following season. The sickle is used for harvesting.

Paddy which is not meant for home consumption is sold soon after drying during the main season. It is not uncommon to find farmers selling wet paddy during the off-season, because of wet weather at harvest time and the lack of drying and storing facilities. The cooperatives and private mills are the biggest buyers of paddy, but some intermediaries operate between the farmers and the big mills. Under the guaranteed minimum price policy of the government, the prevailing price is relatively stable, although somewhat below the level set by the National Rice Authority for each crop season.

Social and institutional factors. Meranti is totally populated by ethnic Malays. Salor has about five percent ethnic Chinese and Thais, with the remainder ethnic Malays. Non-farm employment opportunities in Meranti are quite limited. Because of Salor's proximity to the state capital, non-farm employment is more varied, ranging from operation of pedicabs, to supplying of sand to construction companies, to unskilled and semi-skilled construction jobs. Education is of high priority in these villages; most of the children attend school.

Three major institutions with somewhat overlapping functions are directly responsible for the development of agriculture in these villages. Of these, the Farmers' Association (organized on the Taiwan pattern) and the Agricultural Cooperative have existed for years, while the Agricultural Bank was established only 4 years ago. Although they have similar functions, the Farmers' Association appears to be more effective than the Cooperative, because its varied services for farmers include supplying inputs, marketing paddy, and providing credit and agricultural extension. The Cooperative does not have extension expertise. Until recently, the Farmers' Association and the Cooperative were supervised by different government departments: the Department of Agriculture and the Department of Cooperatives. Even though both of these departments were within the Ministry of Agriculture, their functions were often duplicated, resulting in serious confusion. Because of the confusion between the two major institutions, the government placed them under a single organization called the Farmers' Organization Authority at the beginning of 1973.

Credit seems to be the main interest of farmers who belong to these institutions. Although farmers find it fairly easy to obtain small amounts of credit, they find it difficult to obtain credit in large amounts. The Farmers' Association will only provide fertilizer credit for 1 acre of paddy land at an annual interest charge of between 10 and 12 percent (depending on whether the loan is secured or unsecured).

Introduction of new varieties. New or modern rice varieties in the study area consist of Mashuri (Mayang Embos 80/2 x Taichung 65), released in 1965, and Bahagia, a sister strain of IR5 (Peta x Tanghai Rotan), released in 1966. Two other varieties, Malinja (Siam 29 x Pebifun), released in 1964, and Ria, a selection of IR8 (Peta x Dee-geo-woo-gen), released in 1966, were also tried by farmers but were not adopted. Ria has poor cooking and eating quality, and Malinja is highly susceptible to diseases.

Although Mashuri is highly susceptible to blast, it has heavier grains and better cooking quality than does Bahagia. Mashuri is 130 cm tall and matures in 130 days, while Bahagia is 120 cm tall and matures in 130 days. The major reason for the adoption of these two varieties is their non-sensitivity to photoperiod, which permits them to be grown in the dry season. In Salor, they were adopted as soon as they were released; in Meranti they were adopted in 1968 when installation of the irrigation pumps made double-cropping possible.

It is important to remember that the adoption of new varieties in the study area was simultaneous with the adoption of double-cropping, in which the most important requirement is a short maturing (120 to 130 days) variety. The new varieties identified above have not yielded substantially more than local varieties. The Department of Agriculture in Kelantan has reported that even under ideal conditions, yields of the modern varieties were 3.7 t/ha in Salor and 2.5 t/ha in Meranti in local verification trials.

CHANGES IN RICE FARMING

A two-way stratified random sample was drawn in each of the two study villages. Because farm size and tenure were thought to be important factors affecting the adoption of modern varieties, these two factors were the bases for stratification. Farm size categories were: below 0.6 ha, 0.6 to 1.2 ha, and more than 1.2 ha. Tenure categories

Table 1. Distribution of sample farms by size and tenure (number).

farm size (ha)	owner-operator	tenants	owner-tenants
Salor			
less than 0.6	43	7	16
0.6 to 1.2	37	9	18
more than 1.2	11	2	14
Meranti			
less than 0.6	27	12	12
0.6 to 1.2	18	14	16
more than 1.2	13	10	11

were: owner, tenant, and owner-tenant. There were large differences in the number of farms in each substrata. In particular, few farms were in the large farm and tenant farm categories, so rather than use a constant sampling fraction, we obtained at least 10 sample farms in each substratum, even when it meant including every farm in a substratum. Even then, fewer than 10 sample farms were obtained in each of the three size categories of tenant farmers in Salor. The total number of sample farms was 157 in Salor and 133 in Meranti (Table 1).

Interviews were started during March and April, 1971 when data were collected for the wet season of August 1970, to February 1971. A second set of interviews covered the dry season of March 1971, to July 1971. Additional data were later obtained from a subsample of 57 farmers in Salor and 49 farmers in Meranti, covering the August 1971 to February 1972 wet season.

Extent of use of modern varieties. All of the rice land was double-cropped in the two study villages (Table 2). Modern varieties were used widely during the dry season, but on 30 percent or less of the land during the wet season.

Changes in farm practices and productivity. The greatest change in farming since the modern varieties were adopted has been the large increase in the use of four-wheel tractor (Table 3). The proportion of farmers using two-wheel tractors and chemical fertilizers has increased to a lesser degree. Application of fertilizer increased from 74 kg/ha to 86 kg/ha in Meranti, and from 84 kg/ha to 97 in Salor (in terms of nutrients). Use of organic fertilizer on rice has decreased markedly, possibly due to an increase in tobacco production where organic

Table 2. Basic characteristics of sample farms.

village	farms (no.)		persons in household (no.)	farm size (ha)	farms by tenure category (%)		
	village	sample			full-owners	owner-tenants	tenants
Meranti	536	133	5.3	1.0	43	30	27
Salor	564	157	5.7	0.9	58	31	11

	rice area					principal form of irrigation
	per farm (ha)		double-cropped (%)	irrigated (%)		
	wet season	dry season		wet season	dry season	
Meranti	0.9	0.9	100	94	94	pump-fed canal
Salor	0.8	0.8	100	100	100	pump-fed canal

	modern varieties				year of greatest adoption
	farmers using (%)		rice area planted (%)		
	wet season	dry season	wet season	dry season	
Meranti	50	91	32	67	1970
Salor	32	96	22	89	1970

fertilizer has traditionally been used. The proportion of farmers who use herbicides and insecticides, and who own sprayers has also declined slightly, probably because of the discontinuation of input subsidies which had been introduced with the modern varieties. Mechanical innovations other than tractors, such as weeders, harvesters, threshers, and even pump irrigation, are unknown in this area.

The average levels of fertilizer applied before and after the introduction of modern varieties is shown in Table 4 for each size and tenure class. Amounts of fertilizer applied per hectare declined as the size became larger regardless of tenure status. A positive relationship was found between the average yield and the average fertilizer application among all tenure groups.

Owner-operators in Salor had higher rates of fertilizer application than did owner-tenants and tenants of the same farm size group. In general, tenants, especially large tenants, had the lowest rates of fertilizer

Table 3. Dry season farming practices, before modern varieties and in 1971.

| practices | farmers using (%) | | | |
| | Salor | | Meranti | |
	1966	1971	1968	1971
chemical fertilizers	86	95	77	92
organic fertilizers	30	10	26	5
insecticides	57	37	59	52
sprayer	14	11	59	52
herbicides	13	10	4	2
two-wheel tractors	6	13	6	33
four-wheel tractors	22	85	6	65

application. These pure tenants depend on landlords and fertilizer credit from the Farmers' Association for their supplies of fertilizer. Furthermore, tenants are considered a higher security risk by credit-granting institutions; hence they use lower rates of fertilizer than do owners.

The only consistent yield difference shown by the analysis was the tendency for yields to be lower on larger farms in Meranti for all three tenure groups. The same relationship between farm size and yields was true for all farm categories when the modern varieties were first introduced. In addition, owner-cultivators had the highest yields of the three tenure groups, followed by owner-tenants and tenants, but this relationship was not significant. The increase in yields since the introduction of the modern varieties has been relatively small, ranging from 0.1 t/ha to 0.6 t/ha. The largest increments occurred on the large farms in Salor. No pattern in the yield increments was found for different tenure categories.

Comparing average fertilizer use and yields of modern and traditional varieties for all farmers in the two villages indicates little yield advantage from modern varieties (Table 5). Fertilizer rates on modern varieties are very similar to those used on traditional varieties. There is less difference between average yields of modern and traditional varieties than between the average yields obtained by different size and tenure classes, indicating that other factors affect yields more in these villages than do the varieties planted.

The use of credit.[1] Credit has always been regarded as an important factor that influenced the productivity of paddy farms, but it cannot be considered in isolation. Hence, farm size and non-paddy income are

Table 4. Dry-season fertilizer use and yields before modern varieties and in 1971.

farm size (ha)	owner-operators		tenants		owner-tenants	
	fertilizer (kg/ha)[a]	yield (t/ha)	fertilizer (kg/ha)[a]	yield (t/ha)	fertilizer (kg/ha)[a]	yield (t/ha)
Salor						
less than 0.6						
1966	102	2.4	95	2.1	97	2.3
1971	111	2.7	122	2.4	108	2.6
0.6 to 1.2						
1966	90	2.1	85	2.0	87	2.0
1971	102	2.4	99	2.4	100	2.2
more than 1.2						
1966	84	1.7	50	1.5	78	1.6
1971	95	2.3	61	1.9	94	2.0
Meranti						
less than 0.6						
1968	95	2.0	84	1.8	102	2.2
1971	111	2.4	95	2.2	108	2.3
0.6 to 1.2						
1968	79	1.8	74	1.6	75	1.7
1971	90	2.1	80	1.8	81	1.9
more than 1.2						
1968	70	1.6	55	1.2	62	1.6
1971	81	1.9	62	1.4	70	1.6

[a]Calculated as Kg of $N + P_2O_5 + K_2O$.

considered here along with credit to determine whether an interrelated effect of these variables affects farmers' use of credit. It appears that the limited availability of credit and the small farm size constrain the level of disposable income from paddy, even if the full recommended level of fertilizer is applied.[2] This is especially true in Meranti, which has

[1]This section was prepared mainly from a subsample in-depth study in which 49 out of 133 farmers in Meranti and 57 out of 157 farmers in Salor were interviewed.

[2]The level of fertilizer recommended by Agricultural Department is 67 kg N/ha, 49 kg P_2O_5/ha, and 22 kg K_2O/ha. Under this level of application the estimated yields are about 2.5 t/ha in Meranti and 3.7 t/ha in Salor.

Table 5. Yield and fertilizer use on modern and traditional varieties, 1970/71.

season	Salor		Meranti	
	yield (t/ha)	fertilizer[a] (kg/ha)	yield (t/ha)	fertilizer[a] (kg/ha)
dry season, 1971				
modern varieties	2.5	102	2.1	96
traditional varieties	2.0	96	1.8	88
wet season, 1970/71				
modern varieties	2.4	95	1.9	83
traditional varieties	2.4	99	2.0	91

[a]Calculated as kg of $N + P_2O_5 + K_2O$.

poor soil, and where yield increments from additional fertilizer applications are low and unattractive to farmers. Coupled with the small farm sizes, the absolute increase in paddy income is also low. At the same time, family expenses rise, which encourages farmers to pursue alternative sources of non-paddy income at the expense of further improvements in yields.

The adoption of modern varieties should be accompanied by additional inputs such as insecticide, herbicides, and fertilizers if the full potential of the varieties is to be realized. These inputs were subsidized for a few years after the introduction of modern varieties; more recently, they have been provided on credit. The crucial problem lies in the extent of credit supplied and the degree to which it is being used by farmers.

The adoption of modern varieties in double-cropped areas of Meranti and Salor immediately followed the completed extension of the irrigation canals. This resulted in a doubling of the needs for credit, not only for the purchase of farm inputs and implements, but also for hired labor. Unfortunately, credit was in short supply and many farmers reported problems in obtaining credit even though small amounts were made available to many others.

Farmers could obtain loans in either cash or in kind from a number of credit agencies, but only about 5 percent of the farmers borrowed cash (Table 6). Borrowing in kind, fertilizer in particular, was reported by 56 percent of the farmers in Meranti and by 20 percent in Salor. The higher rate of borrowing in Meranti was attributed to the fact that both paddy and non-paddy incomes were lower than in Salor.

The Farmers' Association was the major source of credit in kind. It furnished a farmer with 63 kg of 16-16-8 and 16 kg of urea, supposedly enough for one acre of paddy land, but actually below the recommended level. Sometimes the fertilizer credit was based on the number of shares a farmer had invested in the association; for each $5.00 share he could obtain 63 kg of fertilizer. This distribution of credit among farmers was irrespective of the farm size and tenure status. The Farmers' Association's policy had been not to provide the full recommended amount of fertilizer, but only part of it, to encourage farmers to obtain some from their own resources.

Low yields and small farm size exert important influences on farmers' attitudes toward production credit. They were considered the main reasons behind the hesitation of farmers to borrow, since they found it difficult to repay the loans (Table 7). More than half of the farmers interviewed refused credit and a third reported difficulty in repaying credit because of low yields. Those who borrowed occasionally ended up in debt since they were not able to generate enough income from the sale of paddy. This in turn affected the profitability of the credit institutions. In fact, in 1972 the Farmers' Association in Meranti ceased to give credit to farmers because of poor repayment.

The failure of loan repayment can also be attributed to the low price of paddy at the farm gate (US$82/t), and, for those farmers with very small farms, the lack of surplus paddy for sale (Table 8). Within a given farm size category, owners have the highest sales per farm, owner-tenants have the second highest, and tenants have the lowest.

Table 6. Use of production credit, 1970/71 wet season.

	Salor		Meranti	
	cash	kind	cash	kind
percent borrowing	5	80	5	44
average loan[a] (US$/ha)	11	13	42[b]	14
percent borrowing from agricultural bank	38	0	29	0
Farmers' Association	0	81	0	65
Farmers' Cooperative	0	3	0	7
relative	25	0	43	0
landlord	0	3	0	12
money lender	37	0	29	0
others	0	13	0	16

[a]Average loan for those borrowing. [b]Excluding one report of over $1000/ha.

Table 7. Production credit problems reported by subsample farmers, 1971/72 wet season.

problem	Percent reporting	
	Salor	Meranti
difficulty in obtaining credit	42	70
lack of credit agency	23	20
procedural difficulties	30	41
lack of needed collateral	25	35
not a society member	33	30
refuse to use credit because	61	51
do not like to borrow cash	56	40
do not like to borrow fertilizer	20	14
low yield makes repayment difficult	35	30
profit benefited landlord	9	4

There is a positive relationship between farm size and paddy sales in all tenure groups. Reported paddy sales may overstate the marketable surplus because farmers might have sold their paddy to get immediate cash to be used for a variety of purposes.

Costs and income. Net returns from paddy were higher for farmers in Salor than in Meranti (Table 9). As expected, net returns for owner-operators were higher than those for owner-tenants and tenants. However, even a return of US$72/ha for owners is low; this represents almost the entire income from paddy since the average farm size is about 1 hectare. Owners and owner-tenants in both villages recorded increases in net farm return from paddy since the introduction of modern varieties, but the increase was higher for Salor than for Meranti.

Table 8. Average sales of paddy per farm in subsample, 1971 dry season (US$/farm).

tenure class	Salor			Meranti		
	less than 0.6 ha	0.6 to 1.2 ha	more than 1.2 ha	less than 0.6 ha	0.6 to 1.2 ha	more than 0.6 ha
owner-operators	24	63	101	7	56	71
tenants	0	8	10	0	10	12
owner-tenants	12	14	50	5	12	16
average	21	30	54	4	26	33

Tenant farmers, although they recorded negative net farm returns, ended up with increases of about 30 percent over their returns before the introduction of modern varieties (because a large portion of the costs included in Table 9 is for unpaid family labor, the cash income of all classes would be positive). The situation seems hopeless for tenant farmers. The smallness of their farms (0.8 ha.), their need to supplement

Table 9. Costs[a] and returns in wet-season paddy cultivation 1966/67 and 1971/72 (US$/ha).

costs, returns	owner-operators		tenants[b]		owner-tenants	
	1966/67[a]	1971/72	1966/67[c]	1971/72	1966/67[c]	1971/72
Salor						
gross value of output	171	208	79	94	165	201
fertilizer	28	31	11	13	26	30
seeds	1	2	1	2	1	2
pulling & transplanting	20	22	19	21	20	21
harvesting & threshing	33	40	30	36	31	38
hauling	6	8	6	7	6	7
tractor charges	21	21	21	21	21	21
land tax and water rate	10	12	0	0	10	12
total cost	119	136	88	100	117	134
net return	52	72	−9	−6	47	67
Meranti						
gross value of output	146	172	63	72	142	156
fertilizer	25	28	10	12	25	27
seeds	1	2	1	2	1	2
pulling & transplanting	18	19	17	18	17	18
harvesting & threshing	29	34	25	28	28	31
hauling	5	6	5	5	5	6
tractor charges	21	21	21	21	21	21
land tax and water rate	10	12	0	0	10	12
total cost	109	122	84	86	109	118
net return	37	50	−21	−14	32	38

[a] A large portion of costs consist of the imputed value of family labor so that if zero opportunity is attached to this the net farm income would be higher. Based on the subsample. [b] Excluding owner's share. [c] 1968/69 in Meranti.

Table 10. Percent of farmers reporting changes[a] in labor requirements following the introduction of modern varieties, 1971.

labor used for	Salor						Meranti					
	family			hired			family			hired		
	+	–	NC	+	–	NC	+	–	NC	+	–	NC
pre-harvest												
nursery	76	0	23	39	5	55	77	2	21	13	11	76
land preparation	34	29	37	73	0	27	8	89	3	84	1	15
transplanting	70	3	27	48	2	50	90	1	9	10	13	77
hand weeding	28	13	57	20	0	80	27	4	69	3	6	91
harvest and post-harvest												
harvesting	56	1	42	40	3	52	79	3	18	25	12	62
threshing	66	1	33	58	2	40	90	1	9	26	13	61
hauling	71	9	20	50	1	49	88	2	10	9	11	80
drying	70	9	21	19	2	79	92	1	7	5	14	81
processing (milling)	21	20	59	60	2	38	11	77	10	92	1	7

[a] + indicates an increase; – indicates a decrease; NC – indicates no change.

their incomes elsewhere, and the grossly unfavorable tenure arrangement have all culminated in low productivity and, consequently, low income. The practice of crop sharing on a 50/50 basis, coupled with the minimal landlord commitments to supply needed inputs, definitely worked against tenant interest. Although the tenants derived income from other sources, the availability of non-farm income opportunities was much lower in Meranti than in Salor. Their paddy production was mainly kept for home consumption, although some records of sales were found. Thus it is unlikely that tenant farmers could be induced to adopt technological changes as effectively as could their owner and owner-tenant counterparts.

Labor use. The adoption of modern varieties and double cropping has resulted in some significant changes in both family and hired labor use in the study villages. These changes were not quantified during the survey, however, so they can be considered only in relative terms. Table 10 shows the proportion of farmers in the sample reporting an increase, a decrease, or no change in labor utilization for the various cultural operations.

About half of the sample in Salor reported an increase in family and hired labor for harvesting, while in Meranti three-fourths reported an increase in family labor and only one-fourth used more hired labor. Although yields were not much higher, farmers reported that the short stalks of the modern varieties required more labor for a given yield. Increases in family labor for threshing, hauling, and drying can be explained by the need to perform these operations in a shorter time period so that work can commence on the next crop. It also appears that labor use for milling is shifting from family to hired.

Because of the low paddy income from the farms, non-paddy employment of the sub-sample of farmers was investigated (Table 11). The 65 percent of the Salor sample with non-paddy income, compared with only 22 percent of the Meranti farmers, reflects the close location of Salor to the provincial capital and, therefore, more employment opportunities. There were no differences in the proportion of farms in each size group reporting non-paddy income; but the amount of non-paddy income was much higher for the small than for the large farmers.

Consumption and expenditures. Farmers were asked whether they felt that their incomes and expenditures had increased, decreased, or stayed the same since they had adopted modern varieties (Table 12). About 60 percent of Salor farmers perceive themselves to be better off since adoption, whereas half of the Meranti farmers saw no change and one-fifth actually felt they were worse off. Food and education expen-

Table 11. Non-paddy employment reported by subsample farmers during 1971/72 wet season.

	Salor		Meranti	
	no.	%	no.	%
total paddy farms	57	100	49	100
carpenters	3	5	0	0
vegetable farmers	14	25	5	10
tobacco farmers	5	9	0	0
rubber and fruit growers	2	4	3	6
small businessmen	7	12	0	0
trishaw peddlers	0	0	2	4
miscellaneous work[a]	6	11	1	2
farmers reporting non-paddy income	37	65	11	22

[a]Contract construction work to supply river sand for building constructions; work in cooperative rice mills; religious teachers; tailors; etc.

ditures increased for most farmers, but few reported increases in other items. Table 13 shows the percent of sample farmers reporting purchases of major consumer durables or reductions in debt since adoption. Salor farmers again seemed to have benefited to a greater extent.

Constraints to higher yield and income. The sub-sample of farmers were asked if they thought they could increase their yields, and if so, how (Table 14). All of the farmers who said they could raise their yields (84 percent in Salor and 86 percent in Meranti) said they could do so by increasing the levels of fertilizer applied. This seems to reflect their feeling of a lack of operating capital, which in turn is a result of

Table 12. Percent of farmers reporting changed income and living standards, 1971.

change in	Salor			Meranti		
	+	−	NC	+	−	NC
rice income	80	10	9	64	24	12
level of living	62	4	34	26	22	52
food consumption	89	2	9	90	3	6
education expenditure	84	4	12	63	12	24
house improvement	50	3	47	16	14	70
savings	31	15	53	17	10	73

Table 13. Percent of farmers reporting purchase of consumer durables and farm investments 1971.

items	Salor	Meranti
household furniture	40	35
home appliances	28	13
bicycle	43	24
motorcycle or scooter	0	0
tractor	9	4
other farm implements	33	10
reduced debts	20	9

credit constraints. About two-thirds felt that lack of sufficient water was a constraint, and half felt that they needed higher yielding varieties.

Surprisingly, about three-quarters of the farmers felt that they could raise yields by using more labor. It is not clear whether they meant more labor at peak periods, which could have been limited by lack of capital to hire more labor, or just more labor throughout the growing period. The latter doesn't seem plausible because of the small farms, which should mean some surplus labor during slack periods. Furthermore, the farmers seek off-farm employment, particularly at the time when more hand weeding might increase yields. There are various

Table 14. Number of subsample farmers reporting possibility of increasing yields, 1971/72 wet season.

farmers reporting	Salor			Meranti		
	farm size (ha)			farm size (ha)		
	less than 0.6	0.6 to 1.2	more than 1.2	less than 0.6	0.6 to 1.2	more than 1.2
total no.	17	17	15	22	23	12
can increase yields	13	14	15	15	22	11
by using						
more fertilizer	13	14	15	15	22	11
more irrigation	10	12	11	13	12	8
higher yielding seeds	8	9	10	10	14	4
more labor	10	11	14	15	21	9

improved practices which, if adopted, could lead to higher yields. Seedlings are often transplanted too late, partly by custom but partly because seedlings must be tall to survive in the uneven topography within the paddies. Disease and pest control practices were found to be minimal even though most farmers recognize these problems.

A discouraging aspect of constraints is shown in Table 15. When farmers were asked to identify what their major problems were before the advent of modern varieties, and at the time of the survey, it was found that farmers seem to be facing the same problems now as they did 3 to 5 years earlier. If there is any change, it is that more farmers now perceive these problems than before.

POLICY IMPLICATIONS

Modern varieties were adopted in Salor and Meranti, not because of high yields, but because of their short maturing period, which enables farmers to grow a second crop. This is obvious when yields of the traditional and modern varieties are compared. The yields of MVs, however, could be further increased with adequate inputs, especially fertilizer, improved water control, and better agronomic practices. The full yield potential of Mahsuri, about 5 t/ha, is difficult to attain under the poor physical and chemical soil conditions in the villages, but yields of about 3.7 t/ha can be attained, compared with farmers' present average yields of about 2.5 t/ha.

The established government policy regarding rice production is basically aimed at:

1. supporting farm income;
2. promoting rice production;
3. ensuring fair consumer prices for quality rice.

In the context of the first two policy objectives a number of important findings in the two villages have implications for policy implementation. Heavy investments have been undertaken to irrigate paddy land for double cropping. The two villages studied fall within the scheme designed to increase domestic production to meet the country's total requirements. While the beginnings of the basic infrastructure, both physical and institutional, have been provided, a number of constraints lie in the way of achieving target production levels. These barriers include lack of credit for inputs, low paddy prices. and uneconomic farm size.

Availability of inputs. While there was no shortage of fertilizer, seeds, insecticides, herbicides, and land preparation services, these inputs were

Table 15. Major rice production and harvest problems before and after the introduction of modern varieties (percent).

problem	Salor		Meranti	
	dry season 1971	dry season 1966	dry season 1971	dry season 1968
pre-harvest				
obtaining seeds	23	16	20	15
obtaining organic manure	14	20	23	17
obtaining chemical fertilizer	83	65	58	52
obtaining credit	43	37	23	25
water-irrigation	68	67	71	64
insects and diseases	31	32	63	54
pests	41	37	62	56
harvest and post-harvest				
harvesting	3	3	19	17
threshing	24	24	26	22
hauling	54	54	41	41
drying	25	24	32	30
storage	29	28	34	33
selling	56	42	61	53
processing (milling)	32	31	45	48

rather expensive in Kelantan. A 15- to 30-percent price differential exists between Kelantan and the western region of West Malaysia. This is a result of high transport costs because the inputs are transported over long distances. In fact, the problem has existed for a long time but concrete steps to alleviate it have only recently been taken in the form of a highway to connect Kelantan to Penang. The 120-km road is expected to be serviceable by 1973.

The ability of farmers to obtain inputs is restricted by the lack of adequate credit, although small amounts of credit were quite easy to obtain. Because the major credit institutions had limited funds for farmers, they were able to provide credit to purchase inputs for only 1 acre (0.40 hectare) per farmer. One result was that larger farmers used less fertilizer and consequently reported lower yields.

The credit institutions have reported high rates of bad debts and the probability of further reduction in credit is rather high. Poor yields have been cited as the major reason for poor loan repayment but this is not entirely the consequence of low fertilizer levels. A number of inter-related problems affect yields. Water availability and management standards need to be improved. One way of obtaining better management is to provide some supervision in the use of inputs. Unfortunately, the present extension coverage is limited, so any policy of tying inputs and credit to management must necessarily be accompanied by a sufficient increase in supervisory personnel which presently operate through the Farmers' Association. There is also a need to provide farmers with short maturing varieties with proven high yielding potential in given environments.

Paddy prices. Although government policy is to ensure a guaranteed minimum price for paddy, it is difficult for farmers to obtain that price. The guaranteed price has been US$105/ton but the prices actually obtained by farmers ranged between $79 and $93. The difference is due to a number of reasons. First, the guaranteed price is for "good clean" paddy with 13 percent moisture delivered to the mill door. Farmers' paddy, however, is subjected to deductions for impurities and moisture. Although farmers complain of exorbitant deductions for dirt and moisture, harvesting of the dry season crop normally coincides with the beginning of the rainy season. Because they lack drying and storage facilities, the moisture content must be high. Second, the smuggling of rice across the border from Thailand has also depressed local paddy prices. Although estimates of the volume smuggled in vary, the effect has always been felt. Millers prefer Thai rice because of its cheap price and premium quality in the domestic market. These two factors, which cause low product prices coupled with high input prices, have been primarily responsible for the low input levels used. These defects must be rectified if the full benefit of the new technology necessary for the succesful adoption and spread of modern varieties is to be obtained.

Uneconomic farm size. Farms averaging about 1 ha, together with poor soil conditions, have resulted in low residual farm incomes. This would be a problem even if farmers were able to attain high efficiency because their total incremental income from greater efficiency would only raise their incomes marginally. The small farms are the results of fragmentation under the prevailing inheritance laws. Some form of land consolidation is imperative to provide farmers with a minimum size of farm to provide a reasonable level of living. Then, given sufficient availability of inputs through adequate credit, farmers with more land could be more easily induced to adopt new technology. One way to increase farm size is to induce small unproductive producers to leave by providing alternate sources of income. This is a monumental task but at the same time very pressing.

Gujranwala, Punjab

H. Ali Chaudhari, A. Rashid, and Q. Mohy-Ud-Din

The adoption of modern inputs was hastened initially by the introduction of tubewells during the early 1960's. The low rate of adoption of modern rice varieties in the Punjab may be attributed principally to the government policy of supporting the price of local Basmati rice to maximize foreign exchange earnings. As a consequence, the new wheat varieties have had a much greater impact on farm incomes than have the new rice varieties.

TOWARD THE END of the 1960's Pakistan, along with some other developing countries in Asia, experienced an influx of improved seed technology in wheat and rice, the major food grains, which resulted in an extraordinary growth in the production of these crops. The rate at which the new fertilizer-responsive modern varieties were adopted was so rapid that it repudiated the image of an illiterate and unresponsive farming community. The first of the Mexican wheat varieties were introduced into Pakistan in 1965. By 1971, 3,037,000 hectares, or about 50 percent of the area, was planted to the new wheat varieties, and the area planted to the new rice varieties IR8 and Mehran 69 (a local selection of the IRRI cross IR6 which was not been offically named by IRRI) rose to 626,000 hectares or 42 percent of the total planted area in 1970.

Over 90 percent of the rice production in Pakistan was concentrated in two provinces – Sind and Punjab. The modern rice varieties were adopted more rapidly in Sind than in the Punjab because the Punjab is the principal area of Basmati rice production. Basmati is a traditional rice variety that does not respond well to fertilizer, but it commands a

H. Ali Chaudhari is Dean of the Faculty of Agricultural Economics and Rural Sociology; A. Rashid was formerly Head of the Department of Agricultural Marketing; Q. Mohy-Ud-Din is instructor of the Department of Agricultural Marketing, all at the University of Agriculture, Lyallpur, Pakistan.

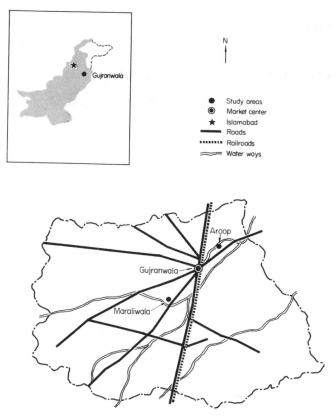

Gujranwala District, Punjab, Pakistan.

very high price on the world market because of its fine quality and aroma.

Gujranwala District. The Punjab, rather than Sind, was selected as the study area so that some of the factors that have influenced the slower rate of adoption of modern wheat and rice varieties in this area could be examined more closely. The Gujranwala District was chosen because it was the largest rice-producing district, in both size and production. In 1970, this district produced 25 percent of all the rice grown in the Punjab.

The crop calendar describes the general cropping pattern and climatic conditions in Gujranwala District. The climate of the district is hot during the period June to September with the major rains occurring in July and August. The winter months are moderately cold (0°−10°C) and dry.

The major crops grown are shown in Table 1. Rice is normally

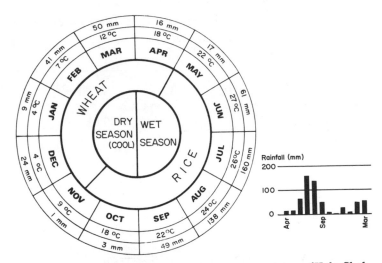

Average monthly rainfall and minimum temperature (Kala Shah Kaku Rice Research Institute, 1967-1971), Pakistan.

planted in June and harvested in October and November. Wheat is planted in November and December and harvested in April.

Two canals irrigated most of the district. With the installation of a large number of government and private tubewells since 1960, irrigation by pumps increased significantly. Government tubewells were installed primarily to reduce the problem of water-logging and salinity.

The villages. The two villages selected for the study were Aroop and Maraliwala. Aroop is located 7 km and Maraliwala 14 km from Gujranwala City (see map), which is a major commercial center with a population over 200,000 and located 64 km north of Lahore.

Both villages have predominantly heavy soils which have a good water-holding capacity and are well suited for rice production. However, in Aroop, because of its proximity to Gujranwala, fodder crops occupy a major portion of the crop area during both the wet and dry seasons. Gujranwala is a major milk-producing area, and much of the fodder is sold for feed for cattle maintained within the city limits.

Aroop is comprised of two main castes, the *Bhindars* and *Chaemas.* The *Bhindars* occupy 60 percent of the village area and the *Chaemas* occupy the remaining 40 percent in two compact blocks divided by a brick wall. The *Bhindars* are a politically active group both at the local and provincial levels and thus were able to arrange many infra-structure facilities in the village.

There are a number of castes in Maraliwala — *Gujars, Arains, Changars, Kakey Zayes, Bhatties,* and *Kasmiries.* The *Gujars* is the main caste

Table 1. Area under different crops in Gujranwala District, 1969–70.

crop	wet-season area		dry-season area	
	(ha)	(%)	(ha)	(%)
wheat	0	0	220	70.1
rice	209	73.6	0	0
fodder	16	5.6	66	21.0
bajra	22	7.7	0	0
sugarcane	14	4.9	0	0
oil seeds	0	0	13	4.1
cotton	11	3.9	0	0
other	12	4.3	15	4.8
total	284	100.0	314	100.0

Source: Department of Agriculture, Government of Punjab.

group and controls the major part of the village economy. Arable farming and milk marketing are the major occupations of the people in Marali-wala. Most *Kakey Zayes* and *Kasmiries* leased out their land and worked in the factories in Gujranwala City. A large number of landless agricultural workers were also found in the village, some of them farming on rented land. The prevailing rental rate for land in Maraliwala was Rs 1,400/ha/year as compared with Rs 2,000/ha/year in Aroop. The land rent in both villages increased by 40–50 percent since the introduction of the modern varieties of wheat and rice.

Aroop showed generally greater signs of prosperity than Maraliwala. All the houses in Aroop were made of brick, while 30 percent of the houses in Maraliwala were constructed from mud. As compared with Maraliwala, the schooling and medical facilities were more adequate in Aroop; the village roads were wider and better drained, and there were twice as many tubewells. In Aroop the credit cooperative society had been successful while in Maraliwala it had accumulated a large amount of bad debts.

The sample farms. A sample of farms was chosen from the list of those planting rice variety Mehran 69 (IR6) in 1971 (Table 2). All adopters in each of the two villages were listed and 18 of the 98 adopters in Aroop and 2 of the 82 adopters in Maraliwala were eliminated.

Aroop and Maraliwala differed markedly in some sample characteristics. Maraliwala had more tenants and fewer pure owners. A large portion of the farm area in Aroop was in crops other than rice and wheat; however, Maraliwala had the largest percentage of farm area planted to Mehran 69.

Since no second crop of rice was grown in this area, the objectives of the second-round survey differed from those of the other studies. The principal aim was to determine the effect of new rice technology on cropping patterns, wet- and dry-season crop intensity, patterns of labor use, changes in income, use of credit and farm supplies, and utilization of rice.

INTRODUCTION OF MODERN VARIETIES

A few progressive farmers in both villages first procured IR8 seed from the Agricultural Department office in Gujranwala and planted it in the 1968 crop season. A year later interested neighbors obtained the seed from these progressive farmers and planted it. However, the farmers were not happy about the market price and the quality of IR8. Even those that adopted IR8 continued to plant most of their rice area to

Table 2. Characteristics of sample farms.

village	farms (no.) in village	farms (no.) in sample	persons in household (no.)	farm size (ha)	pure owners (%)	pure tenants (%)	owner-tenants (%)	pure lease-holders (%)
Aroop	900	80	9	6.7	65	4	2	29
Maraliwala	909	80	11	7.8	23	41	11	25

	rice area			
	per farm (ha)		double	irrigated	principal form
	rice	wheat	cropped (%)	(%)	of irrigation
Aroop	3.7	3.1	84	100	tubewells
Maraliwala	6.0	5.0	85	100	tubewells, canal

	modern varieties		
	farmers[a] planting (%)	rice area planted (%)	year of greatest adoption
Aroop	100	40	1971
Maraliwala	100	49	1971

[a]The sample is of modern variety adopters only. In Aroop 11% of farmers and in Maraliwala 9% of farmers were adopters in 1971.

Table 3. Average farm size of non-adopters and adopters of modern rice varieties, 1971:

village	non-adopters		adopters[a]	
	no.	farm size (ha)	no.	farm size (ha)
Aroop	802	1.2	98	5.5
Maraliwala	827	1.4	82	6.2

[a]Those planting a portion of their land to Mehran 69 (IR6) in 1971.

Basmati-370. Palman-246 and Jhona-344, two other local varieties, continued to be grown but to a lesser extent than Basmati-370. In 1970, most farmers who had been growing IR8 switched to Mehran 69 (IR6), and by 1971, IR8 was no longer grown in these villages. However, even in 1971, the year of highest adoption of modern rice varieties, only about 10 percent of the farmers in Aroop and Maraliwala were adopters, and these adopters tended to be larger farmers (Table 3) who planted only a portion of their rice-growing area to IR6.

What explains the low rate of adoption of the modern rice varieties in this area? The choice in selecting rice varieties to be grown was regulated by:

a. the relative market prices of different rice varieties
b. the relative yield response to inputs
c. the cost of inputs
d. the relative susceptibility of each variety to pests and diseases
e. the growth duration in relation to the crop to be grown in the following *rabi* or dry season; a short season (105—120 days) rice variety allows sufficient time for the farmer to plant on time the subsequent wheat crop.

The government pricing policy was the most important factor in influencing the choice of varieties. The principal objective of the government policy was the maintenance of an adequate supply of Basmati rice, because it was a major source of foreign exchange earnings. The procurement price of Basmati was higher than that of the coarse grain rices such as IR8 and IR6 (Table 4). The 2-to-1 price advantage for Basmati over modern varieties (Table 5) more than compensated for the yield advantage of the modern rice varieties particularly when the added cost of inputs used with modern varieties were taken into account.

Two factors contributed to a sharp rise in the area planted to modern varieties in 1971: (1) a decline in the price of Basmati relative to coarse grain varieties in 1970 and (2) a serious attack of rice stem borer in

Table 4. The government procurement price for fine and coarse varieties of milled rice in Punjab Province, West Pakistan, 1966–72.

year	Basmati (Rp/t)	IR8/IR6 (Rp/t)
1966	750	469
1967	830	509
1968	1018	509
1969	938	509
1970	697	509
1971	1010	509
1972	1125	509

Source: Food Department, Government of Punjab.

Table 5. Trend in adoption of modern varieties in relation to price of modern varieties vs. Basmati rice.

year	village	rice area under MV[a] (%)	price Basmati ÷ price MV (previous year)[b]	yield Basmati ÷ yield MV
1968	Aroop	7.0	1.6:1	1:1.8[c]
	Maraliwala	11.9		
1969	Aroop	5.6	2.0:1	1:2.2[c]
	Maraliwala	7.3		
1970	Aroop	7.0	1.8:1	1:2.9[c]
	Maraliwala	7.9		
1971	Aroop	21.0	1.4:1	1:1.7
	Maraliwala	41.0		1:1.5

[a] M.V. = modern varieties. Figures refer to whole village. [b] Based on Table 4. [c] Yield for district.

1970 (the Basmati varieties were more susceptible than the modern varieties to stem borer damage). The Pakistan government raised the Basmati procurement price to its highest level in 1972 in order to reverse the trend toward the adoption and increased acreage planted to the modern rice varieties. Also, the government took all possible measures to make the plant protection program more effective in controlling rice stem borer. The program included: compulsory spraying of nurseries, more acreage receiving aerial spraying, the transfer of a

Table 6. Approximate procurement and selling price of IR6 and Basmati rice and the gross government profit per hectare.

variety	yield (t/ha)		purchase price of milled rice (Rp/t)	selling price of milled rice (Rp/t)	government gross profit	
	unmilled rice	milled rice			(Rp/t)	(Rp/ha)
IR6	3.2	3.1	509	780	271	569
Basmati	2.0	1.3	1010	2200	1190	1547

major part of the pesticide formulation and distribution program to the private sector, and prohibiting early sowing of nurseries through legislation.

These measures taken by the Pakistan government to promote Basmati rice at the expense of modern higher yielding varieties may seem counterproductive to any goal for increasing the total production of rice. However, the data (Table 6) show that even with the yield advantage of the modern varieties, the monetary return to the government per hectare of Basmati grain procured was more than double that for IR6 with the price relationships that prevailed until 1972.

Finally, the nature of the cropping pattern affected the selection of the rice variety planted. Wheat was the major dry-season crop following rice in both villages. When Mexican wheats were introduced, the area under wheat suddenly increased in the dry-season of 1967/68. Higher yields of the new varieties coupled with a strong support price encouraged expansion of the area planted to wheat. The modern rice varieties are early maturing and thus can be harvested soon enough to

Table 7. Percentages of rice area planted to modern varieties by farm size in Aroop and Maraliwala.

farm size (ha)	Aroop		Maraliwala	
	farms (no.)	area (%) in MV	farms (no.)	area (%) in MV
less than 4	30	49	21	52
4 to 7.9	26	33	31	54
8 to 11.9	14	26	11	54
12 and above	10	42	17	45
all	80	36	80	50

Table 8. Percent of rice area planted to modern varieties by tenure group in Aroop and Maraliwala.

tenure group	Aroop		Maraliwala	
	farms (no.)	area (%) in MV	farms (no.)	area (%) in MV
pure owner	52	34	18	54
pure tenant	3	75	33	58
lease-holder	23	34	20	46
owner and tenant	2	26	9	26
all	80	36	80	50

allow the wheat to be sown on time. Late sowing of wheat normally results in a lower yield.

The adopters of modern varieties in 1971 were the larger farmers (Table 3) and among the adopters, farms were classified by size into four categories (Table 7). In neither village could a clear relationship be discerned between farm size and the percent of the rice area planted to modern rice varieties. The reason for a larger portion of the rice area being planted to modern varieties in Maraliwala than in Aroop was not clear. However, Maraliwala had a higher proportion of tenants and perhaps the tenants were encouraged by their landlords to plant a larger area in modern varieties (Table 8). In the study area the large land owners were the initial and primary adopters of the new rice varieties.

CHANGES IN FARMING PRACTICES

Nitrogen was the major nutrient applied to all rice varieties in both villages. In fact, essentially no phosphorus or potassium was applied to the rice crop in either village. The average level of fertilizer input on IR6 is about the same in each village (Table 9). However, 45 percent of the farmers in Aroop and about 30 percent in Maraliwala were using no fertilizer on IR6. The yield of both modern and local varieties was higher in Aroop principally because of the better quality of soil.

The low level of fertilizer use on modern rice varieties and the high percentage of non-users can be attributed in part to the unfavorable fertilizer-rice price ratio during this period. The price of 4–5 kg of IR6 rice was equal that of 1 kg of nitrogen, and there was also difficulty in obtaining ENGRO urea, the most popular fertilizer brand.

Table 9. Relationship between yield of IR6 and Basmati varieties and fertilizer input.

village	yield (t/ha)		nitrogen[a] (kg/ha)		fertilizer users (%)	
	IR6	Basmati	IR6	Basmati	IR6	Basmati
Aroop	3.2	2.1	30	11	55	26
Maraliwala	2.4	1.4	37	19	70	39

[a] Average of users and non-users.

The modern inputs being used by farmers included new seeds, fertilizer, insecticides, 4-wheel tractors, and water pumps. Herbicide and mechanical weeders were not used in this area. The cumulative frequency distributions over time for the percent of farmers adopting each of the modern inputs in each of the two study villages is shown in figures 1 and 2: Pumps and fertilizer were adopted first, followed by tractors and finally by insecticides and modern rice varieties. The increased profits from installing pumps appeared to be the source of funds for purchasing tractors. Little of the change in farming practices was associated directly with the introduction of modern varieties. Farmers reported that there was essentially no change in the labor requirements, except for harvesting and threshing, with the adoption of the modern rice varieties.

Pumps, tractors, and insecticides were adopted more rapidly in Aroop

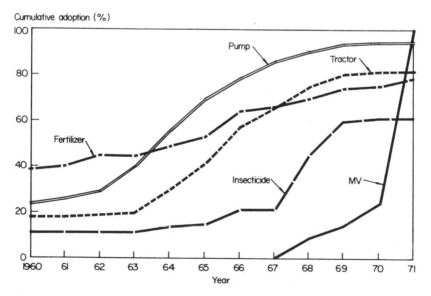

Fig. 1. Cumulative percent adoption of specified improved practices in Aroop, Pakistan.

than in Maraliwala. However, Maraliwala had a higher percentage of area planted to the modern rice varieties, a higher number of fertilizer users, and a higher rate of fertilizer use (Tables 7 and 9).

The number of farmers who had ever used pumps, tractors, and insecticides approximated the number who were still using them (Table 10). However, the percentage of users of modern varieties and fertilizer in the survey year was below the percentage of those who had adopted these technologies, indicating that some farmers had discontinued using these inputs at least temporarily.

In summary, the introduction of many of the newer farming practices in these villages preceded the adoption of modern rice varieties. Furthermore, out of a chosen sample of modern-variety adopters (about 10 percent of the farmers) in 1971, a considerable number had discontinued using IR6 in 1972. As noted earlier, the higher market price of Basmati as compared with that of IR6 was an important factor in the decision to return to growing Basmati.

RELATIONSHIP BETWEEN FARM SIZE AND FARM PRACTICES

The size of farm varied considerably within each of the two villages but there was no apparent effect of farm size on the percentage of rice area planted to new varieties (Table 7). In this section the relationship between farm size, yield, input use, and profitability in rice production

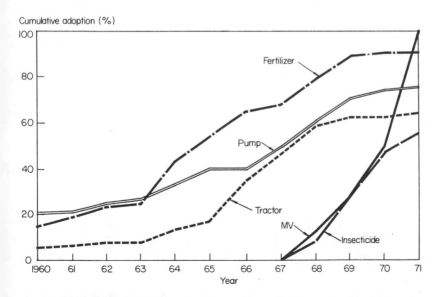

Fig. 2. Cumulative percent adoption of specified improved practices in Maraliwala, Pakistan.

Table 10. Percentages of farmers who had adopted and were still using modern inputs for rice at the time of survey.

modern input	farmers (%) in Aroop		farmers (%) in Maraliwala	
	adopted	still using	adopted	still using
modern varieties	100	74	100	58
chemical fertilizer	77	68	90	85
insecticides	61	61	55	54
tractors	81	80	64	64
pumps	94	90	75	75

is examined (Table 11). However, it should be emphasized that only those farms that were adopters of modern varieties in 1971 were sampled, and these farms tended to be larger than the average farm in the village.

While there was no relationship between farm size and yield of IR 6 in either Aroop or Maraliwala, the very large farms produced lower yields of Basmati. The adoption pattern was mixed and showed no relationship between farm size and adoption of modern rice varieties. The smaller farms had a lower percentage of fertilizer users. In Maraliwala, farms of 4 hectares or less had a lower percentage of tractor and pump adopters than larger farms.

Very few farmers reported increased profits from rice after the introduction of new rice varieties; considerably fewer farmers in Maraliwala reported increased profits as compared with those from Aroop. The groups with larger farm size had a significantly greater percentage of farmers with increased profits from rice. All farmers who reported a gain in profits from rice were planting at least a portion of their land to IR 6. On the balance, however, the benefits from adopting the new rice seeds appear, thus far, to have been minimal.

CHANGES IN CROPPING PATTERN

Included among the wide range of factors that affected the cropping pattern and choice of crop combinations in the study area are:
  a. the changes in government procurement prices for rice (and wheat) and the relationships of these prices to the prices of other crops;
  b. the availability of marketing facilities and the demand for particular crops;
  c. the availability of irrigation water and modern inputs such as fertilizer;

Table 11. Relationship between farm size, yield, use of modern inputs, and higher profits from rice.

farm size (ha)	farms (no.)	yield (t/ha)		MV	adopters (%)			farmers (%) with increased profit from rice
		IR 6	Basmati		fertilizer	tractors	pumps	
Aroop								
less than 4.0	30	3.1	1.9	77	53	53	83	15
4.0 to 7.9	26	3.1	2.1	70	73	73	96	13
8.0 to 11.9	14	3.4	2.1	79	79	79	86	36
12.0 and above	10	3.4	1.0	80	80	80	100	60
Maraliwala								
less than 4.0	22	2.7	1.5	59	73	41	59	10
4.0 to 7.9	30	2.3	1.5	63	83	70	87	3
8.0 to 11.9	11	1.7	1.1	36	90	73	73	0
12.0 and above	17	2.6	1.0	59	100	88	76	24

d. the duration of crop growth;

e. the type of soil;

f. the incidence of pests and diseases;

g. the tenure status and farm size.

Changes in the government's support price for Basmati led to fluctuations in the proportion of area planted to the two types of variety from year to year (Table 5). However, the total area planted to rice before the introduction of modern varieties remained almost constant despite the intensification of the cropping pattern (Table 12).

The introduction of tubewells, followed by tractors, fertilizer, and other modern inputs made possible an increase in the area planted to crops, particularly in the dry season. This added acreage was used to plant fodders and vegetables because they have a short growth duration and there was increasing demand for them. Due to its proximity to Gujranwala and the better quality of its soils, a higher proportion of the farming area was planted to both vegetables and fodders in Aroop than in Maraliwala.

The relatively short growth duration of vegetables and fodders enabled the farmer to prepare the land in time to sow the subsequent crop. The introduction of the early maturing new rice varieties permitted an increase in the area planted to wheat in the dry season. The late-maturing varieties of rice force the farmer to leave the area fallow during the dry season or plant the wet season crop to something other than rice. Two other factors that caused an expansion of the area planted to wheat on some farms in the dry season were the introduction of late-sown varieties of wheat (S.A. 42 variety which can be sown up to the end of December) and the increased availability of mechanical draft power.

Tenure status also affected the choice of a particular crop in a season; for example on tenant-operated farms in Maraliwala more fodders were grown for the feeding of livestock (cattle) raised by the tenants as a secondary source of income. The main crop, such as rice, must be shared in kind by the tenant and the landlord, while the second crops, such as fodders, are not shared but may be sold by the tenant at prevailing market rates.

Finally, the percent of farm area planted to rice did not vary significantly according to farm size; it was about 55 percent for Aroop and 75 percent for Maraliwala.

Utilization of rice. Producers tended to keep Basmati rice for domestic consumption while the coarse varieties were marketed (Table

Table 12. Hectarage under wet season (kharif) and dry season (rabi) crops in 1971/72 and the year before the introduction of modern varieties.

crop	Aroop		Maraliwala	
	1971/72 (ha)	1968/69 (ha)	1971/72 (ha)	1968/69 (ha)
wet season				
rice				
Basmati	81	130	84	179
IR6	40	00	93	0
other[a]	9	12	13	9
fodders	48	na[b]	29	11
vegetables	6	2	1	na
other crops	12	na	4	na
total	196	144	224	199
dry season				
wheat	100	76	145	121
fodders	54	25	22	2
other crops	6	na	2	na
total	160	101	169	123

[a] Mostly Palman. [b] na – not available.

13). In addition, those farm laborers receiving payment in kind preferred Basmati or Palman rice to IR6 rice.

CONCLUSIONS

Government price policy was the most important factor influencing the adoption of modern rice varieties. The objective of the government was to maximize foreign exchange earnings and thus the increase of support prices to maintain Basmati production was consistent with this goal. During the survey year only about 5 percent of the rice area was planted to IR6. Thus, consistent with this policy only in an indirect sense has the introduction of modern varieties made an impact on farm incomes, the major impact on income being felt through higher Basmati prices that were necessary to maintain the volume of Basmati rice needed for traditional export markets.

Table 13. Percent utilization of rice crops.

variety	total production	total production (%)				
		sold	home consumption	payment in kind	payment to landlord	seed
Aroop						
Basmati	353	54	27	16	2	1
IR 6	306	89	2	6	3	0
Palman	47	82	5	12	1	0
Maraliwala						
Basmati	300	42	18	10	29	1
IR 6	567	65	4	8	23	0
Palman	65	69	8	10	13	0

One advantage of the modern varieties of rice in addition to high yield potential is their short growing season, which permits sufficient time to prepare the land to plant the subsequent wheat crop. Additionally, the introduction of "late sown" varieties of wheat made it easier for farmers to follow a rice-wheat rotation.

The larger percentage of farm area in Aroop planted to wet season crops other than rice reflected its proximity to Gujranwala and its favorable soils for vegetable production. However, a larger percentage of crop area in Maraliwala was planted to modern rice varieties. This was particularly true among the tenant farmers. Within each of the two villages, there was no significant difference in the area planted to modern varieties among farms of different sizes.

The relationship between farm size and various factors was examined. The percentage of farmers planting modern varieties, the percentage of the area planted to modern varieties, and the yield of IR 6 did not vary significantly by farm size. The smaller farmers exhibited a lower percentage of adoption of other forms of inputs – fertilizer, tractors, and pumps. Also a significantly greater percentage of large farmers reported increased profits from rice following the introduction of the new rice varieties.

The introduction of most of the modern inputs in the study area preceded the introduction of modern varieties. The major impact to the adoption of other modern technologies was the initial adoption of tubewells in the early 1960's which increased production and profits needed to encourage the use of and provide the capital for other modern inputs. The introduction of the modern varieties of wheat and rice in the late 1960's máde it possible to continue the intensification of crop production. However, the government policy to promote Basmati kept the impact of the new rice varieties (IR8 followed by IR6) minimal in this area.

THAILAND

Don Chedi, Suphan Buri

Jerachone Sriswasdilek, Kamphol Adulavidhaya,
and Somporn Isvilanonda

Villages with different degrees of water control were studied.
Adoption and yield of modern varieties were largely determined
by the degree of water control. The complementary effects of
fertilizer and weed control on yields and income were clearly
evident on farms with good water control. Modern varieties
had the same or higher yields than traditional varieties and a
somewhat greater coefficient of variation. In the wet season,
modern varieties required more labor and gave higher returns
in all three villages. Detailed costs and returns on the farms of
partial adopters are given.

RICE IS THAILAND'S leading earner of foreign exchange, the most
important source of income for Thai farmers, and a major source of
government revenue through the rice export premium. Production has
grown at 6.4 percent annually over the past 10 years, largely because additional land and labor have been used in production, although average
yields increased from 1.5 t/ha between 1961 and 1964 to 1.8 t/ha
between 1968 and 1971 (Table 1). This growth has been adequate to
meet domestic demand as well as to provide a surplus for export.

Because of Thailand's relatively large average farm size, the quality
demands of the export market, and the lack of good water control in
many rice-growing areas, little acreage was put into the early modern
varieties. They did, however, spark interest in developing modern varieties suited to Thailand's needs.

Between 1968 and 1971, a low rate of growth in yield, a slower rate
of growth in land area, and a declining export price put additional pressure on the rice sector to explore the possibility of increasing yield per

J. Sriswasdilek, K. Adulavidhaya, and S. Isvilanonda are members of the Faculty of Agricultural
Economics at the Kasetsart University, Bangkok.

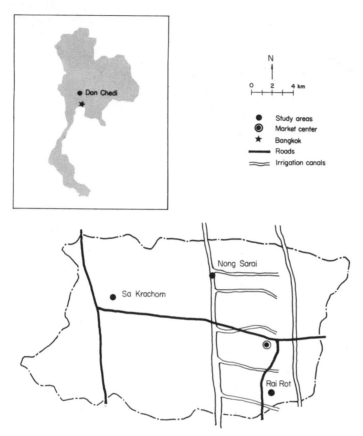

Don Chedi District, Suphan Buri Province.

hectare and lowering unit cost of production to maintain a competitive position in the export market. The world rice shortage in 1973 and the resulting high prices have added to the incentives. In this context, the potentials of the new Thai varieties, RD1 and RD3, released in 1969, and the Philippine variety C4-63, brought into Thailand in 1970, become more relevant. These are superior to the best local varieties in plant type and yield performance when grown in the proper environments, and have good grain type, although their eating qualities are not quite as high as those of traditional varieties.

These varieties are being adopted in some areas of Thailand, particularly in the Central Plain, and are being exported along with local varieties. One major question is how widely they have been adopted; another is how much benefit they have given and will give in terms of yield, cost, and net return compared with traditional varieties.

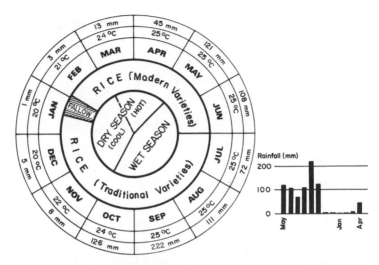

Average monthly rainfall and minimum temperature (Don Chedi, 1967-1971), Suphan Buri, Thailand.

The answers to these questions and others is largely related to the water environment. Rice in Thailand is grown under a wide range of water control conditions. Deep water areas are clearly not suited for short stiff-strawed varieties such as R D 1 and R D 3. To study the yield performance and economic benefits of the high-yielding rice varieties, we chose to study an area where the varieties were being well adopted. Within this area we chose villages representing a range of water control conditions.

RICE PRODUCTION CONDITIONS

The district of Don Chedi is one of eight districts in the province of Suphan Buri, about 200 kilometers northwest of Bangkok. There are four sub-districts and 29 villages in Don Chedi, of which three were selected for our study. The 1969 census showed a population of 28,000 people in Don Chedi, with more than 80 percent engaged in farming. The total area of the district is about 35,600 ha, with 21,600 ha of rice land.

Physical setting. Don Chedi is on the western edge of Thailand's Central Plain, in an area that slopes downward from about 15 meters above mean sea level in the west to about 5 meters above mean sea level in the east. The district has three seasons. The cool season is from November to February, the hot season from March to mid-May, and the rainy season from mid-May to October. The average annual tempera-

Table 1. Thailand's rice area, production, and exports, 1961/62 through 1971/72.[a]

year	harvested area (million ha)	paddy production		exports[b] (million t)
		(million t)	(t/ha)	
1961/62	5.66	8.18	1.44	1.27
1962/63	6.19	9.28	1.52	1.42
1963/64	6.35	10.03	1.58	1.90
1964/65	5.97	9.56	1.60	1.90
1965/66	5.92	9.22	1.56	1.51
1966/67	6.88	11.85	1.72	1.48
1967/68	5.60	9.59	1.71	1.07
1968/69	6.26	10.77	1.72	1.02
1969/70	7.24	13.35	1.84	1.06
1970/71	7.13	13.40	1.88	1.66
1971/72	7.53	14.20	1.89	2.11

[a] Source of data: Bank of Thailand, "Monthly Bulletin," Vol. 13, no. 3, March 1973, p. 50, 81. [b] Milled rice.

ture for Suphan Buri is 28°C, with a range of about 7 degrees between the coolest month, December, and the hottest month, April (when the mean temperature is 31°). Average annual rainfall is about 1,300 mm with a maximum of 220 mm falling in September and practically none in January and February.

Three of the four sub-districts in Don. Chedi are served by a canal irrigation system. The main irrigation canal, the "Makam Tow," originates near the diversion dam in Chainat town about 100 km from Don Chedi. Farm ditches extend to some farmers' fields, but most farmers receive water that has passed through the fields of neighbors.

The irrigation system is divided into a number of zones each with a "zone man," an officer from the Irrigation Department, in charge of allocating water to farmers. The farmers communicate their needs directly to the zone man, who must assign priorities when water is scarce. There is no charge for using irrigation water from the canal; the irrigation system is maintained through government revenue.

Water pumps are commonly used in the study area to deliver water to higher parts of the paddy fields, to bring water from sources such as ponds and ditches to the paddy fields, and to pump out excessive water in the wet season. Shallow well pumping is not common.

Transportation in Don Chedi is mostly by roads. Usually one bank of each irrigation canal carries a laterite road that is passable even in the rainy season. There are also four highways linking Don Chedi with the surrounding districts, one of which is of asphalt while the others are of laterite. Trucks and buses transport goods within the district, while carts and small buses carry goods among villages. Generally, villagers have their own motorcycles.

Institutional setting. Newspapers, radio, and TV from Bangkok regularly reach the area. Official news concerning the marketing situation, agricultural production, and other agricultural information is available at the houses of the heads of sub-districts and of villages.

Farm credit is provided by a number of institutions in the area: the Bank for Agriculture and Agricultural Cooperatives, the Farmers' Association, the People's Irrigation Association, the Agricultural Cooperative Association, and the Land Cooperative Association. Interest rates for short-, medium-, and long-term loans are 12 percent per year from these institutions. However, they provide only a portion of the credit needed for the purchase of inputs. Fertilizer dealers are a major source of credit, charging about 20 percent interest per crop season. This private source is very important to farmers, particularly when they urgently need credit for production.

Fertilizer, insecticides, pesticides, farm tools, and equipment are available in Don Chedi. The price of fertilizer and agricultural chemicals is very high and the price of rice has been relatively low, especially in comparison with other Asian countries. In 1971, the price ratio of a kilogram of nitrogen to a kilogram of paddy rice was about 7 to 1, compared with a ratio of 3 to 1 or less in many other parts of Asia. This unfavorable fertilizer-rice price ratio is largely a reflection of government policies.

Besides credit facilities, agricultural extension is also provided by the government. Government agencies under the Ministry of Agriculture set up demonstration plots in some villages and sometimes help control pests and diseases.

The marketing of farm products is generally performed by local merchants, most of whom come to the farm to buy products. Because local roads are fairly good, moving farm·products to market is no problem. The farmers usually sell their paddy immediately after harvest.

Rice is the major crop grown in Don Chedi. Farmers produce two crops per year on the 20 percent of the land which is irrigated in both seasons. The wet-season crop is planted in July and August and harvested in November and December. The dry-season crop is planted in March and April and harvested in June and July.

There are owners, owner-tenants, and tenants in the area, but most farmers are owner-operators. Most of the tenants pay rent in kind; the normal share arrangement is one-third to the landlord and two-thirds to the tenant.

Rice production in this area is carried on at a relatively low level of management. Weeds are found almost everywhere. Hand weeding is common, but the amount of weeding is generally inadequate to control the weeds. Insecticides are rarely used. Fertilizer is applied at very low levels. Rats are a major problem, finding excellent living accommodations in the unweeded banks of the canals and in the trees and ant hills often found in the paddy fields. This low level of management is partly explained by the high cost of inputs, and the relatively large farm size (4 to 6 ha) which leads to an extensive mode of farming. Despite fairly low yields per hectare, rice production per worker is quite high because of the large farm size.

Tractors have become popular for land preparation. Plowing for most broadcasted rice and some transplanted rice is done by tractor followed by harrowing with water buffalo. Rice is also threshed by tractor (the tractor is driven over the stalk paddy on the threshing ground), although many farmers still thresh by water buffalo. The 50- to 60-hp four-wheel tractors, which are common in this area, provide these services to farmers on custom bases.

CHANGES IN RICE FARMING

Don Chedi was selected as the study area because it is one of the first areas in Thailand in which the modern varieties were introduced, and because the physical environment within the district is highly variable, consisting of both irrigated and rainfed areas.

Stratified two-stage random sampling was used to obtain a list of farmers from whom to gather information. Villages were taken as the primary sampling units and farms as the ultimate sampling units. After selecting the district, all the villages in Don Chedi were divided into three groups based on irrigation conditions. The first group consisted of wholly irrigated villages, the second of partly irrigated and partly rainfed, and the third of wholly rainfed villages. Rai Rot, Nong Sarai,

Table 2. Basic characteristics of sample farms.

village	farms (no.)		persons in household (no.)	farm size (ha)	farms (%)		
	village	sample			owner	owner-tenant	tenant
Rai Rot	98	47	6	7.0	75	19	6
Nong Sarai	125	59	6	7.8	66	29	5
Sa Krachom	78	44	6	7.8	64	23	13

	rice area					
	per farm		double-cropped (%)	irrigated (%)		principal form of irrigation
	wet season	dry season		wet season	dry season	
Rai Rot	5.3	1.4	19	98	100	canal[a]
Nong Sarai	6.1	1.1	13	73	100	canal[a]
Sa Krachom	5.4	0	0	0	0	none

	modern varieties				
	farmers using (%)		area planted (%)		year of greatest adoption
	wet season	dry season	wet season	dry season	
Rai Rot	87	92	41	98	1970
Nong Sarai	75	96	21	96	1971
Sa Krachom	30	0	4	0	1971

[a]Supplemented by pumps for both irrigation and drainage.

and Sa Krachom were chosen at random from the first, the second, and third groups respectively.

A 50-percent sample, which totalled 150 farms, was drawn from the three villages. Table 2 shows some basic characteristics of the sample farms. The three villages are essentially similar in farm and household size and in tenure.

Adoption and constraints to adoption. The modern varieties, RD1, RD3, and C4-63, were made available to farmers in the study area in late 1969. The 1970 dry season was the first season that these new varieties were planted by farmers. By the wet season of 1971/72 they were being planted by more than three-quarters of the farmers in the

Table 3. Farmers' reasons for adopting modern varieties (percent), 1971/72.[a]

reason	Rai Rot	Nong Sarai	Sa Krachom
higher yields	46	30	0
have seen other farms growing	24	50	38
to test the potential	15	11	31
resistance to diseases	15	7	0
shorter time to mature	15	9	0
others	20	9	38

[a] Some farmers gave more than one reason.

irrigated villages and by 30 percent of the farmers in the rainfed village (Table 2).

During the 1971 wet season, 40 percent of the rice area in Rai Rot, 20 percent in Nong Sarai, and 4 percent in Sa Krachom were planted to the modern varieties. During the dry season, nearly all the area planted to rice was in modern varieties but because of limited irrigation water, the total area planted was much smaller.

Although the proportion of adopters was quite high in Rai Rot and Nong Sarai, only 17 percent of the Rai Rot farmers and 3 percent of the Nong Sarai farmers planted all their land to the modern varieties during the wet season. When farmers were asked why they were growing the modern varieties during the wet season it was apparent that a fair proportion were doing so on an experimental basis (Table 3). It is revealing that even one season after their introduction, farmers in the rainfed village of Sa Krachom did not view the modern varieties as higher yielding than the traditional varieties.

Two major reasons were given by adopters for planting traditional varieties on parts of their fields: the water was too deep for modern varieties (adopters in all three villages considered a water depth in the range of 25 to 30 cm to be suitable for modern varieties and water that exceeds 50 to 60 cm to be too deep for modern varieties); and the adopters were not sure that they could obtain high yields from modern varieties.

Farmers who adopted modern varieties in 1970 were asked if they had changed the area planted to them in the wet season of 1971. In Rai Rot, which has better irrigation, three-quarters of those who adopted modern varieties in 1970 expanded their area in 1971. In Nong Sarai,

Table 4. Age, education, farm size, and adoption of modern varieties.

village, class	average age (years)	with primary education (%)	farms (no.)		
			small (4 ha and less)	medium (4.1 to 8 ha)	large (over 8 ha)
Rai Rot					
adopters	47	73	11	24	5
non-adopters	49	67	2	5	0
Nong Sarai					
adopters	45	73	9	27	7
non-adopters	43	73	4	10	2
Sa Krachom					
adopters	43	62	5	5	3
non-adopters	41	42	17	12	2

about half of those adopting in 1970 expanded their area planted to modern varieties in 1971. Among farmers who increased their wet-season area in modern varieties in these two irrigated villages, high yield potential was given as the major reason for the increase. Only two adopters decreased their area planted to modern varieties between 1970 and 1971.

Age and education of farmers were not critical factors in determining adoption (Table 4). Adopters are neither younger nor more apt to have primary education than the non-adopters. Adoption was not related to farm size in the irrigated villages. In the rainfed village there is some indication of a positive correlation between size and adoption.

Irrigation was the major factor associated with the adoption of modern varieties in the study area. Rai Rot, where 98 percent of the total farm area is irrigated, had the highest adoption rate in terms of both percent of area planted and percent of adopters. Irrigation does not guarantee adoption, however; the non-adopters in Rai Rot also had irrigated farms. In Nong Sarai, where three-quarters of the area is irrigated, only 20 percent was planted to modern varieties, but the association between irrigation and adoption is more pronounced than in Rai Rot — only one-third of the farm area of the non-adopters is irrigated. In the totally rainfed village, modern varieties were planted on only a small fraction of the area.

Yields of modern varieties. The farms in each village were ranked from the lowest to the highest on the basis of yield obtained with

Table 5. Factors associated with yields of modern varieties, 1971 wet season.

yield group	farms (no.)	yield (t/ha)	farm size (ha)	modern variety area (ha/farm)	fertilizer (kg/ha N)	hand weeding (man-days/ha)	water control (man-days/ha)	farms with water problem (no.)	cost of pesticide ($/ha)[a]
Rai Rot:									
lowest quarter	9	2.0	5.5	3.0	7	2.8	4.5	2	0.60
2nd quarter	8	2.6	6.0	4.8	16	1.8	3.6	0	1.15
3rd quarter	8	3.2	6.2	2.2	17	2.0	4.5	1	0.40
highest quarter	8	4.2	6.0	1.6	21	11.8	6.5	0	0.95
Nong Sarai:									
lowest quarter	10	1.4	7.3	2.0	3	1.0	7.8	4	0
2nd quarter	9	2.3	6.4	2.0	9	5.2	5.3	3	0.15
3rd quarter	9	2.8	5.2	2.0	8	6.9	6.2	1	0.15
highest quarter	9	4.1	5.0	1.5	18	10.7	10.4	0	0.60
Sa Krachom:									
lower half	6	1.5	7.7	0.8	0	10.2	17.7	6	1.55
higher half	5	2.9	8.5	0.7	2	13.0	14.2	3	1.55

[a]US$1 = Baht 20.8.

modern varieties. The farms in each irrigated village were then divided into four yield groups, and Sa Krachom (the rainfed village) farms were divided into high and low yield groups. Table 5 shows the levels of fertilizer, weeding, water control, farm size, area in modern varieties, and pesticide costs for the yield groups.

There appears to be no relationship between yield and farm size, except in Nong Sarai, or between yield and area in modern varieties in any of the villages. Some factors that do seem to be associated with yields, however, are fertilizer use, labor used for hand weeding, and water problems (usually too little water). Herbicides were seldom used in the study area, so labor used in hand weeding is a good measure of the intensity of weed control.

The association between yield, chemical fertilizer, and weeding labor on irrigated farms without water problems is examined in Table 6. Farms are classified according to levels of fertilizer and weed control. The results emphasize the high degree of complementarity between weed control and fertilizer inputs for obtaining high yields and income. Using high fertilizer or high weeding alone resulted in an insignificant yield increase, but on those farms where high levels of fertilizer inputs were combined with good weed control, yields and net returns per hectare were substantially higher.

Changes in yields and input use. Farmers were asked to recall their yields and input use in 1969 and these levels were compared with their current reported levels. Because a number of farmers in the study villages grew modern varieties on only portions of their farms and others did not grow them at all, we have compared the data for full, partial, and non-adopters.

Table 6. Use of modern varieties, fertilizer use, and weeding labor on irrigated farms, 1971 wet season[a].

fertilizer level[b]	weeding level[b]	farms (no.)	modern variety area (ha/farm)	fertilizer (kg/ha N)	weeding (man-days/ha)	yield (t/ha)	net return[c] ($/ha)
low	low	25	2.7	4	0.4	2.4	79
low	high	8	1.9	6	15.1	2.5	76
high	low	13	3.5	20	0.9	3.0	87
high	high	13	1.4	27	15.2	3.9	127

[a]Farms with water problems are not included. [b]Low fertilizer is less than 12 kg/ha of N, low weeding is less than 3 man-days per ha. [c]Return over variable cost of inputs.

Table 7. Changes in yields since the introduction of modern varieties.

village, class	farms (no.)	yield (t/ha)			
		traditional varieties wet '69	traditional varieties wet '71	modern varieties wet '71	modern[a] varieties dry '72
Rai Rot					
full adopters	8	2.2	na[b]	2.6	3.1[c]
partial adopters	31	2.4	2.4	3.1	na
non-adopters	7	2.6	2.5	na	na
Nong Sarai					
full adopters	2	1.9	na	3.1	2.4[d]
partial adopters	41	1.7	1.7	2.4	na
non-adopters	16	1.3	1.2	na	na
Sa Krachom					
partial adopters	13	1.2	1.0	1.8	na
non-adopters	31	0.7	1.1	na	na

[a]Because nearly 100 percent of the dry season area is planted to modern varieties, all farms on which rice was planted are included as full adopters. [b]na = not applicable because full adopters had no traditional and non-adopters had no modern varieties in 1971. [c]Number of farms = 24. [d]Number of farms = 25.

Table 7 shows that average yields of traditional varieties did not change substantially in these villages between 1969 and 1971. On the other hand, the yields of the modern varieties were between 0.1 and 1.9 t/ha higher than the yields of traditional varieties grown in the same villages during the same seasons. The dry-season yield increment over traditional varieties grown in the wet season was higher in Rai Rot, but somewhat lower in Nong Sarai (no crops were grown in Sa Krachom during the dry season).

The labor used for pre-harvest operations to produce the traditional varieties did not change between 1969 and 1971, but is about 20 percent higher for modern varieties on the farms of partial adopters in the irrigated villages (Table 8). Interestingly, labor use has not changed for full adopters in these same villages, and seems to be substantially lower in the dry season than in the wet season. This may be because the dry season area is much smaller, and the farmers who grow dry-season crops use more machinery and are more efficient producers. The use of fertilizer on modern varieties increased slightly but not substantially.

The variability in wet-season yields is shown in Table 9. In all three

Table 8. Changes in labor inputs since the introduction of modern varieties.

village/class	farms (no.)	pre-harvest labor use (man-days)			
		traditional varieties wet '69	traditional varieties wet '71	modern varieties wet '71	modern varieties[a] dry '72
Rai Rot					
full adopters	8	62	na	62	48[b]
partial adopters	31	49	51	68	na
non-adopters	7	44	45	na	na
Nong Sarai					
full adopters	2	86	na	79	46[c]
partial adopters	41	48	52	64	na
non-adopters	16	32	31	na	na
Sa Krachom					
partial adopters	13	15	18	64	na
non-adopters	31	18	20	na	na

[a]Since nearly 100 percent of the dry season area is planted to modern varieties, all farms are included as full adopters. [b]Number of farms = 24. [c]Number of farms = 25.

villages, modern varieties had wider ranges, higher mean yields and larger coefficients of variation than did the traditional varieties. A few farmers obtained lower yields with modern than with traditional types, but the lower limits of the range for modern varieties were in no cases substantially lower than for traditional.

Although the data and information that have been gathered cannot be directly used to determine if the cropping intensity has been changed after the introduction of the modern varieties, it appears that their introduction has encouraged farmers to grow two crops of rice per year on the irrigated areas. Fifty-two of 150 sample farmers planted dry-season rice in 1972; 49 of the 52 grew modern varieties. In Rai Rot, dry-season rice area increased from 138 ha in 1971 to 913 ha in 1973; in Nong Sarai, it increased from 125 ha in 1971 to 1,312 ha in 1973. Almost all of the rice in both villages was planted to modern varieties.

CONSTRAINTS TO YIELDS

The average yields of modern varieties in the three villages are relatively low, in some cases not much higher than the yields of traditional varieties. Although yields close to 4 t/ha are being reached on some farms in the area, this is exceptional. Some factors that appear to restrict yields below this level on other farms are evident.

Ineffective water control in the wet season is probably the greatest factor holding down yields. In rainfed Sa Krachom, the average yield of modern varieties reached by partial adopters is only 1.8 t/ha, compared with 2.4 t/ha in moderately well-irrigated Nong Sarai. In Rai Rot which has the best irrigation, partial adopters had modern variety yields averaging 3.1 t/ha.

Government price policy has kept fertilizer and chemical prices high and rice prices low, and farmers are using very modest average levels of fertilizer. Higher yields have not been a goal of government policy; in fact, the government indirectly encourages farmers to switch from rice to other crops.

The low level of management is another contributing factor. Rats are a major problem. Weeds are found almost everywhere. Insecticides and herbicides are rarely used. Hand weeding is common, but is usually inadequate, and fertilizer is applied at very low levels. Because relatively large farms provide adequate family incomes at less intensive management levels, there is little incentive to upgrade management.

Table 9. Variability in yields of modern and traditional varieties, wet seasons.

variety type, year	farms (no.)	rough rice (t/ha)		coefficient of variation
		range	mean	
Rai Rot				
modern in 1971	40	1.2 − 6.1	3.2	51
traditional in 1971	39	1.4 − 3.9	2.4	26
traditional in 1969	47	1.4 − 3.9	2.4	23
Nong Sarai				
modern in 1971	43	0.8 − 5.5	2.4	48
traditional in 1971	57	0.3 − 4.1	1.6	49
traditional in 1969	59	0.3 − 4.6	1.6	53
Sa Krachom				
modern in 1971	13	0.3 − 3.6	1.8	58
traditional in 1971	44	0.4 − 2.6	1.1	40
traditional in 1969	44	0.0 − 2.7	0.9	70

Changes in labor use patterns. While no changes were reported in the labor used by full adopters and non-adopters between 1961 and 1971, partial adopters used different levels of labor on their modern and traditional varieties. Table 10 gives pre-harvest labor inputs for each task for the two types of varieties.

Pre-harvest labor inputs for modern varieties were 22 to 33 percent higher than for old varieties in the wet season in the irrigated villages, largely due to substantial increases in hand weeding and labor for water control. Inputs for these tasks during the dry seasons were lower than in the wet seasons, but still higher than for the traditional varieties. The modern varieties in the rainfed village, on the limited area where they were grown, were transplanted, requiring 10 times more labor than the traditional varieties which continue to be broadcast. Farmers also spent much more time on water control when they grow the modern varieties, even in the rainfed village.

CHANGES IN COSTS AND INCOME

Under irrigated conditions returns for modern varieties were about 35 percent higher than for traditional varieties; in the rainfed areas, net returns were about twice as high for modern as for traditional varieties (Table 11). The higher relative benefit should not obscure the higher absolute returns obtained in the irrigated areas, but it did raise somewhat the incomes of those farmers in the rainfed areas who planted limited parts of their land to modern varieties. Benefits were higher still in the dry season for the irrigated areas.

Costs per ton were the same for irrigated traditional varieties and irrigated modern varieties in the wet season, but were lower for modern varieties in the dry season. Costs per ton for the modern compared with the traditional varieties were substantially reduced in the rainfed areas. The benefit-cost ratio reflected this pattern — it was highest for modern varieties grown in Sa Krachom, and substantially higher in the dry season than in the wet season.

Costs and returns per hectare were analyzed separately for full adopters, partial adopters, and non-adopters in the three villages, but there was little difference among the three groups. There were differences between the two types of varieties. To explore these differences in greater detail, the patterns of input use for modern and traditional varieties grown by partial adopters are shown in Tables 12 through 14.

In Rai Rot and Nong Sarai, substantially more fertilizer is applied to

Table 10. Labor inputs used for pre-harvest operations on the farms of partial adopters.

| | Labor input/(man-days/ha) | | | | | | | |
| task | Rai Rot | | | Nong Sarai | | | Sa Krachom | |
	traditional varieties wet '71	modern varieties wet '71	dry '72	traditional varieties wet '71	modern varieties wet '71	dry '72	traditional varieties wet '71	modern varieties wet '71
land preparation	16.1	15.9	10.1	20.0	17.7	10.1	11.8	13.0
seedbed preparation	0.5	1.0	1.1	0.7	1.4	0.9	0	1.3
transplanting or broadcasting	30.7	31.5	30.2	28.3	28.3	27.2	2.1	19.2
handweeding	1.0	7.2	3.3	1.1	5.6	2.1	0.4	9.7
fertilizer application	0.1	1.5	0.9	0	1.0	0.8	0	0.2
pesticide application	0.6	1.6	0.8	0.3	0.8	1.1	0.2	1.0
water control[b]	2.1	9.8	1.3	2.1	9.7	4.2	4.0	19.6
total	51.1	68.5	47.7	52.5	64.5	46.4	18.5	64.0
number of farms	31	31	24	41	41	25	13	13

[a]The labor inputs shown for the wet season are for farms where both types of varieties were grown, while the labor inputs for the dry season (when most producers grew only modern varieties, include all farms growing MVs. [b]Water control includes both pumping water into the paddy fields as well as draining excess water out of the paddy fields.

Table 11. Costs and returns on traditional and modern varieties.

variety type, crop season	farms (no.)	area (ha/farm)	cost ($/t)	cost ($/ha)	return[a] ($/ha)	gross return ÷ variable cost
		irrigated				
Rai Rot						
traditional, '69 wet	47	5.1	15.80	34.85	67.15	2.9
traditional, '71 wet	39	3.6	14.30	31.20	70.80	3.3
modern, '71 wet	39	2.4	16.25	41.50	94.50	3.2
modern, '72 dry	24	2.0	10.66	33.05	100.00	4.0
Nong Sarai						
traditional, '69 wet	45	5.6	13.50	20.60	58.60	3.8
traditional, '71 wet	47	4.3	13.05	19.55	56.35	3.9
modern, '71 wet	36	1.8	14.05	31.00	78.30	3.5
modern, '72 dry	25	1.7	8.35	20.05	83.00	5.1
		rainfed				
Nong Sarai						
traditional, '69 wet	14	3.4	41.50	7.15	22.60	4.2
traditional, '71 wet	10	4.6	18.80	7.95	18.95	3.4
modern, '71 wet	7	1.1	10.35	16.10	58.00	4.6
Sa Krachom						
traditional, '69 wet	44	4.0	15.95	11.40	28.65	3.5
traditional, '71 wet	44	4.1	16.35	12.30	34.45	3.8
modern, '71 wet	13	0.6	11.95	12.85	63.65	6.0

[a]Return over variable cost, with paddy priced at $43/t.

modern varieties, but the levels of other inputs are virtually the same for modern and traditional varieties. Higher yields on the modern varieties resulted in higher returns for the portions of the farms planted to them. Costs of pump irrigation were substantially higher in the wet season than in the dry season because the farmers used their pumps not only for pumping water onto their fields, but also for pumping excess water off their fields.

Partial adopters in Sa Krachom used no fertilizer and practically no pesticides on their traditional rice, but experimented with these inputs to a limited extent on the modern varieties. Their yields and net returns were substantially higher on the areas planted to modern varieties, but

Table 12. Detailed costs and returns for partial adopters in Rai Rot.

costs, returns	traditional varieties wet '69	traditional varieties wet '71	modern varieties wet '71	modern varieties dry '71
variable costs ($/ha)				
seed	1.90	1.90	2.35	2.60
fertilizer	5.30	1.65	9.75	11.50
pesticides and weedicide	.45	.45	.70	.40
hired labor and equipment	15.80	17.10	18.10	16.50
pump irrigation	5.80	8.10	7.05	.75
interest	3.15	1.50	2.10	1.30
total	32.35	30.70	40.05	33.05
area (ha/farm)	5.7	3.8	2.1	2.0
yield (t/ha)	2.4	2.4	3.1	3.1
gross return[a] ($/ha)	103.20	103.20	133.30	133.30
net return[a] ($/ha)	70.85	72.50	93.25	100.25

[a] Assuming a constant price of $43/t of paddy.

their lack of control over water apparently made them reluctant to plant a large portion of their area to the modern varieties.

Changes in the patterns of consumption. In all three villages, farmers who adopted modern varieties increased their returns above variable costs per hectare. Some adopters said that their income was the same or less than before they adopted, however, because the rice price used in our comparison of return was constant while the rice price received by the farmers in the year before the adoption of modern varieties (1969) was relatively high (baht 1047 or $52.35 per ton of rough rice) compared with the price in 1971 (baht 834 or $41.70 per ton).

In Rai Rot, about 40 percent of the adopters reported increased income, and about an equal number reported decreased income, with the balance reporting no change. In Nong Sarai, 60 percent of the adopters reported increased incomes, and about 10 percent reported lower incomes, with the rest reporting no change. In Sa Krachom, one-fourth reported higher incomes, and an equal number reported lower incomes, while about half said they had the same levels of income after adoption.

Table 15 shows how adopters in the three villages changed their patterns of consumption. In all three villages, the largest proportion of

Table 13. Detailed costs and returns for partial adopters in Nong Sarai.

costs, returns	traditional varieties wet '69	traditional varieties wet '71	modern varieties wet '71	modern varieties dry '71
variable costs ($/ha)				
seed	2.55	2.50	2.75	3.20
fertilizer	1.25	.10	6.40	5.90
pesticides	.25	.25	.20	.35
hired labor and equipment	9.40	8.35	9.35	7.35
pump irrigation	5.80	6.60	7.20	1.35
interest	1.60	2.35	2.65	1.90
total	20.85	20.15	28.55	20.05
area (ha/farm)	6.4	4.8	1.7	1.7
yield (t/ha)	1.7	1.7	2.4	2.4
gross return[a] ($/ha)	73.10	73.10	103.20	103.20
net return[a] ($/ha)	52.25	52.95	73.55	83.15

[a] Assuming a constant price of $43/t of paddy.

farmers reported increasing expenditures on clothing. One quarter to one-half of them increased their expenditures on education and food. In each village, more than 20 percent reported increased expenditures to begin a new farm enterprise. Since many adopters had no higher incomes after the adoption of modern varieties because of price changes, other items of expenditure were generally not changed.

SUMMARY AND POLICY IMPLICATIONS

Three villages in Don Chedi representing different water control conditions were selected, and 150 farms were studied. Irrigation was closely associated with the adoption of modern varieties. Both the proportion of farms adopting and the proportion of area planted to modern varieties were higher in the irrigated village of Rai Rot and the irrigated portion of Nong Sarai village than in the rainfed village of Sa Krachom. The large majority of farmers who planted modern varieties were partial adopters, planting only about a third of their farm areas to the new varieties. Even on the irrigated farms, more than one third of the farmers indicated that a lack of water control, which leads to flooding, was the reason they continued to plant a portion of their land to tradi-

Table 14. Detailed costs and returns for partial adopters in Sa Krachom.

costs, returns	traditional varieties wet '69	traditional varieties wet '71	modern varieties wet '71
variable costs ($/ha)			
seed	4.15	3.80	2.80
fertilizer	0	0	.25
pesticides	.10	.10	1.45
hired labor and equipment	2.15	2.10	3.15
pump irrigation	1.80	1.85	1.80
interest	2.45	2.95	3.10
total	10.65	10.80	12.85
area (ha)	6.6	6.8	0.7
yield (t/ha)	1.2	1.0	1.8
gross return[a] ($/ha)	51.60	43.00	77.40
net return[a] ($/ha)	40.95	32.20	64.55

[a] Assuming a constant price of $43/t of paddy.

Table 15. Farmers (%) reporting changes in expenditures between 1969 and 1971.

item of expenditure	farmers (%)					
	Rai Rot		Nong Sarai		Sa Krachom	
	+	NC	+	NC	+	NC
food	27	73	42	58	54	46
clothes	44	56	67	33	62	38
education	37	63	42	58	54	46
house improvement	15	85	14	86	23	77
home appliance	12	88	12	88	8	92
bicycle	12	88	21	79	8	92
motorcycle	2	98	5	95	0	100
farm equipment	12	88	14	86	8	92
radio	0	100	5	95	0	100
savings	0	100	5	95	0	100
paying debts	24	76	23	77	8	92
buying new land	15	85	5	95	8	92
beginning new farm enterprises	24	76	19	81	23	77

[a] + = increase; NC = no change.

tional varieties. This is supported by their behavior during the dry season when nearly all the rice area planted was in modern varieties. The major constraint in the dry season is a lack of sufficient water to irrigate large areas.

Modern varieties showed a significantly higher yield and return per hectare than did traditional varieties on the farms of partial adopters. On irrigated farms the higher yields and net returns of modern varieties were associated with higher inputs of fertilizer and higher costs per hectare. On the rainfed farms, however, the yield and income advantage of modern over traditional varieties was associated with higher labor inputs resulting from the switch from broadcasting to transplanting rice. Adopters on the rainfed farms used almost no fertilizer. In no situation was there a significant difference in variable costs per ton of modern compared with traditional varieties.

The introduction of short duration, non-photosensitive modern varieties has encouraged farmers to grow two crops of rice a year in the irrigated areas. On many of the relatively large farms, the inputs needed to achieve high yields over the total farm area are not being supplied. Instead, there is a tendency among the majority of modern variety users to commit only a relatively small amount of cash for plant protection and fertilizer.

Although the yields of modern varieties are higher than traditional varieties, they are still relatively low. Among the factors that restrict yields are:

- inadequate control over irrigation and rain water;
- government price policy;
- larger farm size; and
- low levels of management.

Only expenditures for food, clothing, and education were increased by more than 20 percent of those adopting modern varieties. Other expenditures that are not important for their livings were not increased. Most adopters did not increase their real incomes over earlier levels because rice prices in the year they planted new varieties were lower than in the year prior to adoption.

PHILIPPINES

Gapan, Nueva Ecija

Romeo T. Herrera

Farmers in two irrigated villages began accepting modern varieties ahead of farmers in the rainfed village. After 4 years, all farmers had adopted them. Little change in the yield of wet season rice was reported despite the use of complementary inputs, but most farmers reported increased profits from rice and higher levels of living since the introduction of the new technology. The implementation of a land reform program and a severe tungro epidemic confounded the analysis of the effect of changes caused by the new technology.

MUCH RELEVANT DATA are available regarding the introduction and spread of high yielding varieties in Gapan, an important rice-farming municipality in Nueva Ecija province of Central Luzon. Gapan was brought under the Land Reform program in 1964. Located along the national highway, most of its barrios are easily accessible by road. The barrios of Mahipon, Malimba, and San Nicolas, with differing degrees of water control were selected for the study. These three barrios vary in land tenure, are at different distances from the town, and all are accessible by road.

THE AGRICULTURAL SETTING

Gapan is located in part of a region that had been an area of peasant unrest in the past, but which has also traditionally been the major supplier of rice to Manila and other towns and cities in the Philippines.

R. T. Herrera was a graduate student at the Department of Agricultural Education, University of the Philippines, Los Baños, Laguna and currently is a faculty member of the College of Community Development and Public Administration, Mindanao State University, Marawi City.

The author wishes to acknowledge the help extended by G. T. Castillo for her sustained support and encouragement throughout the study, A. Gascon in gathering and analyzing the data, A. Zabella of the Bureau of Agricultural Economics, the personnel of the Gapan Land Reform Project team, National Irrigation Administration, and all the people of the areas studied, especially the farmer-informants for their whole-hearted cooperation.

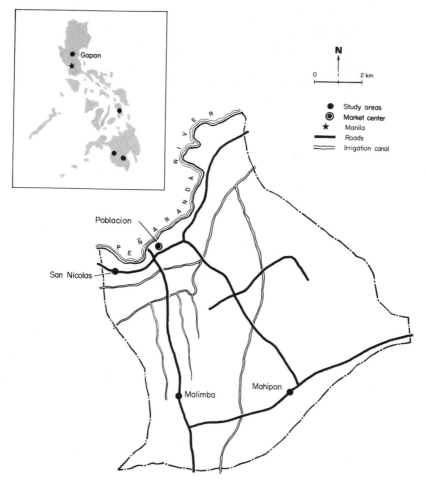

Municipality of Gapan, Nueva Ecija Province.

At the time of the survey, during 1972, the population of Gapan was estimated to be 48,000 persons, residing in 17 barrios. Three of these barrios form the *poblacion* (town center), the seat of the municipal government and center of social and economic activities. The total land area of the municipality is approximately 15,500 hectares, 80 percent of which is utilized primarily for growing rice and other crops. The remaining 20 percent is rolling brushland, which is idle throughout the year except in one location where *bignay (Antidesma binuus), duhat* (Java plum, *Eugenia jambolana*), and other fruits are grown for wine making.

Physical environment. The Central Luzon basin has a highly seasonal distribution of rainfall. It is shielded by the Caraballo mountains when

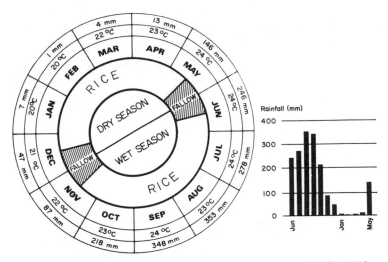

Average monthly rainfall and minimum temperature (1967-1971), Nueva Ecija, Philippines.

the north and northeast trade winds blow, and by the Zambales mountains the remainder of the year. There is a pronounced dry season from November to April. However, the southwest monsoon trade winds bring rains from June through October. The mean monthly rainfall over 20 years averaged 5 mm in January and 383 mm in August. In combination with irrigation, farmers design their cropping sequences to make full use of the rainfall pattern, planting their first crop in June and their second in December.

There are five types of soil in Gapan. The best is *banlik* or *lupain,* a clay soil with 12 inches or more of top soil that is easy to plow. *Mestisong dilain* and *mestisong galas* are shallower, stickier, and somewhat more stony. *Galas* has a shallow top soil layer of 7 inches or less, is sandy with some clay and gravel which overlays hard stone. The poorest soil type is *dilain,* which has a top soil layer of 7 inches or less, is very fine, sticky, hard to dry, and difficult to plow with carabao.

Infrastructure, economic and social environment. The municipality is served by the Peñaranda River Irrigation System, run by the National Irrigation Administration, which has a command area of 18,500 hectares and irrigates 67 percent of Gapan. Since Gapan is located near the system's headworks, it receives a more reliable supply of water than other areas served by the same irrigation system. The general layout of the main canals in relation to the study barrios and the rest of the municipality is shown in the map.

In addition to the national highway that crosses the municipality there is a network of provincial, municipal, and feeder roads serving even the remotest barrios and *sitios* (sub-barrios). Potable water is supplied by the local government to the *poblacion* and adjoining barrios. Electricity for home use is available in these areas.

Gapan is served by a variety of communication and transportation facilities, including postal service, provincial radio network, public and private telecommunication networks, trucks, and various forms of public transportation such as buses, jeepneys (Philippine jitney bus converted from a jeep), tricycles, as well as rail service, which was discontinued in 1972. Gapan is located less than two hours away from Metropolitan Manila by bus.

As a major trade center in Central Luzon, Gapan is a key distribution point for farm inputs, such as fertilizer, chemicals, farm equipment, and machine parts. Rice farming is the main occupation of people in the municipality, but many are also engaged in rice-related businesses, such as buying, processing, and selling rice. Others engage in cottage industries making slippers, shoes, women's underwear, and wine; in livestock production (poultry and swine), and in the culture of cash crops such as watermelon, onions, and other vegetables. Due to its location, Gapan has a number of light industries dealing in the repair and maintenance of land transportation vehicles.

Since Gapan was declared a land reform area in June 1964, the number of leaseholders (tenants paying cash rent) increased and the government's Agricultural Credit Administration (ACA) became as important a source of credit as private money lenders and landlords. The banks (Philippine National Bank and Gapan Rural Bank) catered to more independent farmers or landowners.

The marketing of farm products, especially rice, was facilitated by the buying stations scattered throughout the municipality, some located in the barrios. However, especially during pre-Martial Law times, farmers were at the mercy of middlemen who got a share of the production profits which otherwise would have accrued to the farm operators.

The collapse of the local Farmers' Cooperative Marketing Association a few years before this 1971/72 study did not discourage the farmers from trying "cooperation" again. Through the initiative of private agencies concerned with agricultural development, barrio-based cooperatives were again organized in a few barrios.

The Agrarian Reform Office in Gapan helped farmers change from share tenancy to leasehold (cash rent) status, and finally, following the October 1972 presidential decree on land reform, from leasehold to amortizing ownership. Three government agencies cooperated with the Department of Agrarian Reform: the Bureau of Agricultural Extension, the Agricultural Credit Administration, and the Bureau of Plant Industry. The department of Local Government and Community Development also contributed its share to agricultural development by providing counterpart funds for facilities such as concrete rice drying floors, communal irrigation systems, and feeder roads under its Grants-in-Aid Program. The Philippine Rural Reconstruction Movement and the International Rice Research Institute are two private organizations engaged in agricultural activities in the area.

Conditions in the three selected barrios. Mahipon is a rainfed barrio, producing only one crop a year, while both Malimba and San Nicolas are irrigated, and have the opportunity for growing two crops a year. Inasmuch as San Nicolas obtained its water directly from a main lateral of the Peñaranda River Irrigation System, while Malimba is served by sub-laterals, San Nicolas has relatively more water and is better irrigated especially during the dry season.

Malimba is situated about 5 km from the *poblacion,* while San Nicolas is less than 2 km from the *poblacion.* Mahipon is situated farthest from the *poblacion* — about 10 km — over a bumpy, sand and gravel road.

San Nicolas is the most accessible of the three barrios as well as being closest to the *poblacion.* Public transportation via buses, jeepneys, and tricyles regularly pass through the village enroute to other municipalities. Malimba, which is situated along the national highway has good public transportation with buses and jeepneys passing through the barrio many times daily. Mahipon is less accessible due to its geographic location and poor road. Jeepneys and tricycles serve the transportation needs of the residents during the dry season. This service becomes irregular during the rainy season.

The sample. A preliminary census of rice farmers in the selected barrios was conducted and formed the basis of a master list of those actively farming during the 5 years preceding the survey. The list contained the names of farmers who had used both local and high-yielding rice varieties. A total sample of 193 farmers was drawn from the three barrios in proportion to the number of farmers in each barrio.

While Mahipon is somewhat isolated and has physically unfavorable conditions, it had the lowest percentage of share tenants of the three barrios studied (Table 1). In Mahipon, 25 percent of the sample farmers were owner operators, half were leaseholders, and only about 25 percent were share tenants. Malimba and San Nicolas had less than 20 percent owner operators, more than 50 percent share tenants, and only about 25 percent leaseholders.

Table 1. Characteristics of the sample farms.

village	farms (no.) in village	farms (no.) in sample	persons in household (no.)	farm size (ha)	share tenants (%)	lease-holders (%)	owner-operator (%)	combi-nation (%)
San Nicolas	105	55	7.0	2.5	56	24	16	4
Malimba	85	66	6.0	3.1	59	23	9	9
Mahipon	211	72	6.0	3.8	26	46	25	3

	rice area					principal form of irrigation
	per farm (ha)		double cropped (%)	irrigated (%)		
	wet season	dry season		wet season	dry season	
San Nicolas	2.5	2.5	93	100	100	gravity
Malimba	3.1	3.1	92	100	100	gravity
Mahipon	3.8	n.a.	0	0	0	none

	modern varieties				year of greatest adoption
	farms planting (%)		rice area planted (%)		
	wet season	dry season	wet season	dry season	
San Nicolas	100	100	100	96	1967 and 1968
Malimba	99	100	95	98	1967
Mahipon	99	*a*	75	*a*	1967

*a*No crop during the dry season.

Mahipon lagged in the adoption of modern varieties despite its lower percentage of tenant farmers. In 1969, three years after the first seed of modern varieties reached Gapan, essentially all of the farmers of Malimba and San Nicolas were adopters. Only 11 of the 72 Mahipon farmers studied, or about 15 percent were adopters. However, in 1970, there was a massive shift to the modern rice varieties in Mahipon, with 78 percent of the farmers planting them, and a year later nearly all Mahipon farmers had adopted. In Malimba and San Nicolas all farmers continued growing the modern varieties.

CHANGES IN FARM PRODUCTION

Adoption and yield from new technology. Rice farmers in the three study barrios were classified as "modern" farmers, as far as their

Table 2. Farming practices wet season, before introduction of modern varieties and in 1971.

farming practice	farms (%)					
	Mahipon		Malimba		San Nicolas	
	before MV	1971	before MV	1971	before MV	1971
chemical fertilizer	94	100	58	100	73	100
organic fertilizer	97	93	30	7	18	0
insecticide	79	100	58	97	69	100
sprayer	86	99	65	90	75	100
herbicide	25	44	33	58	67	93
straight-row planting	1	13	6	5	5	0
mechanical weeder	0	6	8	23	9	7
4-wheel tractor	26	42	62	77	87	100
mechanical thresher	100	89	100	83	100	100
gravity irrigation	0	0	100	98	100	100
pump irrigation	7	17	15	36	7	25

awareness and adoption of recommended farming practices were concerned. Many farmers had used improved practices even before the introduction of MV's in 1966 (Table 2). A number of them had discontinued the use of organic fertilizer between 1966 and 1972; but the use of other improved practices increased.

The farmer's belief in the new technology, especially the new varieties was seen in the fact that 93 percent of those surveyed indicated their willingness to plant modern varieties the next season despite a severe outbreak of tungro virus which caused about a 50-percent crop loss during the 1972 wet season. In fact, 97 percent of the farmers surveyed (in irrigated Malimba and San Nicolas) actually planted modern varieties during the 1972 dry season and all continued to use them during 1972 wet season, although there was a marked shift away from susceptible varieties such as IR 5 and IR 22. Similarly, all respondents were willing to use fertilizer while almost all of them were willing to use chemicals (insecticides and herbicides) in the future.

Among the three barrios, San Nicolas had the highest average yields preceding and during the survey year (Table 3). As expected, Mahipon, the rainfed barrio, had the lowest yields and Malimba had intermediate yields. Because of the tungro epidemic in the 1971 wet season, 1970

Table 3. Distribution of yields, average yields, and nitrogen used, by barrio, before and after the introduction of modern varieties.

yield (t/ha)	Mahipon			Malimba					San Nicolas				
	pre-MV	wet 1970	1971	wet pre-MV	wet 1970	dry 1971	wet 1971	dry 1972	wet pre-MV	wet 1970	dry 1971	wet 1971	dry 1972
farmers (no.)													
0.88 or less	6	4	56	2	4	8	61	21	0	0	0	19	0
0.88 – 1.76	41	33	10	29	19	29	4	24	9	3	2	18	3
1.77 – 2.64	22	27	1	28	31	22	0	15	29	9	11	18	20
2.65 – 3.52	3	7	0	6	10	1	0	3	15	22	20	0	16
over 3.52	0	1	0	1	2	1	0	0	2	21	17	0	11
avg yield (t/ha)	1.6	1.9	0.6	2.0	2.1	1.2	0.3	1.7	2.4	3.5	2.8	1.6	3.4
nitrogen applied (kg/ha)	15	25	25	27	52	54	69	67	25	70	93	107	107

yield data are included to give a better reflection of the yield levels in the area.

Between 1966 and 1970 yields in Mahipon and Malimba did not substantially increase, and in the wet season of 1971 tungro caused rice production losses. A promising yield increase was reported only in San Nicolas since the introduction of the new seeds. During the tungro season, yields in San Nicolas averaged 1.6 t/ha while in Mahipon and Malimba they averaged only 0.6 and 0.3 t/ha, respectively.

Farmers in San Nicolas used substantially more nitrogen fertilizer than was used in the other two barrios, especially after the introduction of modern varieties. Mahipon farmers applied half as much nitrogen as Malimba farmers and one-third as much as San Nicolas farmers, but 93 percent of them also applied organic fertilizer compared with 7 percent in Malimba and none in San Nicolas.

No meaningful change occurred in farm size between 1966 and 1971 although the price of land increased markedly. In San Nicolas and Malimba, land values more than doubled, while in the rainfed village of Mahipon the land values increased by 65 percent (Table 4).

Income changes. Aided by the land reform declaration of 1964, a large number of farmers, especially in Mahipon, shifted from share-tenancy to leasehold tenancy between 1966 and 1971. The number of owner-operators remained almost the same (Table 5). Under share tenancy in this area costs and returns are shared between landlords and tenants with each contributing half and receiving half. In addition, the landlord usually advanced cash for many production costs as the tenant often could not put up his own share.

Under the leasehold sanctioned by the land reform, the rental was set by law at 25 percent of the normal yield based on the farmer's harvest during the previous 3 years. During the survey year, 67 percent

Table 4. Land values (₱/ha) before the introduction of modern varieties and in 1971.

barrio	land value (₱/ha)		increase	
	before MV	1971	₱	%
rainfed				
Mahipon	2,982	4,911	1,929	65
double crop irrigated				
Malimba	2,812	6,000	3,188	114
San Nicolas	2,750	6,018	3,268	119

Table 5. Tenure of respondents before the introduction of modern varieties and in 1971.

	respondents (no.)									
tenure	Mahipon		Malimba		San Nicolas		total			
	before MV	1971	before MV	1971	before MV	1971	before MV (no.)	(%)	1971 (no.)	(%)
share tenant	52	19	59	39	45	31	156	80	89	46
lessee	2	32	2	15	1	13	5	3	3	31
owner-operator	18	18	5	6	9	9	32	17	33	17
combination	0	3	0	6	0	2	0	0	11	7

of the lessees interviewed paid their landlords from 6 to 10 sacks of 44 kg/ha per season.

Three-quarters of the farmers interviewed estimated that their profit from rice in the 1970 wet season was higher than during the wet seasons before the introduction of modern varieties; 70 percent thought the same was true for their level of living (Table 6). San Nicolas had the highest percentage of farmers reporting higher profits from rice (93 percent), and Malimba had the lowest (59 percent). In Mahipon 75 percent of the farmers reported increased profits, even though the area was entirely rainfed. With regard to an increase in the level of living, the

Table 6. Change in profit from rice and level of living in wet season 1970 compared to the year before the introduction of modern varieties.[a]

direction of change	farms (%)			
	Mahipon	Malimba	San Nicolas	all villages
	profit from rice			
higher	75	59	92	75
lower	25	39	4	24
same	0	2	4	1
	level of living			
higher	72	50	87	69
lower	27	39	4	24
same	1	11	9	7

[a]Wet season of 1970 is taken as year of comparison because of the tungro infestation in 1971.

Table 7. Items on which expenditures increased since the introduction of modern varieties.

item	increases	
	no.	%
food		
vegetables	142	74
rice	141	73
eggs	140	72
chicken	140	72
fish	139	72
cooking oil	136	70
milk	127	64
coffee	127	64
pork	124	62
canned goods	112	58
beef	97	50
durable goods		
radio	120	62
clothes cabinet	92	48
living room set	70	36
sewing machine	56	29
dining room set	47	24
farm implements	41	21
gas stove	34	18
motorcycle	18	9
bed	16	8
bicycle	16	8
expenditures on		
education of children	106	55
improvement/construction of house	98	51
payment of long-term debts	120	62

villages had the same relative position: 87 percent in San Nicolas, 72 percent in Mahipon, and 50 percent in Malimba. When classed by tenure there was a slight difference in benefits. About 80 percent of the owner-operators, 75 percent of the lessees, and 73 percent of the share tenants reported higher profits from rice, as well as reporting improved levels of living.

Most farmers surveyed reported increases in food consumption and purchases of durable consumer goods as a result of increase in rice profits (Table 7). The leading items purchased since 1966 were: radios, clothes cabinets, sewing machines, living and dining room sets, and farm implements. In addition, about half the respondents reported increased amounts of money spent for children's education, building or repair of house, and payment of long-term debts.

PERCEPTION OF CONSTRAINTS TO HIGHER YIELDS

The presence of insects, diseases, and pests such as rats, were identified by farmers as the main factors most often constraining the yields of modern varieties. The lack of adequate water or irrigation, unavailability of credit, difficulty in obtaining fertilizer, chemicals, and seeds were also considered constraints. More farmers recognized these as problems since the introduction of modern varieties (Table 8).

Before the introduction of the new varieties, the attack of pests, especially rats, was the biggest problem in Malimba and San Nicolas, but in Mahipon such pest problems were not reported by the farmers surveyed. In the wet season of 1971, tungro disease was the biggest problem in all barrios, while rats were equally important in San Nicolas. A majority of respondents in Malimba and San Nicolas again reported the presence of rats as the greatest constraint to high rice yields for the dry season of 1972.

Credit. The four most important problems of Gapan farmers were (a) the sporadic attack of rats, (b) diseases and insects, (c) lack of water, and (d) lack of adequate production credit or working capital. The most critical problem seemed to be the lack of credit because it affected the other problem areas. With adequate working capital available, farmers could purchase chemicals to stop or at least minimize the attack of pests and diseases. With adequate credit, pumps could be purchased to augment the existing irrigation system or to move water from wells and creeks to the crop areas. Likewise, with enough credit, farmers could purchase the recommended amounts of fertilizer and other chemicals and could purchase quality seeds from legitimate sources which were located mostly outside the municipality.

Farmers considered the lack of credit a worse problem in 1971 than in 1966. In 1966, 55 percent borrowed cash for rice production in the wet season, but only 50 percent borrowed cash in the wet season of 1971. In the 1972 dry season, 85 percent borrowed cash. Credit in kind was not very popular in Gapan; none of the farmers surveyed borrowed in kind before 1966 and less than 20 percent borrowed in 1971.

Landlords were the leading source of credit in 1971, especially in Malimba and San Nicolas, where half of the sample farmers were share tenants. In Mahipon, where half of the sample farmers were lease-holders, the government's Agricultural Credit Administration was the major source of credit. Other sources of credit were private money lenders, relatives, neighbors, and banks (Table 9).

Farmers in San Nicolas borrowed an average of ₱232/ha, those in Mahipon, ₱173/ha, and those in Malimba, ₱151/ha during the 1971 wet season. In the dry season of 1972, farmers in Malimba and San Nicolas borrowed an average of ₱423/ha, and ₱395/ha, respectively. The tungro disaster during the wet season did not appear to keep farmers from borrowing even more during the subsequent dry season, although part of those loans were probably for re-finance because of the poor harvest of the previous wet season.

A majority of those who obtained credit from institutional sources (ACA, banks, or cooperatives) borrowed between ₱200 and ₱300/ha in both the wet and dry seasons. Almost half of those who obtained credit from non-institutional sources borrowed less than ₱100/ha in the wet season and more than ₱200/ha in the dry season.

An analysis of the effect of farm size on credit showed that 80 percent of those whose farms were less than 1 ha borrowed from ₱200 to ₱299/ha. Among those with farms between 1 and 2.5 ha, 50 percent borrowed less than ₱200/ha, 45 percent borrowed between ₱200 and ₱399/ha and 5 percent borrowed ₱400/ha or more. A majority of respondents whose farms were over 2.5 ha borrowed less than ₱200/ha. Thus, the smaller the land holding, the larger was the credit per hectare, and vice-versa, suggesting that farmers with larger land holdings were able to meet their production costs without borrowing.

Among those who borrowed cash in the 1971 wet season, 28 percent would have used more credit if it had been available (Table 9). In the succeeding dry season over 60 percent reportedly would have used more credit. In both cases, 85 percent of them wanted the credit for farm production purposes. The others wanted it for family consumption or emergencies. In the dry season of 1972, all those who wanted more credit reported they would spend the money for production purposes only.

About 20 percent of all respondents said that repayment of their loans was more of a financial burden since the introduction of modern varieties, the same number said it was less of a burden and the rest had no opinion or reported it to be the same. However, in Mahipon where there was a noticeable increase in loans from the government Agricul-

Table 8. Perceived constraints to higher yields, before and after the introduction of modern varieties.

farms (%)

constraints	Mahipon		Malimba			San Nicolas			average		
	wet		wet			wet			wet		
	before MV	1971	before MV	1971	dry 1972	before MV	1971	dry 1972	before MV	1971	dry 1972
diseases, insects	1	97	29	91	64	51	93	64	25	93	64
pests	0	4	39	85	94	78	93	80	36	57	88
irrigation, moisture	6	20	33	62	64	33	36	42	23	39	54
obtaining fertilizer and chemicals	1	4	11	24	6	0	9	6	4	12	6
lack of credit	1	2	14	45	51	15	33	24	9	26	39
obtaining seed	6	4	17	35	8	6	27	10	9	21	9

Table 9. Sources, amount, and repayment of credit.

respondents (%)

item	Mahipon		Malimba			San Nicolas			average		
	wet		wet			wet			wet		
	before MV	1971	before MV	1971	dry 1972	before MV	1971	dry 1972	before MV	1971	dry 1972
form of repayment											
cash	30	51	40	68	89	30	40	80	33	54	85
kind	0	19	0	18	15	0	7	5	0	16	11

(Table 9 continued)

source of credit											
landlord	40	28	45	46	46	60	33	57	48	37	50
money lender	56	21	15	6	15	21	25	27	33	17	20
relative/neighbor	2	0	8	13	3	5	8	2	5	7	3
bank	1	5	0	2	0	2	0	2	1	2	1
coop/government	1	46	2	33	36	12	34	12	5	39	26
amount of loan (₱/ha)											
1–199	n.a.	59	n.a.	66	42	n.a.	22	13	n.a.	51	29
200–399	n.a.	28	n.a.	34	49	n.a.	65	47	n.a.	41	48
400 plus	n.a.	13	n.a.	0	9	n.a.	13	42	n.a.	8	23
average loan (₱/ha/borrower)	n.a.	173	n.a.	151	423	n.a.	232	395	n.a.	182	409
would use more credit if available	11	n.a.	48	79	n.a.	25	33	n.a.	28	n.a.	58
case of repayment in 1971 compared to that before MV											
more of a burden	28	n.a.	21	n.a.	n.a.	13	n.a.	n.a.	21	n.a.	n.a.
less of a burden	44	n.a.	9	n.a.	n.a.	9	n.a.	n.a.	22	n.a.	n.a.

Table 10. Distribution of credit by tenure and amount borrowed.

amount (₱/ha)	share tenants		lessees		owner-operators		average	
	wet	dry	wet	dry	wet	dry	wet	dry
borrowers (%)								
	45	91	42	96	48	85	44	92
farmers (%) by amount of loan								
1–199	50	15	14	4	12	9	33	11
100–199	23	15	17	15	23	27	21	18
200–299	17	29	49	46	23	18	26	31
300–399	8	22	14	8	18	0	13	17
400–499	2	14	6	23	12	36	5	18
500 plus	0	5	0	4	12	10	2	5
average loan (₱/ha)								
	132	268	260	292	204	296	194	275

[a]a – family labor. b – hired labor within the barrio. c – hired labor outside the barrio. d – exchange labor. [b]n.a. – not applicable or no response.

tural Credit Administration, 44 percent of the farmers reported repayment to be less of a burden. Among the farmers who borrowed during the 1971 wet season, half considered the cost of credit to be lower than before the modern varieties were introduced, while only 5 percent said the cost of credit was higher in 1971.

In 1971, the number of cash borrowers and the average value of the loan increased substantially from the wet to the dry season for all tenure categories (Table 10). Most of the share tenants borrowed from their landlords while a majority of lessees obtained credit from the ACA. The owner-operators used both institutional and non-institutional sources of credit.

A majority of respondents, regardless of tenure status, believed that credit was not a constraint to getting higher yields before 1966 or even in the 1971 wet season. But in the 1971 dry season, 63 percent of leaseholders considered inadequate credit a constraint probably because of the timing of the release of government loans in the 1972 dry season and the attack of tungro in the previous wet season.

LABOR REQUIREMENT, AND OFF-FARM EMPLOYMENT

In the 3 barrios, 50 percent of all respondents reported that they or some members of their households had other employment besides their

Table 11. Off-farm jobs reported during the wet season, 1971.

	Mahipon	Malimba	San Nicolas	total
	household members (%)			
with off-farm job	49	53	45	50
	household members (no.)			
type of off-farm job				
males	34	21	15	70
agricultural worker	8	4	3	15
laborer (unskilled)	13	3	0	16
laborer (skilled)	0	5	2	7
driver (tricycle, jeep)	10	4	6	20
others	3	5	4	12
females	23	19	27	69
agricultural worker	6	8	2	16
dressmaker	10	0	1	11
factory worker	3	4	8	15
teacher	2	0	0	2
retailer	1	3	14	18
others	1	4	2	7
total	57	40	42	139
	household members (%)			
location of off-farm job				
inside the barrio	61	49	38	51
outside the barrio	39	51	62	49

work on the farm during the 1971 wet season. These were either farming jobs outside their own rice farm, or jobs not associated with farming such as carpentry, dressmaking, teaching, and other skilled or unskilled jobs (Table 11). On the average, extra employment was equally divided between males and females. In Mahipon and Malimba, a majority of those with outside employment were male while in San Nicolas women held more outside jobs. There were almost as many working within the barrios in which they were residing as those working outside.

In the dry season of 1972 about 70 percent of those interviewed reported that they or members of their household had outside employment; 67 were male and 22 were female. Besides taking off-farm employment, some households planted "cash crops" during the dry season (usually vegetables) to augment their income.

In Mahipon about 50 percent of the farmers surveyed increased their off-farm income after the introduction of MV's while about 75 percent

Table 12. ·Percent of respondents reporting changes in farm labor requirements[a] between 1966 and 1971.

change	respondents (%)															
	Mahipon				Malimba				San Nicolas				average			
	a	b	c	d	a	b	c	d	a	b	c	d	a	b	c	d
pre-harvest tasks are:																
greater	29	8	9	0	77	76	3	61	86	82	0	53	63	42	4	36
smaller	7	3	21	7	0	3	0	3	0	0	0	0	3	2	7	4
same	64	89	70	93	17	12	2	24	14	18	7	47	34	43	25	56
n.a.[a]	0	0	0	0	6	9	95	12	0	0	97	0	0	13	64	4
harvesting and threshing tasks are:																
greater	30	15	30	0	71	65	5	62	75	71	0	47	57	48	13	35
smaller	10	13	19	8	0	4	0	3	0	0	0	0	4	6	7	4
same	60	72	43	85	21	23	8	23	25	29	11	53	37	43	22	54
n.a.[b]	0	0	8	7	8	8	87	12	0	0	89	0	2	3	58	7

[a] a. family labor, b. hired labor within the barrio, c. hired labor outside the barrio, d. exchange labor. [b] n.a. not applicable or no response.

of those in the other two barrios reported an increase. No respondent in Mahipon reported lower off-farm income but about 10 percent in Malimba and San Nicolas did. Hence the farmers in Mahipon seemed to experience less changes in off-farm employment.

The introduction of the new varieties and other farming practices since 1966 brought about some changes in the amount of labor needed for specific farming tasks. The rainfed barrio and the two irrigated barrios differed markedly in the pattern of change in labor requirements (Table 12). Over 60 percent of respondents in Mahipon reported no change in the amount of labor used for either pre-harvest or harvest tasks; 60–80 percent of those in the other two barrios reported an increase in most types of labor.

FARMERS' ATTITUDE TOWARD CHANGES

In general, the farmers in the three barrios of Gapan welcomed the introduction of new technology and nearly all had accepted it within several years of its introduction. Ninety six percent of the farmers expressed confidence in the overall effectiveness of the new technology (seeds, chemical fertilizer, and pesticides) even though about 25 percent

Table 13. Expectations for the future.

response	respondents (%)		
	Mahipon	Malimba	San Nicolas
expect higher income in the next 5 years	93	79	93
spend increased income on: education of children	31	5	9
construction/improvement of house	17	11	20
investment	32	20	24
consumption	1	15	3

of those interviewed had experienced problems with some aspects of the technology, including headaches or dizziness from improper use of pesticides, and a crop failure due to tungro disease.

The outlook of the farmers in the area was generally optimistic; 80 to 90 percent expected higher incomes in the future, largely from their own determination to work harder at following the recommended practices (Table 13). The most frequently mentioned plans for the new income expected by the farmers were construction or improvement of housing, education, and farm investment. Very few indicated that the extra income would be used for consumption.

CONCLUSIONS

Farmers in the three barrios studied were familiar with the new technology in rice farming and were using inputs such as fertilizer and insecticides even before the introduction of the modern rice varieties in 1966. Despite the serious outbreak of tungro virus in 1971, which resulted in a reduction of crop yields of 50 percent or more, farmers in all of the barrios were convinced of the value of modern, fertilizer responsive varieties. They continued to grow the modern varieties, selecting those with the greatest resistance to tungro. At the same time, farmers expressed general concern about those factors that would increase their profits from the new technology — land reform, credit availability, adequate irrigation, protection against diseases, insects, and rat damage. A realistic program designed to enhance the crop yields of farmers must take all of these factors into account.

While credit has been emphasized as a major bottleneck in this paper in rainfed barrios such as Mahipon, steps may be needed to improve the infrastructure before credit can be properly utilized. The improvement and extension of irrigation can greatly increase farm production, especially in the dry season. Better extension services are becoming more important given the increased complexity of the new technology. Lastly, a realistic and coordinated land reform program must not only seek to transfer the control of land to the farmers who cultivate the land, but also provide the means (e.g. availability of credit) whereby production can be increased. In short, in what must be regarded as one of the more progressive rice growing communities in the Philippines, the results of this study indicate that there is still much scope for improvement of production.

Baybay, Leyte

Tito E. Contado and Roger A. Jaime

Despite the high rate of adoption of modern varieties and modern inputs, the rate of fertilizer application and yields have remained low. Is it the incorrect amount of applied inputs such as fertilizer, or is it the incorrect use of modern inputs that is the major obstacle to higher yields?

LEYTE IS AN ISLAND - in the central part of the Philippines, on the eastern side of the Visayas region. It is divided into eastern and western sections by a mountain range. The three study villages are located on the western side of the island in the municipality of Baybay.

There is a pronounced wet and dry season. The 5-year rainfall record shows a monthly rainfall average that varied from a low of 62 mm in May to a high of 339 mm in November, with the heaviest rains being received from July through December. The average monthly temperature range is from 22.8° to 25.0°C or a variability of less 3°C during the year.

In 1970, Baybay had a population of approximately 64,000. Its land area is about 46,000 hectares so the population density is more than one person to a hectare. Much of the municipality is forest, only 26,000 hectares are considered developed agriculturally. Roads connect the municipal center *(poblacion)* and the villages *(barrios)*. Jeeps and a few buses serve as the main transport. The coastal villages are also accessible by motorized outrigger boats. Baybay has three telegraph offices and long distance telephone facilities. Most of the electrification is in the municipal center; the villages have none. The Visayas Agricultural College, located 8 kilometers from the municipal center, has its own generator. There are a few privately owned small generators. Baybay has its own pier where inter-island boats from Cebu City and Manila

Tito E. Contado is assistant professor of the Department of Agricultural Extension and Assistant for Extension, Chancellor's Office, University of the Philippines at Los Baños, Laguna; Roger A. Jaime is instructor at the Visayas Agricultural College.

The authors wish to acknowledge the help extended by C. Bantilan in analyzing the data.

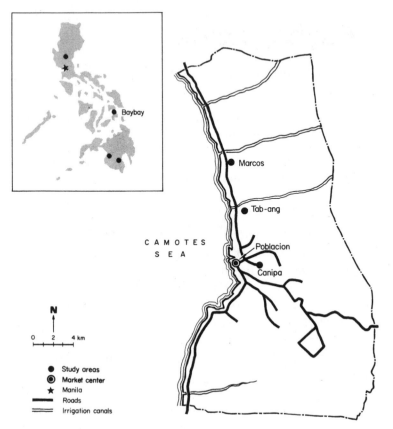

N

0   2   4 km

● Study areas
◎ Market center
★ Manila
━━ Roads
═══ Irrigation canals

CAMOTES
SEA

● Marcos

● Tab-ang

Poblacion

◎

● Canipa

Baybay

Municipality of Baybay, Leyte Province.

load and unload passengers and commercial goods. It is also accessible by air through the Cebu, Hilongos, and Tacloban airports.

The major products in the area are copra, rice, Manila hemp, and bananas. Some white flint corn and root crops are grown for home consumption. There are some backyard-type poultry, swine, and vegetable projects. Since Baybay is close to the sea, fishing is a major economic activity.

Baybay has representatives of the different government agencies like the Bureau of Agricultural Extension, Presidential Arm on Community Development, cooperatives, etc. A new rural bank has been established and the Farmers' Marketing Cooperative Incorporated has been successfully operating for 2 years.

The villages. The three study villages, Canipa, Marcos, and Tab-ang, were chosen from among the 60 barrios in Baybay. Canipa is 2.5 kilometers to the southeast of the municipal center while Tab-ang and

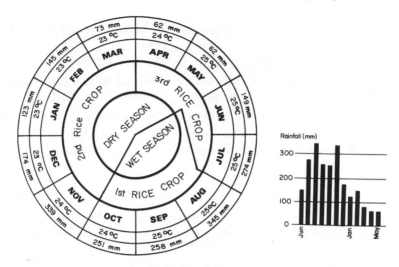

Average monthly rainfall (Philsugin Weather Station, Ormoc City, 1967-1971) and minimum temperature (Weather Bureau, Tacloban City, 1967-1971), Leyte, Philippines.

Marcos are 5 and 9 kilometers, respectively, north, along the national road to Ormoc City.

Despite its proximity to the municipal center, Canipa is in some ways more remote than the other two villages. Access to the village is along a rough and rather steep secondary road. Its rice fields lie high above the river and must be irrigated with pumps. Farmers pay 15 percent of their harvest for the use of water.

Although the bridges along the road between the municipal center and Marcos and Tab-ang are sometimes washed away by typhoons, these villages border on the ocean and are always accessible by water. Their rice fields lie between the mountain range to the east and the Camotes Sea to the west. The silt loam and clay loam soil are well suited for rice. Streams can be easily dammed to divert water to the rice fields for irrigation and there is no charge for the water. Marcos and Tab-ang have the additional advantage of being only a few kilometers from the Visayas Agricultural College.

The sample. A sample of approximately 50 percent of the farm households was drawn at random from each of the villages. The list of farmers was obtained from a village census undertaken before the survey. For the first-round survey, 171 farmers were interviewed between October 1971 and February 1972. Although this covered principally the 1971 wet-season crop, it also included information on varieties grown during the preceding dry season. In the second round conducted from July to September 1972 and covering the 1971/72 dry-season crop, 169 farmers were interviewed.

Although the average farm in the three barrios has about 1.5 hectares, only about half this area is devoted to rice production (Table 1). Share tenancy is high in all three barrios. The only four farmers who reported being on leasehold were all in Tab-ang. Essentially all of the rice area is irrigated and capable of growing two crops. A substantial number of farmers reported growing five crops of rice in 2 years.

THE ADOPTION PATTERN OF MODERN VARIETIES

In the year preceding the introduction of modern varieties the rice farmers in the three villages were growing about 14 improved local

Table 1. Basic characteristics of sample farms.

village	farms (no.) village	farms (no.) sample	persons in household (no.)	farm size (ha)	share tenants (%)	lease-holders (%)	owner-operators (%)	combination tenure (%)
Canipa	110	49	6.7	1.7	77	0	17	6
Marcos	129	66	6.4	1.5	86	0	14	0
Tab-ang	98	56	5.4	1.2	57	4	33	6

	rice area						
	per farm (ha)		double-cropped (%)	irrigated (%)		principal form of irrigation
	wet season	dry season		wet season	dry season	
Canipa	0.8	0.8	100	90	90	pump
Marcos	0.4	0.4	100	90	99	canal
Tab-ang	0.7	0.7	100	99	99	canal

	modern varieties				
	farmers using (%)		rice area planted (%)		year of greatest adoption
	wet season	dry season	wet season	dry season	
Canipa	98	98	95	95	1967, 1968
Marcos	100	100	100	100	1966, 1967
Tab-ang	100	100	100	100	1968, 1969

and traditional varieties. Peta, Apostol, and Tjeremas accounted for three quarters of the total. All three were Philippine Seedboard varieties. This suggests that even before the introduction of modern varieties, the farmers in the villages were aware of the importance of varieties and were trying those that promised high yields.

When the first modern variety, IR8, was introduced in 1966, about 6 percent of the rice farmers in the three villages tried it. By 1970, all three villages had 100 percent adoption of modern varieties. When the farmers were asked which modern varieties they adopted first, 88% said IR8, 6% said IR5, 5% said C4-63, and 1% said C4-137. This is to be expected because from the time IR8 was first planted almost 3 years elapsed before any other variety was introduced to the area. But as soon as other modern varieties were introduced, IR8 was changed easily. Thus in 1970/71 dry season, only 7 percent were planting IR8 while 47 percent were growing C4-63 (Table 2).

Farmers in the area seemed to have seasonal preferences in varieties. While for example nearly half of the farmers planted C4-63 during the dry season, only 18 percent planted it during the wet season. On the other hand, IR8 was planted by 26 percent during the 1971 wet season while it was planted by only about 6 percent during the 1970/71 and 1971/72 dry seasons.

In 1971/72 no single variety seemed to fulfill the requirements of the farmers, so many varieties were being tried again. In addition to high yield, eating quality and resistance to tungro virus disease and bacterial blight influenced the farmers' choices. Few farmers attempted to retain the improved local varieties.

Table 2. Varieties grown in the three villages.

variety	farmers growing (%)		
	1971		1972
	dry	wet	dry
C4-63	47	18	46
IR5	21	22	22
IR20	15	20	15
IR22	9	14	9
IR8	7	26	6
local	1	*a*	2

a Less than 1 percent.

CHANGE IN YIELD AND CROPPING INTENSITY

As a rough way of comparing the yield performance of local and modern varieties we asked each farmer the crop year in which he obtained his highest yield. Eighty percent of the respondents reported the highest yields for both wet and dry seasons were obtained between 1968 and 1971. During this period, practically all the rice farmers were planting modern varieties. This was also before tungro virus was important.

The farmers were then asked the yield of their rice crop immediately before switching to modern varieties and the yield of their modern varieties before tungro disease became prevalent. During the wet season, only in Canipa was the mean yield significantly higher than the yield before the modern varieties were introduced (Table 3). For all three villages taken together, however, mean yields since modern varieties were introduced were significantly higher. During the dry season, the mean yields in both Canipa and Tab-ang were significantly higher than before the modern varieties. And as can be expected, the mean yield in the three villages taken together was also significantly higher than before modern varieties. In Canipa, where the differences in mean yields were greatest, the installation of irrigation pumps since modern varieties were introduced could have contributed considerably to the yield increases.

Although the average yields improved, farmers used well below the recommended level of nitrogen on modern varieties. Based upon our knowledge of nitrogen response, doubling the fertilizer rates should

Table 3. Comparison of yield before modern varieties were adopted and in the year after adoption when the highest yields were obtained.

| village | yield (t/ha) | | | | | | fertilizer used on modern varieties[a] (kg/ha N) | |
| | wet season | | | dry season | | | | |
	before	after	difference	before	after	difference	wet season	dry season
Canipa	1.5	3.1	1.6**	1.7	3.1	1.4**	23	24
Marcos	3.3	4.0	0.7	3.5	4.1	0.6	28	27
Tab-ang	2.5	2.5	0.0	2.2	2.9	0.7*	41	32

[a]In survey year. *Significant at the 5% level. **Significant at the 1% level.

Table 4. Problems encountered by farmers in rice production before and after modern varieties were introduced.

| problem | farmers (%) reporting | | | | | |
| | Canipa | | Marcos | | Tab-ang | |
	before	after[a]	before	after	before	after
insects, disease	68	69	75	76	66	86
pest	3	0	4	6	2	20
irrigation	60	16	4	0	0	2
fertilizer and chemicals	18	10	45	2	38	4
seeds	0	10	0	2	4	7
credit	11	14	2	4	4	4
harvesting	0	0	4	0	0	0
threshing	0	0	0	0	0	4
others	32	14	36	30	36	38
no. reporting	38	49	53	66	47	56

[a] 1971 wet season.

have been highly profitable. But in some years typhoons or other sources of crop damage (such as the recent attack of tungro virus) considerably reduced the payoff from fertilizer.

Barriers to higher yield. In all three villages, farmers said disease and insects were the chief problem both before and after the introduction of modern varieties (Table 4). A serious irrigation problem in Canipa was reduced with the further development of pump irrigation. Fertilizer and chemicals appeared to be more easily available than previously. Credit was not a major problem either, but the demand for credit was stronger in the dry season than in the wet season. One third of the farmers said that they would have used more credit if it had been available in the dry season while less than 15 percent expressed a desire for more credit in the wet season. The farmers' responses (Table 4) suggest, however, that lack of availability of fertilizer and credit was not the the reason behind the low fertilizer input.

Changes in cropping intensity. Almost all farmers in the three villages used double-cropping before modern varieties were introduced (Table 5). Due to the relatively abundant rainfall in the area, it was possible to double-crop even in Canipa. In this village, the introduction of pumps

Table 5. Cropping pattern before and after modern varieties were introduced.

crop/year	farmers (%) reporting[a]					
	Canipa		Marcos		Tab-ang	
	before	after	before	after	before	after
1	0	0	3	0	0	0
2	96	6	94	2	97	5
2.5	0	83	0	73	0	78
3	4	11	3	25	3	17

[a]Includes only 71 percent of the farmer respondents in Canipa and Tab-ang and 79 percent in Marcos who had planted the modern varieties for 5 years prior to the survey.

permitted an increase in farm size and created a more stable water supply. For the three villages, the modern varieties dramatically increased cropping intensity, from double-cropping to five crops in 2 years. Some farmers even claimed to have achieved three crops per year as a result of the early maturity and photoperiod-insensitivity of the modern varieties.

CHANGES IN FARMING PRACTICES

To give the best results, modern varieties require improved cultural practices, more inputs, and more care. Is this reflected in the farming practices of the respondents?

Since the introduction of modern varieties, the number of improved farming practices used in each barrio and the number of users of each practice have increased (Table 6). Of the 16 practices studied, only 10 were used in Canipa, 11 in Marcos, and 12 in Tab-ang before the introduction of modern varieties. In 1971, 13 were being used in Canipa and 14 in Marcos and Tab-ang. The three new practices in Canipa were continuous cropping, use of the *dapog* method of raising seedlings (allowing seeds to germinate and grow on a bed of banana leaves instead of in a traditional seedbed in soil) and use of harvesting knife *(pangapas)* instead of the traditional finger blade harvester *(yatab)*. The use of *dapog* and *pangapas* were also the two newest practices in Marcos and Tab-ang.

The number of farmers using the different recommended practices increased remarkably, especially in Canipa. For instance, before the introduction of modern varieties, only 16 percent of the farmers in

Table 6. Adoption of rice production practices before modern varieties were introduced and in 1971/72.

use of	Canipa			Marcos			Tab-ang		
	before	1971 wet season	1971/72 dry season	before	1971 wet season	1971/72 dry season	before	1971 wet season	1971/72 dry season
organic fertilizer	0	0	0	2	0	0	2	0	0
chemical fertilizer	16	88	84	55	98	99	55	98	99
insecticides	16	95	90	53	98	99	39	98	99
herbicides	2	16	16	3	5	4	2	21	21
straight row planting	31	98	98	64	100	100	70	98	99
hand weeding	98	2	98	98	2	98	100	5	100
rotary weeder	27	98	98	64	98	99	70	98	99
animal power	100	100	100	100	97	96	100	98	97
two-wheel tractors	0	0	0	0	2	2	0	2	2
sprayer	16	96	90	53	98	98	39	98	99
canal irrigation	0	0	0	77	98	98	84	98	100
pump irrigation	35	90	84	0	0	0	0	0	0
mechanical blower	4	94	88	2	53	52	4	96	94
dapog method	0	48	48	0	15	15	0	95	77
harvesting knife	0	80	80	0	85	85	0	76	76

Canipa used chemical fertilizer or insecticides. By the 1971 wet season, 88 percent were using chemical fertilizer and 95 percent were using insecticide. In Marcos, 55 percent were using chemical fertilizers and 53 percent insecticides before modern varieties. In 1971, 98 percent were using each practice. Use of chemical fertilizer and insecticide in Tab-ang was more or less at the same level as in Marcos both before and after the introduction of modern varieties. While the use of hand weeding decreased in all three villages, the use of rotary weeders and herbicides increased.

Although the modern varieties, because of their accompanying cultural requirements, may have encouraged more farmers to use the recommended practices, in Canipa the installation of irrigation pumps may have contributed to the large increase in number of users of the recommended practices. Of course, the promise of high yield from the modern varieties certainly influenced the decision to install the irrigation pumps.

CHANGES IN SOCIAL AND ECONOMIC VARIABLES

Most farmers grew less than a hectare of rice. During the time of the survey, two-thirds of the farmers in the area were share-tenants, one third were owner-operators, and a small proportion were leaseholders. The 50-50 sharing system was predominant, although there were other sharing systems such as 60-40, 65-35, and 70-30 (Table 7). Since the introduction of modern varieties an increase in 50-50 sharing occurred in Canipa and Tab-ang, and a slight decrease occurred in Marcos. This change could be attributed to the relatively high dependency on the

Table 7. Sharing of harvest before and after the introduction of modern varieties.

village	period	tenant-landowner shares reported by farmers (%)					no response (%)
		50–50	60–40	65–35	66–34	70–30	
Canipa	before	23	15	4	17	9	32
	after[a]	44	19	2	12	4	19
Marcos	before	53	5	0	5	11	26
	after	44	12	12	5	7	20
Tab-ang	before	27	6	6	7	9	45
	after	33	9	4	11	9	34

[a]1971/72 dry season.

Table 8. Farmer's share of harvest kept for family use and sold.

village	before modern varieties		1971 wet season sold			1971/72 dry season sold		
	kept	sold	kept	immediately	1 month later	kept	immediately	1 month later
Canipa	64	36	55	14	31	44	25	31
Marcos	62	38	60	33	7	52	19	29
Tab-ang	53	47	48	52	0	45	25	30

(heading spanning over the season columns: proportion (%))

help extended by the landlord to the tenant, in lieu of the easy availability of other sources of credit and other inputs in the area.

Farm size. Although the rice farms are very small in Leyte and inheritance practices encourage fragmentation of land, 13 percent of the farmers in Canipa and 1 percent in Tab-ang reported an increase in rice land area. In Canipa, the availability of irrigation permitted farmers to convert upland areas (planted to sweet potato and coconut) into rice fields.

Rice disposal. Before the introduction of modern varieties, farmers kept about 60 percent of their harvest share for family use and sold the rest. Farmers in Canipa retained the most for family use while farmers in Tab-ang kept the least (Table 8). In the 1971 wet season, only 54 percent of the farmer's share for all villages was kept for family use, the rest was sold. The rice was sold either immediately or 1 month or more after harvest. Postponing the sale of rice may mean that the farmer gets a better price for his produce as post-harvest supply declines, or it may mean better economic stability. It can also be an indication of ability to postpone gratification. In the 1971 wet season, 10 percent of the farmer's share was sold 1 month after harvest. The largest portion of the farmer's share sold 1 month later was in Canipa (Table 8). In Tab-ang, the farmer's share was marketed entirely within the first month after harvest.

During the 1971/72 dry season a big change occurred. Overall, the proportion retained for the family declined to 47 percent. Of the 53 percent sold, 30 percent was sold 1 month later and only 23 percent was sold immediately. Even the farmers in Tab-ang sold 30 percent of their share 1 month or more after harvest.

Table 9. Distribution of farms by source of credit, cash, and kind.

source	Canipa		Marcos		Tab-ang	
	1971 wet season	1971/72 dry season	1971 wet season	1971/72 dry season	1971 wet season	1971/72 dry season
cash loans						
private moneylender	40	50	91	85	95	87
landlord	27	27	3	6	0	3
relative and others	26	11	6	9	3	10
rural bank	7	8	0	0	2	0
cooperatives	0	4	0	0	0	0
loans in kind						
private lender	50	11	0	15	86	31
landlord	0	67	0	66	14	35
relative and others	50	11	0	8	0	30
cooperative	0	11	0	11	0	4

The good price for rice in 1972 may have encouraged the farmers to sell more of their rice share than before. This points to a changing attitude — that of regarding rice as a cash crop in contrast with the traditional view of rice growing for family consumption alone.

Credit. The sources of credit and the proportion of farmers using them seemed not to have changed. The private moneylender and the landlord still predominated. In Canipa, however, there was a noticeable increase in the number of farmers using the rural bank and the cooperative between the 1971 wet season and the 1971/72 dry season (Table 9). The amount of credit used by the farmers also increased between the two seasons (Table 10). If increased credit means more production inputs and therefore more yield, this trend towards bigger credit has positive value.

Labor use and costs. Farmers' views of the labor requirement of the modern varieties in comparison with that of local varieties was not clear-cut. Most farmers thought that the new rice technology required as much or more of all kinds of labor (Table 11). Few thought that modern varieties had made labor requirement smaller. As long as the added labor pays off, and as long as there is farm labor surplus, the

Table 10. Amount of credit per hectare used in the 1971 wet season and 1971/72 dry season.

village	amount borrowed (₱/ha)			
	wet season		dry season	
	cash	in kind	cash	in kind
Canipa	104	47	155	100
Marcos	111	0	139	128
Tab-ang	182	55	172	80

added labor requirement is good for the economy. The cost of labor has nearly doubled for all job operations excluding harvesting (Table 12).

Land values. Another indicator of the impact of the new rice technology is its influence on the value of land. While little land has changed hands in the area, it is nonetheless clear from the responses of the majority of farmers that land values have risen dramatically:

	Canipa	*Marcos*	*Tab-ang*
1965	₱ 2,600	₱ 2,701	₱ 3,737
1972	16,650	10,065	14,312

The fantastic increase suggests that many more people are attracted to the purchase of rice land than before. Just how much of this can be attributed to the influence of modern varieties is not possible to determine, but we think it is large.

CHANGE IN THE LEVEL OF LIVING

If the rice farmer has had a little more money to use since modern varieties were introduced, how did he spend it? About half of the farmers in the three villages reported an increase in food consumption and house improvement (Table 13). Fifty-seven percent reported payment of long-standing debts; in Tab-ang, 70 percent reported this. The primacy of such needs is clearly pointed out here. Purchase of farm implements, purchase of furniture and appliances, and education, were also given high priority. It seems that increased savings, purchase of motorcycles and bicycles, and investment in new enterprises are higher level needs that must wait until the more basic needs are fulfilled and and the income is much larger.

Table 11. Labor needed for modern varieties compared with that for local varieties.

labor source	farmers (%) reporting								
	Canipa			Marcos			Tab-ang		
	more	less	same	more	less	same	more	less	same
pre-harvest tasks									
family	32	6	34	45	2	33	23	14	34
hired from village	8	0	4	11	0	9	7	2	7
hired outside village	6	4	16	17	3	11	20	4	13
exchange labor within village	10	2	44	12	2	22	29	4	33
harvest tasks									
family	24	2	30	33	2	33	18	6	34
hired from village	2	0	6	7	3	10	7	4	5
hired outside village	0	2	18	9	0	5	9	2	11
exchange labor within village	12	6	40	18	2	24	25	5	39
exchange labor outside village	0	0	0	0	0	0	2	0	2

Table 12. Cost of labor by job operation before modern varieties were introduced and after (1971/72 dry season), average of three villages.

activity	laborer supplies	food supplied by farmer	cost (₱) before	after
land preparation	labor only[a]	no	83.00/ha	175.00/ha
plowing, harrowing, etc.	draft animals	yes	3.50/day	5.80/day
	draft animals	no	3.30/day	7.70/day
	machine	no	14.00/day	30.00/day
	labor only	yes	1.25/day	2.40/day
	labor only	no	1.25/day	3.00/day
pulling seedlings	labor only	no	0.01/bundle	0.015/bundle
	labor only	yes	1.40/day	2.40/day
	labor only	no	1.00/day	3.40/day
transplanting	labor only[a]	yes	44.00/ha	55.00/ha
	labor only	yes	1.20/day	2.10/day
	labor only	no	1.70/day	3.40/day
weeding	labor only[a]	yes	n.a.	30.00/ha
	rotary weeder	yes	1.40/day	2.30/day
	rotary weeder	no	1.90/day	3.40/day
	labor only	yes	1.30/day	2.00/day

Table 13. Changes in consumption and investments since the introduction of the modern varieties.

item	farmers (%) reporting		
	Canipa	Marcos	Tab-ang
increase in food consumption	61	49	48
house improvement	45	62	47
purchase of furniture and appliances	45	36	39
purchase of bicycles	8	0	0
purchase of motorcycle or scooter	0	0	13
purchase of farm implements	57	51	22
increase in savings	2	0	9
pay off long standing debts	49	53	70
new farm enterprises	2	1	2
educational expenditures	41	33	39

When the farmers in 1971 were asked how their yields, profits, and level of living compared with the period before the modern varieties, most did not report higher achievement (Table 14). If the yield figures and the reported improvements were correct, then these impressions may have been affected by their higher levels of expectations or perhaps by the tungro outbreak at the time of the survey.

CONCLUSION

No miraculous changes occurred in rice farming in these three villages in Leyte. But the adoption of modern varieties was rapid, comparatively higher yields were attained with modern varieties in general (although not in all cases), more farmers adopted more of the recommended rice production practices, the sharing arrangement tended to weigh more in favor of the landowner, many farmers reported some improvements in their socio-economic life. Little change occurred in the use of the different sources of credit although considerable changes were reported in labor requirements and the cost of labor about doubled since the introduction of the modern varieties. Farmers said the value of irrigated land increased considerably which makes acquisition of rice land by the small farmer even more difficult in a free land market.

Certainly the new rice technology created changes in the farmer himself, for it provided him with new learning experiences and stimulated

Table 14. Farmers' views of their yields, profits, and level of living for the period since the introduction of modern varieties compared with before.

village	rice yield			profits			level of living		
	higher	lower	same	higher	lower	same	higher	lower	same
Canipa	52	10	17	42	52	6	19	5	31
Marcos	32	41	12	18	80	2	2	78	20
Tab-ang	24	45	20	51	47	2	13	51	36

a greater willingness to try new things and new practices. The relatively rapid change in the variety used in the area suggests the increased innovativeness of the farmers. Furthermore, there was evidence that rice farmers were beginning to view rice as a cash crop, not merely a subsistence crop.

This study suggests the need for further investigation of certain questions. In spite of the high rate of adoption of recommended practices such as the application of fertilizer or the use of rotary weeders, the yield of the modern varieties did not reach the expected level. What might be lacking in the application of such practices? Adoption as a variable of change has two aspects — the act of using a recommended practice, and the quality with which the act was carried out. It has been much easier for us to observe the former than the latter. But, for example, if fertilizer is to be used efficiently and reward the user with a high return, it has to be the right fertilizer, in the right amount, applied at the right time, in the right combination with other production practices and inputs. Is it the right quantity of what is applied, as in the case of fertilizer, or is it the right use of these modern inputs that is the major obstacle?

PHILIPPINES

Hagonoy, Davao del Sur

James C. Stewart and Antonio B. Arellano

Whether farmers are really better off since the introduction of
modern varieties is difficult to ascertain. Risk-avoidance appears to be important in explaining the low level of input use
and profits have been reduced by a series of poor harvests
culminating with the loss due to the tungro virus attack in the
dry season 1971/72. Despite this, farmers have generally increased consumption of goods in the period of adoption of
modern varieties, and are optimistic about the future.

MINDANAO HAS OFTEN BEEN CALLED the Philippines' land of promise.
Lured by the prospect of land, employment, and a better life, thousands
of immigrants have flocked to Mindanao during the past half-century.
For some, the promise has been fulfilled. For others, their hopes and
dreams have yet to materialize. Indeed, in many cases, it seems the life
they have found in their new home may not be so different from what
they have left behind.

We studied farm conditions in an area of high tenancy in Southern
Mindanao. In particular, we attempted to determine the effects of
modern rice varieties on farm practices, farm returns, and the general
welfare of the people in this area.

Mindanao, the second largest island in the Philippines, is one of three
major regions into which the country is commonly divided. Historical,
cultural, demographic, and climatic factors have combined to make it
somewhat distinct from Luzon and the Visayas to the north.

About 1,913 streams of immigrants from Luzon and the Visayas
began entering Mindanao, some of them with government assistance.
With the exception of the years during World War II, the influx of
settlers has continued to the present. The pioneers from the north
cleared most of the arable land, and logging companies stripped away
much of the island's forest. Before the war, most of the new farmers

James C. Stewart and Antonio B. Arellano are members of the Faculty of the Social Sciences
Division at the Ateneo de Davao College, Davao City.

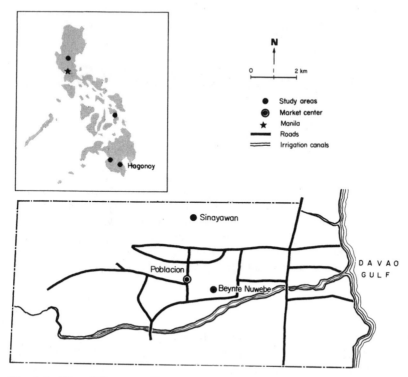

Municipality of Hagonoy, Davao del Sur Province.

planted corn, coconut, root crops, and a limited amount of rice. In the past 20 years or so, however, this cropping pattern has changed as more land has been brought under irrigation. The irrigated area in Mindanao is currently estimated to be 130,000 hectares.

The plantation sector has also developed rapidly in recent years. Much of the island has long been used for coconut plantations, but recently there has also been extensive development of pineapple, rubber, and banana plantations.

The province of Davao del Sur is located in the southeastern part of Mindanao on the west coast of Davao Gulf. The most fertile lands in the province lie in the Digos-Padada Valley, an area of approximately 700 sq m of coastal and river flood plains, piedmont, and low foothills. The valley is bordered on the northwest by Mount Apo, the Philippines' highest mountain, and on the southwest by the Alip Mountains. Between the two mountain ranges is a pass leading to Cotabato Province.

The municipality of Hagonoy, where this study was conducted, lies at the coastal end of the valley. It is 11 km south of Digos, the provincial capital, and 68 km south of Davao City, the largest urban

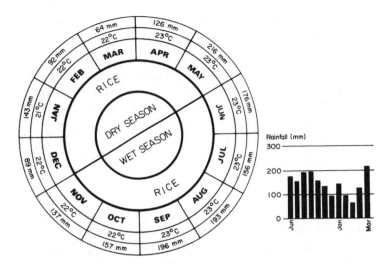

Average monthly rainfall and minimum temperature, Davao del Sur (Davao City, 1967-1971).

center in Mindanao. Hagonoy has several natural advantages for wet rice farming. Most of the soil within the municipality is San Miguel silty clay loam, a highly productive soil for rice. This part of Mindanao is south of the typhoon belt (although typhoons occur from time to time) and it has no pronounced wet or dry season. The area receives 1,500 to 1,750 mm of rainfall annually. Rain is generally heavier in the months from May to September, averaging 150 to 200 mm or more per month but in most years farmers can rely on 60 mm of rain even during the driest month, March.

Hagonoy is crossed by the two major rivers in the valley — the Balutakay and the larger Padada River. In 1953, the National Irrigation Administration began to develop the Padada River for irrigation. This system now serves 1,241 hectares, nearly all of which is planted to rice. Hagonoy was selected for study because it seems fairly representative of areas served by small-scale, recently developed irrigation systems scattered throughout Mindanao. These systems may seem small by many standards, but taken together, they make up the 130,000 hectares of the irrigated area in Mindanao. Assuming that these systems may have their counterparts in pioneer areas elsewhere in the Philippines and Asia, it seems essential to have information on such areas to understand the situation of a very large number of farmers who, taken collectively, farm a very substantial amount of land.

The municipality of Hagonoy is a typical agricultural town. Although it can be reached by public utility vehicles, it still has to contend with the problem of bad roads. As an interior town, business activity is rather slow. The major agricultural crops are rice, corn, sugarcane, and coconut. Two big coconut plantations are located in the municipality and a sugar central has been in operation since 1971.

The villages. Sinayawan and Beynte Nuwebe, the two villages selected for this study, are typical of the rice growing villages in Hagonoy in several respects. Among the similarities are basic rice technology, varieties grown, access to irrigation water, availability of inputs, and credit and marketing facilities. The two villages may have slight advantages in their accessibility to both the town proper and to the provincial capital, and transportation may be better for both people and farm products. On the other hand, these villages are located at the lower end of the irrigation system which accentuates problems of water management and especially of drainage. They are also adjacent to two large coconut plantations, giving them the advantage of off-season employment, but, at the same time, the disadvantage of competing for available labor during peak farming activities such as planting and harvesting.

The two villages are connected to the *poblacion* (municipal center) and to the national highway by unpaved roads, most of which are passable by jeep except after heavy rains. Communications are good, many persons have transistor radios and several telegraph offices are located in nearby Digos. Newspapers are available on the day of publication in Digos for those who can afford to buy them. There is no public electricity in Hagonoy, although some houses have their own generators. In the study villages, houses are along the roads, but otherwise dispersed. Small groups of houses are located here and there and occasionally a house is isolated from its neighbors by several hundred meters of rice fields.

Much of the land in Hagonoy was originally acquired in parcels of 24 hectares under the Homestead Act. The land has since been divided through sale or inheritance. In 1972, the 118 hectares of irrigated rice land in Beynte Nuwebe were owned by 15 individuals with an average holding of 8 hectares. In Sinayawan, 175 hectares were owned by 76 individuals whose average holding was 3 hectares. These averages obscure the concentration of ownership. In Beynte Nuwebe, five individuals with holdings of 20 hectares or more owned nearly 80 percent of the land. In Sinayawan, 11 individuals whose average holding was 8 hectares owned more than half the land.

The construction of the irrigation system in the early 1950's brought about significant change in land use in Hagonoy. Previously most of the farm area in the municipality was planted to corn and coconut. A scatter of these coconut trees is still visible in the present rice farms. Rice cultivation in the area expanded only after the opening of the irrigation system.

Most farmers in both sample villages were migrants. Only 13 percent were born in Mindanao. The majority had lived in the region for 10 to 30 years. In Beynte Nuwebe, most of the migrant-farmers came from the Visayas — Ilongo speakers from the islands of Panay and Negros, and Cebuano speakers from Cebu. Sinayawan had a more mixed group — a quarter from the Ilocos Region of Luzon and another half from the Visayas. In the Philippines, the Ilocano has the folk image of being a frugal, hardworking, astute, and efficient farmer. On the other hand, the "Visayan," a broader ethno-linguistic category, is viewed generally as fun-loving, easy-going, fatalistic, and correspondingly adapted to the less rigorous occupation of corn farming.

On typical farms in Hagonoy the dry-season crop is usually planted between December and February, and the wet-season crop between June and August. This flexibility in planting reflects the lack of pronounced seasons and the general availability of irrigation water. Most farms begin their land preparation by hiring a hand tractor to plow their fields at least one way, and sometimes, two ways. The remaining preparation, usually including two or three harrowings, is done by carabao. Transplanting is done with the aid of hired labor, mostly from within the village. The daily wage for these laborers has been ₱2.50 plus food, coffee, and bread in the morning, rice and sidedishes for lunch, and coffee and bread again in the afternoon. Sometimes transplanting is done with use of a marking board, making the plants approximate a linear pattern in one direction.

Farmers generally visit their farms daily but care of the growing plants is mainly limited to weeding unless insects or signs of disease appear. Hand weeding is usually supplemented by the use of herbicides. Topdressing with fertilizer is rare. Farmers own or have access to sprayers and chemicals and they consult with agriculturists as well as with each other about the most effective sprays to use, but most farmers have had inadequate resources for the proper chemicals. Because of this, there is little preventive spraying and even when outbreaks of disease occur, application of chemicals is usually insufficient. Also, the farmers' use of insecticide and herbicide and other chemicals was reported to have had some negative effects — poisoning of livestock, nausea on the part of the farm laborers, damage to rice stalks, and the stunting of the rice plant's growth.

Harvesting is done by hand, with the aid of labor drawn mostly from within the village. The common share for harvesters is one bundle in every twelve harvested. These bundles, however, are of different sizes and the farmers interviewed could not estimate the volume of rough rice per harvested bundle.

The sample. During the first-round survey covering the 1971/72 dry season 93 heads of households in Sinayawan and 66 in Beynte Nuwebe were interviewed. Several household heads — about 10 percent of those in the two villages — were eliminated from the original random sample on the basis of occupation or because they had moved into the barrios too recently to be included. Another 10 percent of the original sample were not interviewed due to evasion or nonavailability. During the 1972 wet season, some farmers interviewed in the first round could not be located. Hence, during the second round survey, additional farms were picked at random to replace those that were unavailable and to make the number of interviews equal in each village for both seasons.

The high rates of tenancy in these villages have already been noted. Since the two villages are adjacent to each other, and have similar physical resources, it is not surprising that they differ little in most characteristics (Table 1). All of the area planted to rice was under irrigation and double cropped. All of the rice area, which accounts for over 90 percent of the farm area, was planted to modern varieties in the survey year.

THE ADOPTION OF MODERN VARIETIES

The first of the modern varieties planted in Hagonoy farms was IR8 which reached the farmers through the local farmers' cooperative in 1967 when the variety, popularly known as "miracle rice," was introduced on a national scale for the first time. Prior to the introduction of IR8, the rice farmers in Hagonoy were planting and experimenting with the Philippine seedboard varieties such as Peta, Intan, and Tjeremas. Farmers seem to have been particularly successful with Peta. Making allowance for difficulties of recall, it appears that before 1967, yields of 2.9 t/ha were common for Peta. This yield was much better than that for older varieties though it was nearly doubled by the yield of IR8 during the first season of its adoption. The subsequent experience with the modern varieties has been mixed. At the time of the first round survey, the farmers in Hagonoy had tried IR5, IR20, IR22, IR24, BPI-76, C4-63, and C4-63G.

All the farmers during this study period were planting modern varieties. IR20 was planted on 70 percent of the farms. Other varieties were IR5, IR8, IR22, IR24, and C4. Since the introduction of IR8, other

Table 1. Characteristics of sample farms.

village	farms (no.) in village	farms (no.) in sample	persons in household (no.)	farm size (ha)	share tenants (%)	owner-cultivators (%)
Sinayawan	103	93	7	2.2	86	14
Beynte Nuwebe	73	66	6	1.7	92	8

	rice area				
	per farm (ha) wet season	per farm (ha) dry season	double cropped (%)	irrigated (%)	principal form of irrigation
Sinayawan	1.9	1.9	100	100	canal
Beynte Buwebe	1.7	1.7	100	100	canal

	modern varieties				
	farmers using (%) wet season	farmers using (%) dry season	rice area planted (%) wet season	rice area planted (%) dry season	year of greatest adoption
Sinayawan	100	100	100	100	1967
Beynte Nuwebe	100	100	100	100	1968

modern varieties were adopted but later dropped for one reason or another. The use of IR 8 was ended because farmers found it highly susceptible to diseases and because it commanded a relatively low market price primarily because of its poor eating quality. High susceptibility to diseases was among the major reasons farmers gave for discontinuing the use of some of the other new strains and of the Philippine seedboard varieties.

Some farmers seemed to find no differences among the various rice varieties, which suggests a peculiar system in seed selection. In general, farmers apparently have followed what the leading farmers decided to plant. These leading farmers were usually the owner-cultivators. The owner-cultivators had less difficulties than tenants in financing farm operations and they were also usually the ones who produced the "good seeds" which were used when "certified seeds" were unavailable. This "following-the-leader" system was rather informal and implicit. Although the tenants maintained that they decided what variety to use, their seemingly independent decisions were actually a reflection of previous ones made by the owner-cultivators or the leading farmers.

Most farmers, 101 out of 159, considered IR 20 the best variety for both the dry and the wet seasons. The selection of IR 20 as "best" for both seasons may result from the reliable supply of irrigation water and the absence of pronounced wet and dry season in the study area, and from the successive poor crops which occurred before the 1971/72 dry season. And in the 1971/72 dry season a tungro virus epidemic struck. IR 20 was the most tungro resistant of all the new strains available. Peta was also considered as highly resistant to diseases and insects and also to drought. Both IR 20 and IR 5 were considered good varieties when droughts, floods, or typhoons occurred. Because of the advice given by agricultural technicians, the practice of the owner-cultivators, and the farmers' own experiences with various varieties, most farmers during the 1972 wet season planted IR 20. Other varieties planted included IR 5, IR 22, IR 24, and C 4.

YIELD PERFORMANCE AND FARM PRACTICES

Generally, the 1972 wet-season harvest was much better than the 1971/72 dry-season harvest due undoubtedly to less damage from tungro virus. The average yield for both villages was about 2.5 t/ha in the dry season and 2.9 t/ha in the wet season. These yields (Table 2) are based upon figures reported by farmers. A known source of error, one which may be common elsewhere as well, is that farmers frequently fail to include the harvesters' share when stating their total yield. Given the prevailing harvester's share of 1 in 12, this could lead to a considerable underestimation of yield.

During the 1971/72 dry season, nearly half the farmers in both villages produced less than 2.4 t/ha (Table 3). Only 14 percent reported above 3.5 t/ha. During the wet season, one quarter reported below 2.4 t/ha while another quarter reported yields above 3.5 t/ha.

In the villages studied, different ethnic groups were farming under identical economic and ecological conditions and their performance seems to indicate no relation between cultural differences and actual productivity (Table 2). In Sinayawan, the Ilocano and Ilongo farmers produced an average of 2.6 t/ha while the Cebuanos reported 2.3 t/ha (Ilongos and Cebuanos constitute the "Visayans"). In Beynte Nuwebe, the Ilongos produced an average yield of 3 t/ha while the Cebuanos had an average yield of around 2.9 t/ha. Obviously the difference in the average yields is not significant. In fact nothing conclusive can be deduced from this information for various reasons. The dry-season harvest was greatly affected by the tungro epidemic which caught the

Table 2. Yields, 1971/72 dry season and 1972 wet season.

village	all farms		by ethnic groups in dry season			by tenure status			
						tenant		owner	
	dry season	wet season	Ilocano	Ilongo	Cebuano	dry season	wet season	dry season	wet season
Sinayawan	2.3	2.6	2.6	2.7	2.3	2.2	2.8	2.4	3.5
Beynte Nuwebe	2.7	3.3	n.a.[a]	3.0	2.9	2.8	3.3	2.7	6.1

yield (t/ha)

[a]Not applicable.

Table 3. Distribution of yields, 1971/72 dry season and 1972 wet season.

yield category (t/ha)	farms (%)					
	Sinayawan		Beynte Nuwebe		both	
	dry season	wet season	dry season	wet season	dry season	wet season
4.8 − 6.0	4	5	9	11	6	8
3.6 − 4.7	4	13	12	29	8	19
2.4 − 3.5	34	47	49	50	40	47
1.2 − 2.3	43	28	21	11	33	22
under 1.2	15	7	10	0	13	4

farmers by surprise, resulting in heavy losses to almost all of them. Thus, comparing and relating productivity differences to cultural differences among these ethnic groups at this point could at best be informative but hardly conclusive.

Another yield comparison was made between owner-cultivators and share tenants. In the wet season, the owner cultivators, who account for 10 percent of the total sample, had an average yield of 4.2 t/ha. The share-tenants' yield was 3.0 t/ha. This difference could be attributed to differences in financing capacity. Lack of capital hindered the tenant farmers from using adequate amounts of the required inputs such as fertilizer and chemicals as well as additional labor for the necessary regular hand weeding. In Sinayawan, the farmers with the highest average yields used ₱88/ha of fertilizer and ₱99/ha of insecticides. Those in Beynte Nuwebe applied ₱95/ha of fertilizer and ₱146/ha of insecticides. On the other hand, farmers with yields under 2.4 t/ha used much lower rates of application − in Sinayawan, ₱22/ha of fertilizer and ₱49/ha of insecticides; in Beynte Nuwebe, ₱23/ha of fertilizer and ₱41/ha of insecticides.

Farmers reported that the yields of the modern varieties had declined considerably since IR8 was first planted. Whether the decline was due to the recent disease and weather problems or other factors as well was unclear. The decrease, however, was associated with a decline in fertilizer users (Table 4).

Fertilizer. Compared with the period before modern varieties, fertilizer use had increased, but many farmers in both villages applied no fertilizer at all (Tables 4 and 5). Yields of users and non-users were not significantly different, however (Table 5).

Table 4. Changes in farm practices.

period	farmers reporting (%) use of						
	chemical fertilizer	insecticide	herbicide	straight-row planting	mechanical weeder	two-wheel tractor	mechanical thresher
				Sinayawan			
before 1967	10	46	45	16	0	9	7
1967[a]	77	95	89	32	0	49	62
1971/72 dry season	41	100	97	17	0	87	96
1972 wet season	53	100	95	n.a.	0	71	97
				Beynte Nuwebe			
before 1967	19	64	67	25	0	14	7
1967[a]	62	100	100	46	0	52	86
1971/72 dry season	39	100	99	18	0	73	94
1972 wet season	65	100	99	n.a.	0	71	100

[a]Year modern varieties were first introduced.

During the 1972 wet season, the number of farmers using fertilizer increased. In the wet season the average production loan in both villages was much larger than in the dry season:

	season	amount borrowed	source
Sinayawan	dry	₱187	dealer
	wet	314	dealer
Beynte Nuwebe	dry	227	moneylender
	wet	320	rural bank

Since the 1971/72 dry-season harvest was greatly affected by tungro, most of the farm expenses for the wet season probably were financed through credit. These expenditures include the amount spent for fertilizer. The data seem to indicate that the farmers borrowed more money and spent more of it for fertilizer than in the previous season.

This change from the dry season to the wet season can be explained in part by the opening of the Rural Bank in Hagonoy in 1972 which issued loans to farmers at an interest rate of 6 percent payable every harvest. This made borrowed capital relatively cheaper and the burden lighter to many farmers. In addition, fertilizer prices dropped after the dry-season harvest from ₱34 per bag of urea to ₱29 per bag. Similar decreases occurred in the prices of the other types of fertilizer.

Labor saving practices and labor use. Accompanying a rise in the use of yield-increasing inputs such as new seeds, fertilizer, and insecticides, has been an increase in the use of potentially labor-saving technology — herbicides, hand tractors, and threshers (Table 4). Farmers regarded the use of the thresher and hand tractors as the most labor-saving of the

Table 5. Fertilizer use, 1971/72 dry season and 1972 wet season.

village	season	avg use (kg/ha)			yield (t/ha)	
		N	P_2O_5	K_2O	users	non-users
Sinayawan	dry	16	n.a.	n.a.	2.4	2.3
	wet	10	0.7	0.4	2.8	2.4
Beynte Nuwebe	dry	16	n.a.	n.a.	2.8	2.7
	wet	33	25.0	13.0	3.6	2.8

practices adopted (Table 6). Use of sprayers was considered the most labor-increasing practice.

Most respondents felt that the adoption of new strains increased the the amount of labor hired (from within the village) for both pre-harvest and harvesting and threshing tasks (Table 7). Many farmers indicated they used less family labor for both pre-harvest and harvest tasks, no doubt because of the introduction of hand tractors and mechanical threshers.

FARM INCOME

Based on estimated rice production costs and returns for the wet season (Table 8), the income in Beynte Nuwebe was larger than that in Sina-yawan mainly due to higher yield. But the net return in both villages is relatively low. A return of ₱400/ha, for example, would be equivalent to approximately 20 sacks (44 kg/sack) of rough rice. Probably 25 or

Table 6. Changes in labor requirements following the introduction of the modern varieties, 1971/72 dry season.

| use of | farmers reporting (%) | | | |
| | Sinayawan | | Beynte Nuwebe | |
	family labor	hired labor	family labor	hired labor
	labor-reducing practices			
thresher	28	68	23	59
tractor	58	42	54	65
hired labor	2	0	3	0
fertilizer	1	1	4	4
sprayer	2	2	3	2
herbicide	8	2	9	9
sickle	8	15	0	0
	labor-increasing practices			
sprayer	43	22	82	68
fertilizer	3	3	6	4
hand weeding	5	1	50	45
herbicide	1	0	4	4
insecticide	3	0	4	4
modern varieties	12	8	3	3

Table 7. Change in use of farm labor after adoption of modern varieties.

labor source	farmers reporting[a] (%)					
	Sinayawan			Beynte Nuwebe		
	more	less	same	more	less	same
	pre-harvest tasks					
family	46	29	15	35	6	46
hired within village	73	5	10	50	3	32
hired outside village	5	13	10	3	0	3
exchange	39	19	13	9	2	39
	harvesting and threshing					
family	15	64	5	21	6	52
hired within village	56	30	2	48	5	30
hired outside village	6	10	9	0	2	3
exchange	26	20	12	17	3	36

[a] Rows do not add up to 100 percent because of non-response.

30 sacks would be needed just to meet the annual rice requirements of a family of six or seven. The farm income from two crops of rice on 1.8 hectares would be about three times the amount needed to meet the rice consumption requirements for the family.

One explanation of this low rate of return was the prevailing price of rough rice *(palay)*. Generally, during the wet-season harvest, the price of rough rice was ₱0.47/kg or ₱20.68 for every sack of 44 kilos. This low selling price could also be due to the prevailing practice of selling immediately after harvest. The government support price of ₱25 per sack was not implemented in the area for lack of funds.

Over 40 percent of the farmers said that their households' income was supplemented from sources other than rice farming. In Sinayawan, the farmers reported an average household income from other sources of of ₱1,759 in 1971. In Beynte Nuwebe, the reported outside income was ₱1,666. The household members who had other sources of income included the farmer himself, his wife, daughter, son, and brother. The other sources of income included livestock raising, retail store business, income from tractor and thresher operation, public school teaching, work in coconut plantation, rice mill business, office employment, work in a fishpond, and corn farming.

Sugarcane was a potential source of income, especially in Beynte

Table 8. Production costs and returns (₱/ha), 1972 wet season.

Item	Sinayawan	Beynte Nuwebe
land preparation	56	83
seed	46	49
pulling seedlings	55	47
transplanting	96	73
fertilizer	32	35
insecticides	39	65
herbicide	16	14
handweeding	6	14
harvesters' share[a]	108	130
threshing	96	113
hauling	3	4
landowner's share	279	392
debt payment	41	50
irrigation fee	16	17
total costs	889	1086
gross return	1222	1551
net return	333	465

[a]Harvesters' share estimate is based on the 1:12 sharing ratio. Sacks of rough rice (*palay*) converted to pesos using the standard 44 kg per sack and the most common price of ₱0.47 per kilogram of *palay*.

Nuwebe. Some farmers had decided to shift from rice to sugar. The effect of this decision on other farmers could not be determined, but according to the farmers, sugarcane offers a ₱4,000/ha net return annually, a rather attractive figure compared with the ₱400/ha per harvest of rice or an annual net return of ₱800/ha.

FARM PROBLEMS

The reported yields were relatively low given the potential of the modern varieties. Tungro disease may have reduced the yield of IR 20 and it certainly reduced the yield of the other varieties which were more susceptible. Added to this are the general disease and insect problems rice farmers face. The majority of farmers identified disease and insect factor as a production constraint in both the dry and wet seasons (Table

9). Another problem was the extremely limited use of fertilizer. In the dry season, farmers in the two villages used an average of only 16 kg/ha N and only 40 percent of all farmers applied fertilizer. Furthermore, only five of the 159 sample farmers applied 70 kg/ha N or more. The use of chemicals such as herbicides and insecticides was also negligible. In fact, during the dry season, more than half the farmers had difficulty obtaining fertilizer and chemicals (Table 9).

Input use. Since the performance of the modern varieties is greatly determined by the extent the required technology is applied, the farmers' use of inputs such as fertilizer and chemicals is disturbing. One possible explanation is that the 1972 wet season followed on the heels of successive crop losses due to typhoon damage, rat infestation, and the tungro epidemic. All the farmers surveyed experienced losses from one or more of these causes. These poor crops taxed farmers' financial resources and some had exhausted their credit. Another closely related reason is that tenant farmers felt they were shouldering too much of the risks of production. They complained that most of the landlords did not share the costs of certified seeds, fertilizer, and farm chemicals, yet

Table 9. Production problems 1971/72 dry season and 1972 wet season.

problem	farmers reporting (%)					
	Sinayawan			Beynte Nuwebe		
	before 1967	dry season	wet season	before 1967	dry season	wet season
obtaining seed	8	17	5	29	38	24
obtaining fertilizer and chemicals	13	26	15	44	76	45
obtaining credit	19	41	20	35	44	30
irrigation	8	23	0	15	24	24
disease-insects	40	84	61	79	95	88
harvesting	2	3	1	0	0	0
threshing	5	6	0	3	3	0
hauling	11	25	0	9	12	0
drying	6	8	0	0	0	0
storage	2	16	0	2	0	0
selling	1	1	0	11	15	0
processing	4	5	0	0	0	0

they reaped their usual share of any additional production resulting from these inputs. The tenants had to absorb most of the losses during the previous several seasons and they were obviously growing tired of it.

The farmers also seemed to be developing a pattern of "risk-avoidance." Evidence of this is the gradual decline in expenditures for inputs from 1970 to 1972. This is especially apparent in their conservative use of fertilizer and pesticides. It is also indicated by the desire that several farmers expressed to return to using Peta as their main variety. Peta, which requires fewer inputs than the dwarf varieties, was producing pre-1967 yields comparable to those currently being realized from the modern varieties. The farmers remember that Peta had a fairly high resistance to disease, a prime consideration after the experience with tungro, and it certainly required less care than the new strains. But they may have forgotten some of Peta's weaknesses, among them its susceptibility to lodging. If poor harvests continue, more and more farmers may develop attitudes of conservatism and "risk avoidance" which could be a major barrier to further agricultural development. •

Credit. As previously observed, the low use of fertilizer also reflects poor supply and inadequate credit. Over 40 percent of the farmers indicated that credit was a difficulty in the dry season (Table 9). This could be expected from rice farming in areas where most of the inputs are acquired through cash outlays. In addition, the services from institutional sources of financing were inadequate. Most of the production credit of the farmers in the two villages was supplied by the rice dealers or a private moneylender, at varied terms of payment. The opening of the. Rural Bank in Hagonoy in 1972 seems to have relieved the credit problem somewhat in the wet season (Table 9).

The most common rates of credit repayment were 100 kg of rough rice for every ₱100 borrowed, or two sacks for every ₱100 loan, in both cases payable every harvest (Table 10). If a sack of rough rice can sell at the government support price, ₱25 per sack, then the rate of interest for every ₱100 loan goes as high as about 50 percent every 6 months. Some dealers also lend money without interest but the farmer-borrower must sell his rice exclusively to the dealer. Usually this arrangement is supplemented by other forms of relationships like friendship, the *"paisano"* relationship of being of the same ethnic group, or the *"kumpadre* system" or being a sponsor in either a baptism or wedding.

Over half of the farmers interviewed were unwilling to use additional credit even if it were available (Table 11). This observation could reinforce the idea of "risk-avoidance" among farmers. But the farmers might have seen no sense in spending more for the farm operation since

Table 10. Rate of interest on cash loans, dry season.

interest rate	farmers reporting (%)	
	Sinayawan	Beynte Nuwebe
100 kg rough rice per ₱100/harvest	31	3
2 sacks of rough rice per ₱100/harvest	3	27
3 sacks of rough rice for every ₱100/harvest	4	6
20% every harvest	5	17
12% every harvest	3	3
10% every harvest	0	4
6% every harvest	0	4
5% every harvest	0	2
5% every month	3	0
no interest	27	14

the cost of capital was high and the possibility of events such as the tungro epidemic would only make additional investment futile. Nonetheless, the farmers' volume of loans in the 1971/72 dry season was much greater than in the pre-1967 period with the burden of repayment having similarly increased. This probably was due to the shift of varieties from the traditional low-input-requiring varieties to the high-yielding but high-input-requiring strains.

Staggered plantings. Another serious farm management problem in Hagonoy was the lack of a coordinated planting schedule. Locally, this was known as the problem of "staggered planting." There is no pronounced wet and dry season in Davao del Sur, so the agricultural calendar is not strongly influenced by climatic factors. The entire area studied is irrigated, shortage of water is rare, so water is always potentially available to the farmers. This fact combined with the short maturation period of the high yielding varieties, has led many farmers to replant their land as quickly as possible after harvest. They probably have been encouraged to do this by the availability of hand tractors to assist them in land preparation. The speed of "hurry-up" land preparation, as they termed it, varied from farmer to farmer, even between neighbors. This was particularly true where some farmers had money to hire tractors while others had to rely on their carabaos or where only a

Table 11. Production credit.

item	farmers reporting[a] (%)	
	Sinayawan	Beynte Nuwebe
borrowed money for production	49	55
would not use more credit if available	56	70
would use more credit if available	44	28
would use added credit for production	43	26
borrowings, 1972 vs. 1967[b]		
more	34	23
less	6	11
same	17	15
repayment burden, 1972 vs. 1967[b]		
more	34	23
less	6	11
same	17	15

[a]Interviewed in 1971/72 dry season. [b]Does not add up to 100 percent because of non-applicability of question.

limited number of tractors were available to service a large number of farmers.

As a result, in a single contiguous area, rice plants were in virtually all stages of development. Farmers only short distances apart might be preparing land, transplanting, weeding, or spraying their half-grown plants or harvesting, all at the same time. Naturally, this has created a problem of water management, and may lead to conflicts between neighboring farmers. It also has greatly increased the problems of pest and disease control, and it may have affected the availability of additional manpower during the critical periods of transplanting and harvesting. The farmers themselves recognized staggered planting as one of their most serious problems and considered the solution rather difficult.

Extension. Extension services and farmers' organizations were two other problems. A municipal agriculturist and two agents of the Agricultural Productivity Commission were assigned to work with farmers in Hagonoy. The farmers said that these extension workers visited them infrequently, although they saw the municipal agriculturist more often than the APC agent whose office was in Digos. A common criticism was that the extension agents visited farms along the main roads but seldom went to the fields or to the less accessible farms. Even those farmers who were visited complained that there was little depth to the inquiries of the extension personnel which were often limited to the "how are things?" level of discourse.

The one active farmer organization was the Hagonoy Producers Cooperative Marketing Association, Inc. It was organized in 1967 to cooperatively market farm products, especially rice, and to provide services including trucking, milling, warehousing, and a cooperative store. It was the local channel for farm loans extended by the Agricultural Credit Administration.

The original membership was 143. In 1972, there were 258 members of which only 50 were listed as active. This points to the chief difficulty of the organization, which was described as lack of support from the membership. The cooperative's officials said farmers needed education about the cooperative and its operations and objectives. Other major problems cited were the cooperative's low volume of business and the failure of the first phase of the loan program due to rat infestation which destroyed much of the crop. To overcome some of these difficulties, the cooperative planned an educational drive among farmers and closer coordination with other government agencies. With regard to loans, beginning in June 1972, it extended funds to groups of 5 to 10 farmers who as a group shared liability and responsibility for repayment.

LAND TENURE

Although the Department of Agrarian Reform had been conducting a series of seminars on land reform in Hagonoy, there was no significant change in the tenure arrangement governing the two villages. In Sinayawan, 85 percent were still tenants while in Beynte Nuwebe the tenancy rate was 91 percent. It was expected, however, that before the end of 1973, most of the land in the area would be converted to leasehold.

The majority of the farmers questioned favored the shift from tenancy to the leasehold system. The main reason was the consequential increase in the farmer's share of the farm output. Also, many considered the shift as a form of independence. With leasehold, the farmers felt they would no longer be bound to the landowner beyond the payment of the fixed rental. Under the existing tenancy system, the farmers felt obliged to perform services and tasks other than those required by rice

Table 12. Benefits and expenditures, 1971/72 dry season compared with before modern varieties were introduced.

item	farmers reporting[a] (%)					
	Sinayawan			Beynte Nuwebe		
	higher	lower	same	higher	lower	same
rice profits	23	58	12	30	42	15
level of living	18	27	45	29	26	29
expectations of income next						
5 years	45	38	17	80	14	6
expenditures for						
food consumption	70	0	30	74	0	4
education	39	0	44	45	0	26
clothing	56	0	40	80	0	3
repayment of long-term debt	48	0	50	59	0	30

[a] Rows do not add up to 100 percent because of non-response.

farming, such as providing household help or being a driver. Some preferred the shift merely because it was decreed by the government.

On the other hand, some farmers preferred the existing system to leasehold. They felt that the leasehold system would open farmers to more risk than tenancy. Under the existing system, the "rental" was relative to yield — in case of crop failure, the landowner suffered along with the tenant. Under the leasehold system, some farmers contended that regardless of the outcome of the harvest, the rental is fixed and the loss is entirely the farmer's loss. Another reason for preferring the existing tenure arrangement was the "special relationship" between the tenants and landowners as friends or relatives. Some tenants also regarded their landlords as kind and considerate and felt that supporting the shift to leasehold would be ingratitude.

EFFECTS ON INCOME AND GENERAL WELFARE

In the 1971/72 dry season, farmers were asked to compare their level of living to that in the period before the introduction of the modern varieties. The largest group found no difference at all (Table 12). About a quarter of the farmers felt that the present was relatively better and another quarter reported just the opposite. More than half of the farmers found their rice production profits much lower than before the

Table 13. Purchases between 1967 and 1971/72 dry season.

item	farmers purchasing (%)	
	Sinayawan	Beynte Nuwebe
radio	66	67
sewing machine	18	35
wardrobe	4	35
dining room set	1	21
bicycle	28	32
motorcycle	2	6
tractor/farm implements	40	12

introduction of modern varieties. Among the reasons given were infestation (disease, pests, insects), higher costs of production inputs, and increases in overall levels of prices. But those who considered the present as relatively better gave reasons such as higher yields, increases in the market price of rice, and additional income from other sources.

Whether the farmers are really better off since the introduction of modern varieties is difficult to ascertain. The 1971/72 dry-season crop was rather disastrous, primarily because of the tungro epidemic, hence, the overall low level of living and profits. But the farmers' changes in food consumption, clothing expenditures, expenditures on household appliances, expenditures on education, and payment of long-term debts seem to indicate a different condition. Nearly three-fourths of the farmers said their consumption of food has increased and that most of the money spent came from rice farming. Similar increases were registered in clothing expenditures and spending for household appliances. Two-thirds had bought a radio and another quarter were able to acquire sewing machines through the use of rice farm income (Table 13). Some bought additional farm implements, others spent more to send children to high school and college, while others were even able to pay long-term debts.

All these changes in expenditures were made during the whole period after the modern varieties were introduced and are not confined to the dry season studied. The farmers' low profits and living levels could be due to the series of poor harvests. In spite of the losses, however, the farmers were optimistic and had bright hopes for the coming years. More than half were expecting their rice farm income to increase within the next 5 years.

PHILIPPINES

Pigcawayan, Cotabato

Eva Kimpo Tan

The nearly 100 percent adoption of modern rice varieties has been accompanied by a sharp rise in the use of insecticides, herbicides, and tractors. However, the level of fertilizer input and rice yields remain very low. This is attributed principally to inadequate irrigation facilities and extension services. The Muslim population occupied the poorest land area and received no aid from the government.

THE COTABATO REGION IN MINDANAO is known as a rice granary of the Philippines, second only to Central Luzon. The numerous rivers which criss-cross its plains and valleys are used for irrigation and transportation, but are also the source of destructive floods.

Three villages were selected for this study in the municipality of Pigcawayan. This municipality is representative of those in the region both socially, physically, and economically. It was only slightly affected by the trouble between Muslims and Christians that recently upset the region's economy. It is one of the biggest rice-producing areas and the one nearest Cotabato City, which is the major market and outlet for agricultural products.

One important objective of this study is to compare the adoption of modern rice technology by the predominant Christians and the Muslims who inhabit part of one of the three villages.

Geophysical environment. Pigcawayan's 450 square kilometers are divided into 36 barrios. Pigcawayan is bounded by mountains in the north and west, by the Rio Grande River in the south, and the Libungan River and marsh in the southeast. Almost two fifths of the area is flat, one-fifth is rolling, and the rest is mountainous.

Eva K. Tan is a member of the Faculty of the Socio-Economic Research Center, Notre Dame University, Cotabato City.

The author wishes to acknowledge the help extended by D. Silva in the analysis of the data; the government agencies of Cotabato, the municipal officials of Pigcawayan, Fr. E. Gonzales, and all the farmer respondents who cooperated with the survey team.

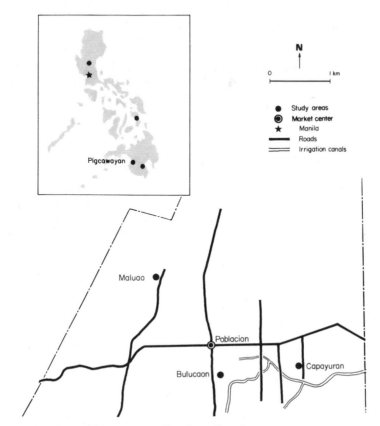

Municipality of Pigcawayan, Cotabato Province.

The soil is greatly influenced by the topography. In the south and east, the soil is dark brown to almost black, soft and slightly sticky when wet, friable when dry. Water retention is good, making the area susceptible to floods, but ideal for irrigation. In the west and upper central portion, the soil is dark gray to black — plastic and sticky when wet, hard when dry. Drainage is excessive externally, fair internally. Topography is rolling. Irrigation might be possible from the many streams and rivers of the area but dams are needed. Riverbed stabilization is also needed because rivers now shift course frequently. In the north, the soil is dark gray to light gray, slightly compact, coarse and granular clay loam. External drainage is excessive, internal drainage poor. This area has been exploited by lumber operators and slash-and-burn farmers *(kaingineros),* causing silting of riverbeds and floods in the southern portion during heavy rains. Pigcawayan, like most of Cotabato, has no dry season and no pronounced rainy season.

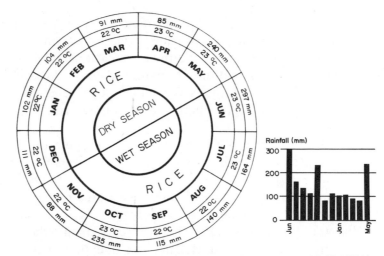

Average monthly rainfall (Midsayap Weather Station, 1967-1971) and minimum temperature (Weather Bureau, General Santos City, 1967-1971), Cotabato, Philippines.

Pigcawayan is 26 kilometers from Cotabato City. The national highway has some cemented portions but is mostly gravel. In the southern portion of Pigcawayan people prefer to use river transport on the Libungan River to Cotabato. The Libungan River is a major tributary of the Rio Grande which drains the basin into Illana Bay.

Four bus companies ply the Cotabato-Davao route and jeepneys are available from Cotabato City to Pigcawayan. Operations are suspended during the night due to unfavorable peace and order conditions, however. Within the municipality, motorized tricycles operate in the municipal center *(poblacion)* and the adjacent barrios. Pigcawayan has a post office and a government telecommunication. An electric plant was put up in 1965 by the municipal government but due to inefficient operation, the officials were planning to sell the franchise to a private company providing electricity to Cotabato City.

About 80 percent of the farmers own a radio. Cotabato City has three English-Tagalog stations which can be heard in Pigcawayan. National newspapers reach Pigcawayan every afternoon.

Socio-economic environment. The population of the municipality was 35,600 in 1970. Twenty percent are natives — Maguindanao, Iranon, and Manobo, and 80 percent are migrants — mostly from the island of Panay. Largely because of migration the average annual rate of population increase is 5.8 percent, which is much above the national average. The average farm household has six· members, which is similar to the national average.

Two-thirds of the population are farmers engaged in rice and corn production while the rest provide services to farmers – rice and corn processing, storage and marketing, educational and medical services, government, and recreation. On market days in Pigcawayan – Wednesday and Sunday – farmers from the south bring fish caught in the Libungan River to market and those from the north bring vegetables and crops.

There are 22 rice mills and 11 thresher operators. Several farmers own hand tractors, and many others rent tractors for land preparation. There are four dealers in farm inputs in the municipality and one farm machinery dealer. Small threshers are manufactured in the nearby municipalities of Libungan and Midsayap.

Farmers in Pigcawayan obtain credit from the rural banks of Cotabato, Midsayap, and Malang, but due to the time taken in processing loan applications, they prefer to borrow from the rice mill operators and the rice dealers. The rice mill operators charge 20 percent interest on loans. The rice dealers seldom charge interest but use credit as an instrument for controlling the marketing of rice. Those in debt to the dealers have no recourse but to sell their produce even if the price offered is very low. Due to difficulty in obtaining credit, cooperatives have been formed, both private and government. There are three cooperatives whose business is to give credit to farmer-members.

The government, aside from encouraging the formation of cooperatives, also has financed construction of multi-purpose pavements to barrios for drying rice and for recreation. Through the farm management technician of the Agricultural Productivity Commission (APC), modern methods of farming were introduced. The APC has a demonstration farm in Bulacan and the Bureau of Plant Industry has an experiment station in the nearby municipality of Midsayap. The biggest boost to farming has been the development of the Libungan River System. Floods caused by the river have been minimized and 12,000 hectares are now irrigated. The other areas serviced by the irrigation project are Libungan and Midsayap.

Religious and civic organizations also contribute to the improvement of agricultural practices and facilities. The most active is the Federation of Free Farmers which conduct seminars on scientific farming and the legal rights of farmers. The Notre Dame Social Action of the Catholic Church and the Cotabato Rural Uplift Movement of the Protestant Domination help in the formation of credit cooperatives and lending farm equipment.

Agricultural environment. As in all municipalities situated at the bottom of the Cotabato River basin, the major crop in Pigcawayan is rice. Forty percent or 8,815 hectares of the total land area of Pigcawayan is planted to rice with an average yield of 1.6 t/ha (which is slightly higher than the regional average of 1.4 t/ha). The second major crop is corn with an estimated 7,150 hectares yielding an average of 0.9 t/ha. Part of the 7,150 hectares classified as cornland is planted to rice during the wet season and to corn during the dry season.

The size of farms in the area varies with the tenure status of farmers and the availability of water. In areas with high incidence of tenancy, the total operated area averages about 2 hectares. Well-irrigated areas have smaller farms than the rainfed and marshy areas. The better irrigated farms, however, are those cultivated by tenants and are more intensively used for rice production.

There is no definite time for planting and harvesting in the area because of the absence of a pronounced wet and dry season and a well-programed irrigation system. Generally, two rice crops are grown in one year. Some fields are usually in the transplanting stage while the rest are still harvesting. This occurs not only among farmers but also within farms, but this pattern is more common in poorly irrigated or rainfed areas than in areas irrigated by the National Irrigation Administration.

The sample. The three barrios chosen for this study, Maluao, Bulucaon, and Capayuran, differ from each other in several ways. Maluao is rolling, Bulucaon is a choice area in the plains, and Capayuran is partly swampy. Maluao is partly rainfed and partly irrigated, Bulucaon is completely irrigated, and Capayuran is irrigated but flood prone. Bulucaon has much higher tenancy rates than Maluao and Capayuran (Table 1). Most of the population in the three villages is Christian, but a remote swampy portion of Capayuran is Muslim. Traditional varieties are still being used in the rainfed areas of Maluao while farmers in Bulucaon and Capayuran are 100 percent adopters of modern varieties (Table 1).

The most highly tenanted village, Bulucaon, has the most productive land. The population here is 100% Christians. Capayuran, which has also a high incidence of tenancy among the Christians, is partly populated by Muslims who claim to be owner-cultivators. Although they pay no rent, neither do they possess legal title to the land which they farm. These Muslims were natives of Pigcawayan who were pushed back to the marginal lands when the Christians came.

A total of 160 respondents made up the sample for the region – 40 from Bulucaon, 36 from Maluao, and 84 from Capayuran. The sample size was originally intended to be in proportion to the population in the area, but to examine farming practices among the Muslims, a sample of 48 Muslim respondents were selected in Capayuran together with 36

Table 1. Basic characteristics of sample farms.

village	farms (no.)		persons in household (no.)	farm size (ha)	share tenants (%)	lease- holders (%)	owner- operators (%)
	village	sample					
Maluao	80	36	6.0	2.9	53	3	44
Bulucaon	93	40	6.5	2.0	91	3	6
Capayuran							
Christians	181	36	6.5	1.9	86	0	14
Muslims	171	48	6.8	3.9	0	0	100[a]

	rice area					
	per farm (ha)		double- cropped (%)	irrigated (%)		principal form of irrigation
	wet season	dry season		wet season	dry season	
Maluao	1.6	1.6	100	90	84	canal
Bulucaon	1.8	2.0	100	100	100	canal
Capayuran						
Christians	1.3	1.2	100	100	100	canal
Muslims	1.4	1.3	95	100	100	canal

	modern varieties				
	farmers planting (%)		rice area planted (%)		year of greatest adoption
	wet season	dry season	wet season	dry season	
Maluao	83	78	90	88	1969
Bulucaon	100	100	100	100	1967, 1968
Capayuran					
Christians	100	100	100	100	1969
Muslims	100	100	82	100	1969

[a]The Muslims do not pay rent, but have no legal title to their land.

Table 2. Comparison of modern varieties with local varieties by modern adopters.

reason for preferring[a]	farmers (%) reporting preference			
	Maluao	Bulucaon	Capayuran	
			Christians	Muslims
modern varieties				
resistant to disease	86	38	11	85
yield	86	95	61	31
resistant to drought	58	52	28	18
resistant to flood	14	30	8	14
eating quality	0	0	0	31
short maturing variety	0	10	0	7
resistant to lodging	0	5	0	0
local varieties				
resistant to disease	25	2	16	2
resistant to flood	0	2	4	0
resistant to drought	6	0	0	0

[a] Some farmers gave more than one reason.

Christian respondents. The names of the respondents were taken at random from a list supplied by the Population Commission Office of the local Bureau of Census.

CHANGES IN FARMING PRACTICES

Adoption of modern varieties. IR8 was the first modern variety introduced in the area in 1968 through the municipal branch of the APC in Pigcawayan which conducted an intensive campaign of field demonstrations and radio announcements. Lowland irrigated farms were the first to adopt. The high productivity of the new variety and its resistance to disease were the main reasons why farmers adopted it (Table 2).

Bulucaon led the others in adopting modern varieties and by 1969, it had 100 percent adoption. Capayuran had 100 percent adoption by 1972 but Maluao had only 78 percent adoption since upland farmers of Maluao refused to use modern varieties. Their main complaint was the tendency of modern varieties to lodge and their poor performance due to the scarcity of water. Contour farming, which might alleviate these problems, is not used by upland farmers in the region because of its high labor requirement.

Adoption of other practices. The adoption of fertilizer, insecticide, herbicides, and other practices can be directly or indirectly traced to the introduction of modern varieties. Among the inputs for production, fertilizer use has increased very slowly among the farmers (Table 3). The increase in adopters in Bulucaon has been very slow, and although Capayuran registered almost 50 percent adopters, this can be wholly attributed to the Christian farmers in the village. The Muslim farmers have never applied fertilizer on their land. Twelve percent of Maluao farmers tried fertilizer when they first tried planting modern varieties but then gave it up because, they said, fertilizer was not needed or too expensive, or they did not know how to use it.

Among other modern inputs, insecticides were the most popular due to the high incidence of pests and diseases in the municipality and in the region as a whole (Table 3). Insecticides were even used by Muslim farmers.

Herbicides were widely used. Bulucaon had 100 percent acceptance followed by Capayuran and Maluao. Handweeding and rotary weeding were used in Bulucaon and to some extent in Maluao. Capayuran farmers, however, barely use either. Muslim farmers seldom removed the weeds from their farms. They did not use straight-row planting (both ways) and few planted in a straight line (either practice makes weeding easier). Other respondents (Christians) in Capayuran and Maluao planted in straight lines (one way). Bulucaon farmers used straight-row planting (both ways). The topography of Maluao made the water buffalo more widely used than tractors, especially when heavy rains come. Water buffalo and tractors were both used in land preparation in Bulucaon. In Capayuran the Muslim respondents used primitive methods in land preparation. No Muslim farmers owned a buffalo, but many expressed the desire to buy one if income increased.

Since threshers were rented, their adoption was dependent on the accessibility of farms. Bulucaon had 100 percent adoption, but in Maluao and Capayuran the roads were not as good so fewer farmers could make use of threshers.

The cropping pattern depended on water availability. In irrigated areas, farmers planted twice a year, especially after the introduction of modern varieties. In Maluao, even in the rainfed areas, modern varieties were planted twice a year. In Capayuran the swamp was flooded part of the time and during the survey year, five were not able to double crop. Nevertheless, the total rice area planted each season was approximately the same. Even though this was true for the village, the area planted to rice by the sample farms within the village varied significantly from wet to dry season.

The three villages differed in their farm practices, but there was a sharp increase in the use of modern inputs following the introduction of the new varieties in 1968 and 1969 (Table 3). Bulucaon farmers were the most receptive to modern technology. The Muslim farmers in Capayuran adopted modern varieties and insecticides, but unlike the Christian farmers, they did not use fertilizer, or herbicides, or tractors and threshers. Both environmental and social factors undoubtedly influenced this sharp contrast between ethnic groups.

Changes in labor requirements. Following the introduction of the new varieties, no change in labor use occurred in the Muslim portion of Capayuran. In all other areas most farmers said the use of labor before, during, and after harvest both within and outside the village increased (Table 4). Apparently, however, some hired labor was substituted for family labor particularly among those farmers who hired tractors for land preparation and threshers at harvest. For example, the amount of family labor for pre-harvest and harvest activities declined on most farms in Bulucaon where the use of tractors rose from 52 percent before the new varieties to 92 percent in the survey year. The use of mechanical threshers rose from 60 to 100 percent over the same period (Table 3).

FACTORS INFLUENCING FARM PRODUCTIVITY

Only in Bulucaon during the dry season did a significant gain in yield occur following the introduction of the modern varieties (Table 5). Despite nearly 100 percent adoption of modern varieties in the other two villages, the yields remained extremely low. Part of the low yield in the wet season can be attributed to the drought; however low yields were closely associated with low levels of fertilizer input (Table 6). The recommended level of nitrogen input on rice would be at least 60 kg/ha in this area. But most farmers used no fertilizer at all, and even among those farmers using fertilizer in Bulucaon and Capayuran, the level of input was extremely low. Analysis of constraints to yield and fertilizer input is necessary to explain this poor performance.

Institutional factors. Government support is a most influential factor in increasing productivity. In most underdeveloped countries the infrastructure which is necessary for improving agriculture is the primary

Table 3. Changes in farming practices at three stages: before modern varieties, year modern variety was adopted, and during survey year.

| village | year | modern varieties | chemical fertilizer | farmers (%) using | | | | | |
				insecticide	herbicide	mechanical weeder	straight-row planting	tractors	mechanical threshers
Maluao	before		3	25	19	0	11	6	17
	adoption	78	12	86	72	17	27	47	61
	survey	100	0	89	75	95	27	50	64
Bulucaon	before		12	68	68	60	10	52	60
	adoption		20	90	95	80	15	78	82
	survey	100	32	100	100	100	20	92	100
Capayuran									
Christians	before		6	14	17	5	8	14	22
	adoption		33	83	83	5	19	42	89
	survey	100	44	97	89	11	22	75	97
Muslims	before		0	0	0	0	0	0	0
	adoption		0	98	0	0	0	0	0
	survey	100	0	100	0	0	0	0	0

Table 4. Changes in farm labor requirement following introduction of modern varieties.

type of labor	Maluao			Bulucaon			Capayuran[a]		
	more	less	no change	more	less	no change	more	less	no change
pre-harvest									
family	89	6	5	18	80	2	72	12	12
hired within village	100	0	0	87	13	0	88	0	50
hired outside village	81	19	0	75	25	0	58	22	3
exchange	66	31	3	2	48	48	55	22	4
harvest and after harvest									
family	91	6	3	2	95	2	55	25	12
hired within village	94	6	0	90	10	0	80	22	4
hired outside village	60	40	0	87	13	0	52	22	4
exchange	68	26	6	0	68	32	49	30	52

[a]Christians only. The Muslim respondents reported no change in farm labor requirement.

Table 5. Rice yields for modern and local varieties.

| village | yield (t/ha) | | | | |
| | before modern varieties introduced | 1971/72 dry season | | 1972 wet season | |
		modern	local	modern	local
Maluao	1.7	1.9	1.1	1.6	1.2
Bulucaon	2.9	3.4	–	2.9	–
Capayuran					
Christians	2.4	2.9	–	2.6	–
Muslims	0.6	0.7	–	1.0	0.9
avg	2.2	2.4	–	2.1	–

Table 6. Fertilizer use.

| village | fertilizer used (kg/ha) | | | | | |
| | 1971/72 dry season | | | 1972 wet season | | |
	N	P_2O_5	K_2O	N	P_2O_5	K_2O
	all farms					
Maluao	0	0	0	0	0	0
Bulucaon	5	0	0	10	1	1
Capayuran						
Christians	8	1	1	12	1	1
Muslims	0	0	0	0	0	0
	users only					
Maluao	0	0	0	0	0	0
Bulucaon	16	8	4	15	11	6
Capayuran						
Christians	20	22	22	24	21	10
Muslims	0	0	0	0	0	0

responsibility of the government. Roughly half the farmers in the three villages felt they were beneficiaries of government aid (Table 7). This aid came in the form of visits by the community development officer and the farm management technician, and provision of roads, bridges

Table 7. Proportion of farmers receiving aid from extension organizations and affiliation of farmers with farmers' organizations.

organization	respondents (%)			
	Maluao	Bulucaon	Capayuran	
			Christians	Muslims
receiving government aid[a]				
Presidential Assistance for Community Development	17	20	30	0
Agricultural Credit Administration	0	38	24	0
Agricultural Productivity Commission	33	28	45	0
Total	50	85	99	0
affiliated with[b]				
Federation of Free Farmers	25	65	24	0
Free Farmers Cooperatives	0	58	0	0
Notre Dame Credit Union	0	2	0	0
Ansarol Islam Farmers' Association	0	0	0	100

[a] Some farmers receive aid from more than one government agency. [b] Some farmers in Bulucaon belong to more than one farmers' organization.

and irrigation facilities. All Muslim respondents in Capayuran listed government aid as the most important way in which farming could be improved (Table 8).

Farmers' organizations also play an important role in increasing production. The Federation of Free Farmers was the most influential organization in the area since it conducts meetings on scientific farming for its members. It is significant that Bulucaon had the largest number of affiliates to the organization (Table 7). Capayuran and Maluao had few members and although the Muslim farmers were members of another organization, the latter was more political than educational (Muslim farmers were working for the separation of their *sitio* into a separate *barrio.*)

Lack of credit prevented many farmers from applying modern rice technology. The credit problem seemed to be more serious in Maluao and Capayuran than in Bulucaon (Table 9). In Maluao nearly all farmers listed credit as a constraint and say that they would use more credit if it

Table 8. Farmers' views of ways rice farming can be improved, 1971/72 dry season.

what must be done	farmers (%) reporting			
	Maluao	Bulucaon	Capayuran	
			Christians	Muslims
have sufficient farm capital	0	33	3	0
apply new technologies	41	18	38	0
solve irrigation/water problems	17	23	0	0
cooperation among farmers	0	5	9	0
ask government help and aid	0	12	3	100
proper application of fertilizers	14	2	6	0
construct feeder roads	0	2	0	0
proper maintenance of rice fields	28	0	25	0

were available. By contrast, in Bulucaon the credit seems to have become less of a problem since the introduction of modern varieties, and few farmers indicated that they would use more credit if it were available. This is rather surprising since fertilizer use was at such a low level (Table 6). Bulucaon had the largest loans and the largest number of farmer-borrowers (Table 10). Maluao had a larger proportion of borrowers than Capayuran, but smaller loans. Bulucaon farmers borrowed less during the wet season than the dry season, while Capayuran farmers maintained the same average. Credit and yield in both barrios were positively correlated: yields of Bulucaon farms also decreased during the wet season while yields in Capayuran remained the same. Maluao showed a negative correlation between credit and yield.

Since two barrios showed a positive correlation between credit and production, an increase of credit facilities may contribute to increased yield. The region sorely lacks institutional credit sources. Private moneylenders were still the major source of credit and interest rates are exhorbitant (Table 11).

Tenure status is another factor to consider in farm productivity. Share tenants made the largest contribution to production due to their number. However, a correlation is hard to establish because the share tenants were located on choice lands. In interviews on tenure preferences, 85 percent of Bulucaon farmers preferred leasehold or cash rent to 15 percent who preferred share tenancy. This is significant considering that 90 percent of Bulucaon farmers are presently share tenants. Maluao

Table 9. Major problems encountered in rice production, before the introduction of modern varieties, 1971/72 dry season, and 1972 wet season.

| | | | | | | | Capayuran | | | | | |
| | Maluao | | | Bulucaon | | | Christians | | | Muslims | | |
problem	before	dry season	wet season	before	dry season	wet season	before	dry season	wet season	before	dry season	wet season
pre-harvest												
disease/insect/pests	100	100	100	70	70	88	97	78	78	100	100	90
obtaining fertilizer	100	100	25	5	15	5	81	50	38	100	10	0
irrigation water	97	97	25	33	8	58	50	42	9	100	100	46
obtaining seeds of modern varieties	92	97	61	38	38	2	67	83	25	0	0	15
obtaining credit	0	100	54	32	30	0	83	47	53	0	28	49
would use more credit if available	–	97	–	–	5	–	–	83	–	–	27	–
harvest and post-harvest												
harvesting	0	0	0	5	2	0	2	0	0	0	0	0
threshing	0	0	7	15	0	0	0	0	6	0	0	0
hauling	0	0	0	42	0	0	0	0	0	100	31	21
drying	0	0	0	2	0	0	0	0	0	0	0	0

Table 10. Use of production credit, 1971/72 dry season and 1972 wet season.

village	season	borrowers (%)	amount (₱/ha)		source[a] (%)				
			village avg	borrowers only	private money-lender	landowner	relative	ACA[b]	farm input dealer
in cash									
Maluao	dry	63	53	83	78	17	0	0	0
	wet	55	44	99	56	9	20	0	0
Bulucaon	dry	82	328	497	66	3	0	21	0
	wet	87	186	186	68	2	0	0	0
Capayuran									
Christians	dry	66	213	320	66	33	0	0	0
Muslims	dry	20	20	98	40	0	50	0	0
Christians	wet	72	166	230	75	12	0	0	0
Muslims	wet	31	14	46	6	0	94	0	0
in kind									
Maluao	dry	36	13	35	60	0	0	0	30
	wet	25	10	36	43	14	10	0	0
Bulucaon	dry	10	10	104	0	75	0	0	0
	wet	72	26	36	34	3	0	0	0

Capayuran

Christians	dry	38	14	37	57	35	0	0	7
Muslims	dry	0	0	0	0	0	0	0	0
Christians	wet	33	22	66	63	27	0	0	9
Muslims	wet	6	3	51	43	0	57	0	0

aSome farmers had more than one source of credit. bAgricultural Credit Administration.

Table 11. Interest rates per season on production loans.

		farmers (%) reporting[a]								
		cash loans					loans in kind			
village	season	no interest	6–12%	10%	20%	30%	no interest	6–15%	20%	30%
Maluao	dry	14	0	0	0	69	46	0	0	31
	wet	43	37	0	0	7	72	14	0	0
Bulucaon	dry	2	15	15	37	24	0	25	75	0
	wet	17	0	6	40	20	52	48	0	0
Capayuran										
Christians	dry	62	0	8	12	12	70	0	14	0
Muslims	dry	90	10	0	0	0	0	0	0	0
Christians	wet	38	17	29	4	0	81	9	0	0
Muslims	wet	80	10	0	10	0	45	16	16	6

aSome farmers had more than one source of credit as well as more than one form of repayment.

and Capayuran farmers on the other hand preferred share tenancy, which may reflect their high risk situation. Since high productivity is assured in Bulucaon, the farmers believe that they can afford the lease-hold system which will give them incentive to produce more. Since productivity is low in the other two areas, farmers are reluctant to be independent from the landlord who usually is at the losing end when harvest is poor. But the landlord stands to gain during good harvest so share tenants may have less incentive to produce more.

Environmental factors. The major problems that were difficult to control even after the introduction of modern varieties were water availability and diseases, insects, and pests (Table 9). Water was more of a problem in Bulucaon during the wet season and in the other two villages during the dry season. Possibly the irrigation system which serves the farmers in Bulucaon did not function well during the drought experienced in the wet season. Bulucaon is at the end of the government irrigation system that serves this area. Little if any improvement in irrigation has been made in Maluao and Capayuran. Maluao has always been deficient in irrigation water. It tried putting up a communal irrigation system which broke down time and again. Capayuran, although partly irrigated by the National Irrigation Administration, always faces the danger of flooding from the Balogo river. The swamp of Capayuran becomes a lake when the rains come, particularly affecting the Muslim section.

Disease and insects were problems common to the three villages but to a lesser extent in Bulucaon and Capayuran. Maluao had the biggest problem because unlike the two villages which are government irrigated (the cropping pattern is more or less controlled by water rationing), Maluao farmers used overlapping cropping patterns which induce diseases and insects to move from one field to another the whole year around.

Managerial factors. Farmers agreed that application of scientific methods and proper caring of the farm would improve rice production. Nevertheless, farmers in the three barrios differed in their ideas of the proper way of farming.

Almost all lowland farmers were adopters of modern varieties. Upland farmers of Maluao on the other hand believed that modern varieties could not be planted on their farms. When informed that this is possible through contour farming, they shy away due to the labor required. Hence, when the rains come, the water carries surface soil which is dumped on the lowland and as a consequence the upland farms rapidly become less productive. This partly explains the low yields of Maluao farmers, especially those planting local varieties.

Table 12. Increases in income and living standards since 1969.

item	farmers (%) reporting			
	Maluao	Bulucaon	Capayuran	
			Christians	Muslims
increase in				
rice profits	81	75	91	52
level of living	78	75	86	48
education expenditure	86	62	63	25
house improvements	53	37	36	58
savings	86	62	75	30
food consumption	97	85	88	80
invested in or purchased				
living room set	63	7	31	0
dining set	52	0	22	12
clothes cabinet	33	5	17	0
bed	66	5	42	2
radio	75	57	86	11
sewing machine	27	12	31	6
gas stove	0	2	3	0
bicycle	19	7	31	0
motorcycle/scooter	0	5	0	0
tractor and other farm implements	0	35	0	8
other farm enterprise	3	0	11	0
reduced debts	75	100	69	8

In view of this it is surprising that Maluao farmers used virtually no fertilizer because they believed that their farms were fertile. Although fertilizer use and yield in Capayuran and Bulucaon farms was very low, still the attitudes of farmers were encouraging.

The availability and low prices of insecticides put them within the reach of every farmer. Insecticides, however, could not combat the incidence of insects and pests in Maluao. The overlapping cropping pattern in this village encouraged the proliferation of insects and pests. A change in cropping pattern is needed before insecticides can help. Bulucaon and Capayuran farmers were getting results from insecticides, but they needed more training especially in the use of systemic types.

Another factor to consider is weeding. Muslim farmers did not weed as a rule. Handweeding, however, was not sufficient especially on farms over 1 hectare. Bulucaon farmers solved their problem by using rotary weeders which required the adoption of straight-row planting.

Income and welfare. The introduction of modern varieties and scientific farming changed the standard of living of the respondents. Seventy percent reported an increase in their level of living. This was primarily due to increase in profits from rice production (Table 12).

For the farmers whose yields did not increase after the introduction of modern varieties, the reasons given for higher standard of living is income from off-farm occupation. This, however, is a minority. Rice production is still the major source of income of farmers. Maluao has the highest proportion of respondents showing changes in income and standard of living after the introduction of modern varieties despite the low yield levels. This may be because there are relatively more owner-cultivators in Maluao than in Bulucaon. Although yield is low, all of it goes to the farmer.

But most of the expenses of Maluao farmers were on household consumption. No one spent on tractors or other farm implements. On the other hand, 35 percent of Bulucaon farmers invested on farm implements.

POLICY IMPLICATIONS

This study of rice farming in Cotabato shows the receptivity of farmers to scientific methods. There are, however, two major constraints to success in rice production. These are the lack of irrigation and marketing infrastructure and the need for a widespread information campaign on modern methods of farming.

Infrastructure — the most important of which is damming rivers for irrigation — would help solve a variety of problems. First of all, dams would distribute water to rainfed areas and minimize floods in the plains. This is important considering that rainfall in Cotabato does not have a definite pattern. Secondly, controlled irrigation could minimize the incidence of pests and diseases by establishing a uniform cropping calendar for farmers. Thirdly, roads and bridges could lower marketing costs and thus increase the profits of farmers. It would also enable rented machinery such as tractors and threshers to enter the inner farms. This would allow farmers to use part of their labor in off-farm occupations.

An information campaign is needed to teach farmers correct ways to use modern production inputs. Farmers relied on hearsay, most of which was inaccurate. The most productive farmers were members of organization engaged in giving seminars on farm production.

Other needs of the region were more credit facilities offering lower interest, fertilizer, and other inputs at prices within the reach of farmers.

Diversity in unity: the social component of changes in rice farming in Asian villages

Gelia T. Castillo

RICE IS RICE is rice but unlike Gertrude Stein's rose, it does not "smell as sweet" when grown at different times in different places by different people. Furthermore, it could be "miracle rice" in the Philippines, *padi ria* in Malaysia, PB-8 in Indonesia, RD-1 in Thailand, Mehran 69 in Pakistan, and Jaya in India. Nevertheless, by whatever name it is known, most of Asia depends on rice as its staple food. Whatever else it may mean in terms of growth, equity, and employment, one must never forget that it was the need for more food which originally inspired the search for new and better ways of producing rice. After the policy-makers decided to use the new rice technology as a major means to pursue the objective of increased rice production, the rhetoric and controversy surrounding its impact followed as its most bountiful harvest.

This chapter summarizes observations distilled from the studies discussed in the other chapters — studies of 36 villages in 14 research sites in 6 Asian countries: India, Pakistan, Indonesia, Thailand, Malaysia, and the Philippines. If one is asking for the nature and magnitude of the changes in national, regional, or global terms, he cannot find the answers in these studies. Or at least, it would be misleading to extrapolate far beyond the data provided by these village-level studies. Despite this caution, however, there is a built-in tendency to refer to villages X, Y, or Z as Thai or Indian villages, and an inherent predisposition on the part of the reader and the writer to intellectually treat them as if they were representative of Thailand or India. In the absence of an effective defense against this predisposition to generalize beyond limitations, the most one could aim for is to highlight the complexities which underline the changes that are remotely or directly associated with the new rice technology. These complexities which characterize the physico-socio-cultural environment of rice farming deserve to be highlighted because broad, general policies seldom touch these micro-level problems. Quite often, even sound policies fail to produce the desired effects because these problems are bypassed either because of the lag between policy and implementation, or because of the inability of national policies to cope with the idiosyncracies of micro-environments which ultimately determine how the rice crop fares and how the harvest is distributed.

The diversity in environmental and institutional conditions, not only among countries but also among villages and among farms, makes comparability of results more of an illusion than a reality. However, there are common trends across countries and villages, although the empirical manifestations of the trend may be peculiar to an area. Keeping all of these caveats in mind, significant patterns of unity and diversity have been identified from this series of studies.

PATTERNS OF ADOPTION

Regardless of what international development experts have to say about the "evils" or the "blessings" of the new rice technology, one can safely generalize that Asian rice farmers are not resistant to change. They responded to innovations with measures to temper risk. Irrigation by whatever means has influenced the rate of adoption of the modern varieties. Where it was more advantageous to plant them during the dry season, they did so. Another approach taken was to plant more than one variety for each crop season, thus providing insurance against the possible failure of the new seeds. There are interesting variations in risk taking. In Andhra Pradesh, where use of the new varieties is associated with farm size, complete adoption was more frequent on farms of less than 4 ha than on larger farms.

> "Complete adoption in this area, was more frequent on farms under 4 hectares (80% of adopters in both seasons) than on the large farms (24%)" (p. 51).[1]

It was likewise noted that farmers who grew the modern varieties had better results with local varieties than did those farmers who grew only local varieties, suggesting that adopters probably have superior managerial skills. While the early-adopter-large-farmer used partial adoption as a means of reducing risk, the smaller farmers had a "wait-and-see" attitude. With demonstrated results from the larger farms, the small farmers were then willing to go all the way with the new seeds.

Another indisputable and almost universal impact of the modern varieties is the change in cropping pattern which they have brought

---

[1] Quotations in this chapter are from the other chapters in this volume as indicated by the page numbers in parentheses.

about in combination with irrigation. In fact, their adoption is almost synonymous with the adoption of double cropping. Although high yield capacity is the characteristic most associated with the new varieties, their yields did not exceed those of the local varieties, in many villages where adoption has taken place; they were adopted because of their shorter growing period and non-photoperiodism. In Uttar Pradesh, it was possible to have a rotation of modern varieties of rice and wheat. The practice of keeping land fallow in the kharif season to grow wheat in the rabi has declined due to irrigation and the new seeds. In Cuttack, the growing of pulses and vegetables has been replaced entirely by a second rice crop. In the Philippines, both the desire to grow five crops in two years where water is always available, and the fact that the new seeds can be planted anytime (as in Davao and Cotabato) led to the phenomenon of staggered planting. Within a small contiguous area, one can see rice plants in all stages of development. In Pakistan and Uttar Pradesh the rice-wheat rotation is also made possible because the short maturity of the modern rice varieties permits wheat to be sown on time.

The repercussions of increased cropping intensity on the insect and disease problem deserve serious and immediate attention. Where a second crop of rice has replaced pulses and vegetables, its impact on the diet of the farm family needs to be analyzed. Poorer nutrition does not necessarily follow because much depends on how the income from the second rice crop is spent. Of course there are other obvious implications for labor absorption and more potent arguments for tractor use to speed up land preparation between growing seasons. The short maturity of the new seeds, rather than their high yields, may yet prove to be their most important asset. To the ecologists, however, this quality might be viewed as a potential liability if it leads to unmanageable disease and insect problems associated with continuous cropping. On the positive side, more intensive cropping of the same farm land not only makes for greater labor absorption but also for more even distribution of labor demand throughout the year.

LABOR ABSORPTION

The effects of the introduction of modern varieties on labor requirements were positive despite tractor adoption in several places. Both family and hired labor increased in all of the study sites except for the two Pakistan villages which reported practically no labor changes. The Malaysian villages had the highest proportion of tractor adopters but pre-harvest labor also increased. Because more laborers were hired, the changes in rice farming have provided more employment to landless farm laborers. In Mysore, agricultural laborers reported that they have been employed more days in a year since the advent of modern varieties, and that their living conditions have improved. However, the increase in farm wages has in some instances, as in Central Java, led to greater use of family labor. In Kelantan, Malaysia, although 75 percent of the farmers felt that they could raise yields by applying more labor, they could not do so because they lacked the capital to hire labor.

One cannot always presume that hired labor is landless labor because in some communities the farmer-cultivators themselves hire out their services to other farmers, especially if their particular labor needs do not occur at exactly the same time.

Adjustments to the existing land-labor ratio are depicted by Java and Thailand which offer quite a contrast in *intensification* and *extensification*. Farm size in Javanese villages is the smallest of all places, but the Javanese farmer utilized roughly twice as much labor as does the Filipino farmer. Improved cultural practices which have been in use since 1942 have been further intensified; hence their rice fields are well-manicured compared with those of other countries, notably Thailand, where very low levels of management are practiced. Thailand's yields per hectare are low, but rice production per worker is high because of large farm size. The predominance of weeds over rice plants is a far cry from the tiny garden-like (almost all available space utilized) weedless rice plots in Central Java. To further intensify production, the *petukan* method is used. To save time, seedlings for a new crop are prepared before the old crop is harvested, thus shortening the growing period between harvesting and transplanting. Where tobacco planting is required, the objective is to obtain four crops of rice plus one crop of tobacco over a 2-year period. In the Javanese villages studied, the tractor is nowhere in sight. As a matter of fact, harvesting is done mostly with a small knife called the *ani-ani* instead of the sickle. The share-and-share-alike philosophy in the village sustains the use of the *ani-ani* so that more labor can participate in the harvest. In addition to intensive rice cultivation, farmers are engaged in backyard production of livestock and of other plants such as papaya, bananas, and vegetables. Smaller rice farms tend to derive larger incomes from their backyard production. The pressure to *share poverty* is beginning to weaken as reflected in the appearance of the *tebasan* systen under which the standing rice crop is sold long before it is harvested. Under this system the buyer, who is responsible for harvesting the crop, is relatively free from the usual cultural obligations to allow as many harvesters as possible on a privileged sharing basis. The system has even encouraged the use of the sickle rather than the small knife. The extent to which community norms will allow the continuous spread of this practice, however, remains to be seen.

On the other hand, farmers in Don Chedi, Thailand, are just beginning to shift from broadcasting to transplanting, and more labor is saved by the use of four-wheel tractors for land preparation and even for threshing. Don Chedi seems to suffer from a labor shortage to which farmers adjust by a fairly low-yield, low management system of rice farming carried out on large farms. What aggravates this state of affairs is the twin problem of irrigation and drainage in the area.

Patterns of labor utilization are influenced by social obligations and by cultural constraints, as evident in Cuttack, India. There, the number of family members potentially available for farm work appears to be sufficient to meet the labor requirements on the farms, but this potential is not realized because female members rarely, if ever, take part in agricultural operations. Hence, supplemental labor has to be hired. Therefore, a labor surplus and shortage can exist simultaneously at the local level. This paradox is nowhere more dramatically described than in Uttar Pradesh:

> "Hired laborers that worked in the Tarai migrated from other regions, particularly eastern U.P. and Bihar where there was a labor surplus. Large farms maintained a permanent labor force, but during the peak seasons there was frequently a labor shortage. In Tarna and Barain where labor was more plentiful, large farms experienced labor shortages during peak seasons because some laborers left for jobs in the nearby city of Varanasi" (p. 111).

Tractor use is another intriguing aspect of rice production. Small farm size caused by extreme fragmentation in Cuttack, for example, discouraged tractor use even when the machinery was available. But Salor and Meranti in Kelantan, Malaysia, which also have small fragmented landholdings, reported 91 and 88 percent of farmers using either two-wheel or four-wheel tractors. What differentiates Cuttack from Kelantan? Obviously small farm size cannot explain a shift to tractors in one place and not in another place. In Andhra Pradesh, land mortgage banks provided liberal loans for tractor purchase. Consequently the ownership of cattle and carts declined and many farmers have become dependent on hired tractors. In Pakistan, the increased profits from installing pumps provided money for buying tractors.

An analysis of changes in rice farming which narrowly concentrates on rice production alone does not really tell the story because of complementary, supplementary, and inseparable elements such as non-rice agricultural enterprises and non-farm employment. Where rice production has contributed to increased profits, the demand for goods and services has increased, and employment has been generated in other sectors. Where rice production has not been as fortunate, off-farm and non-farm incomes have quite a bearing on the survival and well-being of the farm family. The extent to which earnings from non-farm employment are invested on rice farms and vice-versa was not investigated, although many farmers reported increases in off-farm and non-farm incomes. The issue is also related to tenure status and farmers' willingness to apply more of their own labor on land which is not their own. One assumption of land reform is that an owner-operator will apply more labor on his farm because he owns it.

TENURE STATUS AND FARM SIZE

Farm size *per se* has little meaning. It acquires significance only when viewed within the context of the community, the productivity of the land, the infrastructure, the services available, the intensity of land use, population pressures, the tenure system, and the social and economic values attached to land ownership. Half a hectare of land in Java may be "equivalent" to 2 hectares in Thailand. In the Philippines 2 hectares of land in Nueva Ecija does not mean the same thing as 2 hectares in Cotabato. 'Large' and 'small' are relative terms conditioned by the above-mentioned factors.

Social equality or inequality on the basis of farm size and land ownership depends on the level at which one wishes to make the assessment. The impact of the new rice technology on farms of differing sizes and tenure is very much affected by the extent to which a set of factors are linked together in a mutually reinforcing favorable or unfavorable manners. For example, in the villages of Tarai and Varanasi, Uttar Pradesh, all the farmers studied were owners – hence in this respect and at this level there is equality in ownership status. In the Tarai, land was allotted in the early 1950s to agricultural graduates, political refugees from Pakistan, and some of the most progressive farmers in India. The area is also characterized by rich soils and is further favored by the location of the G.B. Pant University of Agriculture and Technology. The equality in land ownership status is made unequal by the differentials in farm size and by the concomitant of these differentials, shown by the fact that medium and large farms are 100 percent gravity and pump irrigated, while one-third of the small farms are not irrigated and those which are irrigated have only one source of water. The large farmers also use better management practices because they are in greater contact with influential farmers outside the locality. They have an advantage in obtaining inputs from institutionalized sources, in selling their outputs, and in getting credit from agencies in the village. However, if one took Tarai and Varanasi Districts as a whole, despite the equalities in ownership and inequalities in farm size, the farmers in the area generally would be quite privileged relative to farmers of other Indian regions. So where does one begin and end the issue of social equality? What is the reference point for equity? If the existing structure is unequal, one can expect anything that is introduced into the structure to have an unequal impact. This is aggravated by the fact that the positive factors tend to occur together as much as do the negative factors.

In Pedapulleru, Andhra Pradesh, where the use of modern varieties is associated with farm size, adopters were from upper castes. Small owners and tenant farmers who were aligned with the dominant caste group tended to be by-passed by the program. Among adopters, small tenant farmers obtained higher yields than did owner-operators because landlords financed them. With respect to farmers' assessments of their rice profits since 1965/66, only a third of the Pedapulleru farmers reported increases. The proportion was higher among owners than among tenants and among larger farmers than among small farmers. From the analysis of indirect evidence, Parthasarathy concluded:

> "Taking all things together, it is reasonable to infer that the already existing inequalities of the rural structure were worsened rather than lessened by lags in rates of adoption between big and small owner-operators, the bias of the new technology in favor of owners, and the unfavorable position of the small tenants and owners in the credit, inputs and produce markets" (p. 70).

The focus on the income distribution issue which emphasizes the relative gains made by the "rich" and the "poor" farmers has led to a neglect of the other issue which pertains to farmers' gains relative to where they were before the advent of the new rice technology. Preoccupation with the first issue leaves the reader with the impression that tenants and small farmers would have been better off in terms of incomes and levels of living if they had remained with traditional varieties. If this were the case, there would be no rationale for wishing for the wider spread of the new seeds. Table 1 illustrates the significance of the second issue. From the data, it is obvious that tenants and small farmers believe they are better off with modern than with local varieties. Of course, owner-operators and large farmers were much better-off than tenants and small farmers. How else could it have been? It is truly asking for a miracle to expect that the new seeds would bring about social equality

Table 1. Increase in rice income and standard of living since 1964/65 in relation to tenure of all farmers and size of holding of landowning farmers.

growers of	farmers reporting (%)					
	by tenure			by farm size		
	owners	tenants	all farms	less than 4 ha	4 ha and over	all farms
	increase in rice profits					
modern varieties only	59	33	50	50	87	82
some modern varieties	82	33	78	50	75	59
combined[a]	73	33	65	50	84	73
local varieties only	20	1	12	6	6	6
all farms	44	10	32	26	66	44
	increase in standard of living					
modern varieties only	27	42	32	25	47	44
some modern varieties	44	33	43	21	38	27
combined[a]	38	40	38	22	45	38
local varieties only	6	6	6	2	17	6
all farms	21	14	18	8	36	21

[a]Value for all farmers who grew any modern varieties.

where centuries have failed to produce a dent on institutional rigidities. As Parthasarathy admitted:

> "Given a persisting inegalitarian land structure, modern varieties contributed little to the reduction of rural inequalities, though with an egalitarian land structure they would have the potential for rapid growth consistent with equity" (p. 70).

In villages where the caste system is important and where it reinforces the inegalitarian land structure, the new rice varieties could never hope to level the caste hierarchies so that everyone would gain equally from whatever benefits go with them, especially if the dominant caste also controls the local institutions such as the cooperatives and the *panchayats*. However, if these benefits have contributed toward heightened consciousness of the inequalities and toward realization of those at the lower ends of the status hierarchies that they should participate as much in the gains as do the upper ends, then the technology has served an unanticipated function — that of facilitating a confrontation with the status quo. The natural course of history has apparently failed to produce alternations in social structures because those who are privile   continue to benefit more from anything beneficial than those who are less privileged.

In the Philippines, share tenancy and small farm size have not deterred the adoption of the modern varieties. In other words, being an owner-operator and cultivating a large farm showed no particular advantage either in innovativeness or productivity per hectare. In fact, farm size tended to have an inverse relationship to productivity, with smaller farms exhibiting higher productivity. In Nueva Ecija, Central Luzon, where the land reform program has been most actively pursued, the shift from share tenancy to leasehold (fixed rentals) has resulted in increased shares of the output for the lessees, but their productivity per hectare did not differ significantly from that of share tenants or owner operators. Farmers themselves believe that they benefited as much, if not more, than did the landlords when they entered into leasehold. Ironically, in Davao and Cotabato, where land was acquired by the original owners through homesteads, share tenancy rates have been reported which are higher than those reported in Central Luzon. In the Davao villages, owner-operatorship is positively related to yields per hectare. This was explained by better financing capability of the owner-operators. While most of the farmers prefer a leasehold to a share tenancy arrangement, some prefer the latter because the risks are shared with the landlord. Under the leasehold system, the fixed rental has to be paid regardless of production. In Cotabato, the village with the lowest yield showed the highest overall proportion of farmers reporting increases in income, household consumption, and savings. The low yields were mitigated by the fact that they had more owner-cultivators among them than did the other villages. Hence, although yields were low, all of the production went to the farmers. A contrast to the Davao case of higher productivity for the owner-cultivator is the observation from Andhra Pradesh that small tenant farmers had higher yields with modern varieties than did owner-operators who had outyielded tenants with local varieties. The explanation given for higher yields among tenants who planted new varieties is the financing provided by landlords.

Cuttack presents a curious example of tenants gaining more than owners because of a fortuitous event. The owner-operators in the villages studied have the smallest farm size due to the acquisition of land for the construction of a railway from Cuttack to the Paradeep sea-port which affected owners more than others. Ninety-one percent of the pure tenants reported receiving higher rice profits since 1966, while only 87 percent of the pure owners did so. Seventy-three percent of pure tenants and only 53 percent of pure owners reported higher levels of living.

These observations indicate that in the final analysis, welfare and income distribution depend on the peculiar interactions among several factors, and not on farm size, productivity, or tenure status alone. The situation of the Muslim farmers in Capayuran and Pigcawayan, Cotabato, is a classic illustration of an "interlocking chain of negatives;" larger farms but in the swampy areas; adoption of modern varieties but not fertilizer; no extension assistance from government agencies; lowest yields; no access to institutional credit; lowest proportion of farmers reporting increases in rice incomes, levels of living, and consumption. Two factors at first glance appear to be positive: larger farm size and interest-free loans. The former can hardly be an asset because the farms are located in a swampy area. The latter occurs because the sources of credit are mostly relatives, which undoubtedly implies corresponding obligations to compensate for the favor of credit without interest. Given this set of circumstances, it is not surprising that when asked what must be done to improve rice farming, all the Muslims replied "ask government help and aid."

For an illustration of the "interlocking positives," there is the case of village leaders in Central Java. Although farms are very small, a high proportion of the rice farmers are owner-operators. Those who own land also share-crop or lease land to increase the area they cultivate because they can afford to pay the high land rentals. Peculiar to the area is the practice of giving village officials (*pamong desa*) plots of village ricefields substitutes for their salaries. These plots usually have the best fertility and irrigation and are also two to three times larger than those owned by the common villagers. With these advantages, the *pamong desas* and the owner-operators have been able to adopt modern varieties and the needed inputs. Increased yields have enabled them to add more land to their farms through leasing or share-cropping. On the other hand, most of the landless operators (share-croppers and lease-holders) still plant the local varieties. The stronger positions occupied by the *pamong desas* and owner operators have enabled them to decide the most profitable tenure arrangements since they can afford to provide the necessary inputs. Shortages of alternate employment opportunities in the area also make it possible for these two groups to obtain the cheapest labor. In short, the *pamong desas* are responsible for the implementation of government programs at the village level but at the same time are in the best position to capitalize on the benefits coming from government programs. It is again ironic that a system of incentives for village officials has at the same time become an instrument for increasing inequality. How does one reconcile the objective of equity with the need for incentives to local officials?

CREDIT AND EXTENSION SERVICES

Despite the proliferation of government efforts in every country to set up institutional sources of credit such as rural banks, farmers' associations, cooperatives, etc., the traditional sources of credit such as the landlord, private money lenders, and relatives, remain important. In Tamil Nadu, India, where cooperative societies were mentioned as a major source of credit both in cash and in kind, large farmers and owner-operators had greater access to credit than did small farmers and tenants. To promote the new varieties, credit was made more easily available to farmers who used them. This was specifically reported in Java and in Tamil Nadu, India. Davao and Cotabato, in the Philippines, observed no interest on loans from rice dealers but credit was used as an instrument for controlling the price of rice because farmer-borrowers had to sell their rice to these rice dealers. In Nueva Ecija, farmers who shifted from share tenancy to leasehold were cut off from landlords' credit but were given preference in institutional sources. In Java, where the requirement was to repay credit in cash 1 month after harvest time, the need for cash becomes more acute. This requirement may have encouraged the *tebasan* system whereby the crop is sold to a harvest contractor before harvest. The most welfare-oriented agency ever mentioned in all these studies seems to be the Marginal Farmer and Agricultural Laborer Agency in Cuttack. Under this scheme farmers with less than 1 hectare of land will get 33 percent subsidy on loans for agricultural purposes. The study did not mention, however, how many farmers had taken advantage of this scheme. In Salor and Maranti, Malaysia, the Farmers' Association normally extends fertilizer credit to cover only 1 acre of rice land. Quite often this amount is used for the whole farm, thus resulting in minimal fertilizer application. Although credit was cited as a constraint in many places, the phenomenon of *risk avoidance* was observed in Davao where many farmers were not inclined to use more credit even if it were made available because they have had a series of crop failures and were therefore inclined to use less inputs. The use of fertilizer, for example, definitely declined.

In most places the role of agricultural extension services was clearly recognized and the need for them was expressed definitely in Mysore, India, in Davao and Cotabato, Philippines and in Kelantan, Malaysia.

Other areas appear to be serviced more or less adequately. In Mysore, farmers wanted to know more about the technical side of growing modern varieties. It was observed that technical advice was passed on to a small group of farmers, but that most were by-passed by officials responsible for extension. In Davao, the complaint was that extension workers visited only the farms along the main roads and even among those which were visited, there was little depth in the inquiries made. In Cotabato, the most progressive farmers were members of organizations giving seminars on rice production. Non-members, especially the Muslims, had minimal or no exposure to extension. In Malaysia, the limited extension coverage is believed to affect the low management levels and use of inputs. Where credit procedures are tied to extension services of some kind, or where the farm management technician is the link between the farmer and the agrarian reform program as in the Philippines, a scanty extension coverage impedes improvement of farmer's welfare. In general, participants in government programs, whether in India, Java, or the Philippines, have greater access to credit and extension. Usually the use of modern varieties and the complementary inputs are the *sine qua non* of such programs.

RICE POLICY

Research sites in Thailand and Pakistan reported low rates of adoption of the modern varieties. Both countries are rice exporters and are therefore quite protective of their fine quality rice. Furthermore, Thailand maintains an unfavorable price ratio between fertilizer and rice; in 1971, the price of a kilogram of nitrogen was 7 times that of a kilogram of paddy, compared with 3 to 1 or less in other parts of Asia. It is interesting how Thailand's policy affects rice production in Kelantan, West Malaysia, which is near the Thai border. Because Thai farmers get a better price for rice in Kelantan than in Thailand, smuggling of rice across the Thai border has depressed local prices. In addition, Malaysian millers prefer Thai rice not only because of its lower price, but also because of its premium quality. Kelantan farmers mentioned selling, hauling, and processing as important problems in rice production. Relevant to these problems is the existence of a guaranteed minimum price which is difficult to obtain. The guaranteed price is different from the actual price received by farmers because of farmers' inability to meet the requirement of "good clean paddy with 13 percent moisture delivered to the mill door." Lack of drying and storage facilities results in deductions for dirt and moisture. Low prices for output and high prices for inputs encourages low input levels and, consequently, low yields.

The situation in Gujranwala, West Pakistan, is especially significant because the existing policy is a disincentive to the growing of modern varieties. To increase the production of fine rice, mainly for export, the government has substantially increased procurement prices of such varieties while leaving static those of the new coarse varieties. But pests have caused huge losses of the Basmati fine variety crop; this has led to increased areas planted to modern varieties. West Pakistan is the only study site where compulsory measures to protect the Basmati crop are enforced. The net income from modern varieties is lower than for Basmati, despite higher yields, because their price is only about half that of Basmati. Among those who grow both varieties, Basmati is used more for home consumption and for payment in kind to labor (farm laborers insist on payment in Basmati) while the coarse new varieties are normally sold. Despite the price discount for the new varieties, certain advantages have contributed to their spread. Their early maturity, in combination with irrigation, availability of mechanical draft power, and short-duration wheat varieties, have brought about increased cropping intensity. Short-duration crops such as fodder and vegetables have also been fitted into the cropping pattern. Tenancy status has an important bearing on the choice of particular crops in a season. On tenant-operated farms, fodder was more likely to be produced for the livestock because a main crop such as rice has to be shared in kind between the tenant and the landlord, while the fodder is not shared and its price is paid to the landlord at prevailing village rates. Thus fodder becomes a secondary source of income. Here is a case where modern varieties were adopted despite policies to discourage adoption because they offered certain advantages which fitted into the cropping system, and because they were resistant to pests to which Basmati was susceptible.

CROP DISPOSAL

In most of the villages studied, farmers tended to sell their rice crops soon after harvest. This was often necessary to meet the farm family's subsistence need for other food, clothing, education, and other expenses. The repayment of loans is also a critical factor in the early disposal of crops. Given this predominant farmers' practice, we should determine the extent to which rice farmers are net purchasers of rice (we usually think of them as rice producers and only incidentally as purchasers and consumers). In practically all of the study sites, where farmers grew both local and modern varieties, they almost always kept the local for home consumption and sold the modern. Understandably, their taste preferences for rice have been less amenable to change than their responses to market forces.

A final and general observation may be made on the interaction of physical and institutional factors to re-emphasize a point made earlier. Physical environmental factors such as irrigation, flood control, pests and diseases, and soil quality appear to be as important as the institutional factors of farm size, tenure, credit, and price policy, in determining the nature, magnitude, direction, and beneficiaries of the new rice technology. Poor environmental and institutional conditions tend to go hand in hand with occasional mitigating circumstances which cushion the extremes of consequences. Therefore, policies designed to modify, improve, or control the institutional factors will have far-reaching implications as to who benefits. The influence of the second set of factors is very dependent on the nature of the physical environment. An area with good irrigation may also have good roads, extension services, credit, a research station, more available inputs, and better prices for products. In a swampy remote area, very few, if any, of these facilities and services can be found. The interlocking chain of "positives" or "negatives" has to be broken somewhere in order to improve the lot of the disadvantaged.

Appendices

Note: "This past ___ season" and "the ___ season" refer to the last season harvested before the survey, which will be the wet season in most cases (exceptions are Indonesia and Malaysia). In the local questionnaire the season referred to could be identified by name (e.g. Kharif, Palagad, etc.) in the blank space for this purpose. Questions of this type are marked with an "*". The year "19__" is to be identified in each village as the first year MVs were introduced there. Questions reffering to that year are marked with "**"

Appendix A. Changes in Rice Farming in Selected Areas in Asia –
FIRST ROUND SURVEY QUESTIONNAIRE

Location: Region (Province) _____ Date of interview _____
District (Town) _____ Interviewer _____
Village _____
Name of farmer _____
Is your farm in the same location now as it was before 19 ** ?
Yes/No ___ (IF NO, DO NOT PROCEED, BUT SELECT A REPLACEMENT)

I. Current farm practices

1. How large is your total operated farm area (excluding homelot)? ___
2. How much of this were you cultivating this past * ___ season? ___
3. How much was irrigated this past * ___ season? _____
4. Please tell us the areas you planted to different rice varieties in * ___ season and the amount of seed used (USE TABLE 1).
5. Please tell us the areas you planted to different rice varieties in the previous season (USE TABLE 2).
6. What other rice varieties are grown in your village?

Names	Have you ever planted it? Yes/No	Why don't you use this variety now?
_____	_____	_____
_____	_____	_____
_____	_____	_____

7. (a) If you consider all the local and MV's that you have planted in the past during the *wet* season, which one gives the best results? variety ___ why best? _____
   (b) Which one gives the best results in the *dry* season? _____ why best? _____
8. If you consider all the varieties that you have planted in the past, are there any varieties which clearly give better results when the following problems occur?

	Yes/No	If yes, name varieties
Disease & insect	_____	_____
Drought	_____	_____
Flood	_____	_____
Typhoon or strong wind	_____	_____

9. How much chemical fertilizer did you use on your total rice crop this past * ___ season?

Type used	Quantity
_____	_____
_____	_____
_____	_____

10. What type and how much did you put on each variety planted in this past *___ season? (USE TABLE 1).
11. What type and how much chemical fertilizer did you put on each variety planted in the previous season? (USE TABLE 2).
12. Would you have liked to have used more chemical fertilizer this past *___ season? Yes/No. ___
    If yes, why didn't you use more? _____
13. Did you use any organic fertilizer this past ___ season? Yes/No ___
    If yes, what type _____ and how much _____
    If no, why not? _____
14. Between transplanting time and harvest time, how many times per week do you visit your rice fields? _____
15. What crops other than rice did you grow this year?

Crop	Area planted	
	Irrigated	Non-irrigated
_____	_____	_____
_____	_____	_____

II. **Change in practices**

A.1. *We would like to know which of the following practices you have used on your rice farm, when they were first adopted and whether they are still used.*

Practice	Date first adopted		Still used (yes/no)
	Season	Year	
MV (specify first variety used _____)			
Fertilizer Chemical Organic			
Insecticide			
Herbicide			
Hand weeding			
Straight-row planting			
Double-cropping			

	Borrowed, owned, or rented
Rotary weeder	
Animal power	
Tractor for land preparation	
Mechanical harvester	
Mechanical thresher	
Irrigation -gravity flow -pump	

Sprayer

2. What other changes have you made in the way you produce rice in the last five years? _____

3. If any of the practices in (1) above were adopted and discontinued, when were they discontinued and why?

Discontinued practices	When?	Why?
_____	_____	_____
_____	_____	_____

4. Does the use of insecticides or herbicides have any undesirable effects in or around your rice fields? Yes/No ____
If yes, specify _____

5. What is (are) the source(s) of water supply for your rice crop in the *____ season?

If irrigated, what kind of facility(ies)	When did it first become available?	Does it meet your needs? Yes/No	If no, why not?
_____	_____	_____	_____
_____	_____	_____	_____
_____	_____	_____	_____

B. Employment effect of practices adopted after MV's
1. Since 19**___, have any of the practices that you have newly adopted caused a *reduction* in the amount of labor needed for specific tasks? Yes/No ____
If yes,

| List these practices | Caused reduction in | | |
	Family labor	Hired labor	Both
_____	_____	_____	_____
_____	_____	_____	_____
_____	_____	_____	_____

2. Since 19**, have any of the practices that you have newly adopted caused an *increase* in the amount of labor needed for specific tasks? Yes/No____
If yes,

| List these practices | Caused increase in | | |
	Family labor	Hired labor	Both
_____	_____	_____	_____
_____	_____	_____	_____
_____	_____	_____	_____

III. Change in farm size, land value, yields, and rice disposal
A. *Farm size and land value*
1. Since 19** have you bought or sold any rice land? Yes/No ____
If yes, area bought _____
area sold _____
2. Since 19** have you begun to lease-in or share crop-in more rice land for the ____ season? Yes/No ____
If yes, *change* in area *leased out* or *share cropped-out* _____

3. Since 19<u>**</u> have you begun to lease-out or share crop-out more rice land for the _____season? Yes/No ____
If yes, *change* in area *leased out* or *share cropped-out* _____
4. Since 19<u>**</u> has there been any change in the area double-cropped? Yes/No ____ If yes, area of increase _____ decrease _____
5. Has the value of your good irrigated land increased since 19<u>**</u>? Yes/No ____
If yes, what was the value then? _____ now? _____ (per unit)
to what do you attribute this change? _____

B. *Rice disposal*
1. How did you use your <u>*</u>___ season rice crop before 19<u>**</u>?

	Estimated %
Kept for family use	_____
Sold	_____
Given out for	_____

2. How did you use your rice crop production from this past <u>*</u>___ season?

	Amount	
	MV's	Other varieties
kept for family use	_____	_____
sold immediately after harvest	_____	_____
sold within month after harvest	_____	_____
sold more than 1 month after harvest	_____	_____
Given out for _____	_____	_____
Other _____	_____	_____

C. *Yields*
1. Can you tell us what yield you obtained for each variety planted this past <u>*</u>___ season? (USE TABLE 1).
2. a. Which variety was planted on your best irrigated rice plot this past <u>*</u>___ season? (REFER TO TABLE 1).
b. What yield did you use to get on this piece of land in the _____ season before 19<u>**</u>? (RECORD IN TABLE 1).
c. What type and quantity of fertilizer did you normally use then? (RECORD IN TABLE 1).

IV. **Change in tenure and credit situation**
A. *Leased-in*
1. How much of your operated rice area did you lease-in this past <u>*</u>___ season? _____ How much share crop-in? _____
2. How much of your irrigated rice area did you lease-in this past <u>*</u>___ season? _____ How much share crop-in? _____
If NONE, proceed to (6) below
3. What varieties of rice did you plant on this leased-in land? _____
share cropped land? _____

4. What is the rental/sharing arrangement in the *____ season with the owner of the leased-in land? _____
   · share cropped land? _____
5. What does the owner contribute to costs of inputs and other production costs on the leased-in land? _____
   share cropped land? _____
6. Did you lease-in or sharecrop rice land in the *____ season before 19**? Yes/No ____
   If yes, did the owner share input and production costs then? Yes/No__
7. What was the rental/sharing arrangement in the ____ season with owner at that time? _____
8. (If change occurred) Who do you think benefited from the change in tenure arrangements? You ____ owner ____ both ____ Why? _____
9. This past *____ season, who decided what varieties you planted on this land? You ____ Owner ____

B. Leased-out

1. Do you lease-out or sharecrop-out any of the rice land that you own? Yes/No ____ If YES, ask (2) to (7).
2. What area did you lease-out? ____sharecrop-out? ____
3. What rice variety was grown on this land this past *____ season? _____
4. What inputs did you supply to the tenant? _____
5. Who decided what variety to plant on this land? you ____ tenant ____
6. Did you share production costs on land leased-out by you before 19**? Yes/No _____
7. (If there is a change from (4) to (6)) Why has this change occurred? _____

C. Credit

1. How much money did you borrow this past *____ season to pay cost of rice production?

Amount	Borrowed from	Used for	Terms of repayment (in cash or kind, duration of loan, amount to be repayed or interest rate)
____	____	____	____
____	____	____	____

2. Besides money borrowed, did you take fertilizer, seed, or other inputs on credit this past *____ season? Yes/No _____
   If yes,

Amount	From whom	Used for	Terms of repayment (in cash or kind, duration of loan, amount to be repayed or interest rate)
____	____	____	____
____	____	____	____
____	____	____	____

3. If more production credit had been available to you this past *____ season, would you have used it? Yes/No ____
   If yes, how? _____

4. Did you buy inputs on credit or borrow money for production costs before 19**? Yes/No ____
   If no, why not? _____
   If yes, did you borrow more ____less ____or the same amount ____ as now? (check one)
   If yes, during that time did you find repayment of production credit more of a burden ____less of a burden ____about the same ____? (check one)
   If more or less, why? _____

5. In what ways have the terms or costs of credit/input loans changed since 19** ?

6. What were the main sources of your loans or credit then? _____
   (check one or more) Commercial bank ____, gov't agency _____
   landlord ____ private money lender ____ Other (specify) _____

V. Change in family size and employment

A. Household size and income

1. How many people are fed in your household?

	Now		in 19__	
	male	female	male	female
persons under 10				
10 – 50				
over 50				

2. Which of these persons earn an income outside of your farm?

			Source of income	
Name	Sex	Age	(type of work)	(inside or outside the village?)
_____	__	__	_____	_____
_____	__	__	_____	_____
_____	__	__	_____	_____

3. Has the total income from off the farm increased or decreased (including remittance) since 19__? increased ____ decreased ____ same ____

B. Farm labor requirement

1. Compared to the period 19** is there any difference now in the amount of family labor, hired labor or exchange labor that you use on your farm in the *____ season.
   a. Specifically, is the amount of *family* labor used for pre-harvest tasks greater ____ smaller ____ or the same ____
   b. Is the amount of *hired labor from within the village* used for pre-harvest tasks greater ____ smaller ____ or the same ____
   c. Is the amount of *hired labor from outside the village* used for pre-harvest tasks greater ____ smaller ____ or the same ____
   d. Is the amount of *exchange* labor used for pre-harvest tasks greater ____ smaller ____ or the same ____
   e. Is the amount of *family* labor used for harvest and threshing tasks greater ____ smaller ____ or the same ____

f. Is the amount of *hired labor from within the village* used for harvesting and threshing tasks greater _____ smaller _____ or the same _____

g. Is the amount of *hired labor from outside the village* used for harvest and threshing tasks greater _____ smaller _____ or the same _____ .

h. Did the amount of *exchange* labor used for harvest and threshing tasks greater _____ smaller _____ or the same _____

VI. Changes in production problems

A.1. Were you fully satisfied with the harvest you obtained from your rice crop in this past *_____ season? Yes/No _____

2. What used to be the main constraints in getting higher yields from the rice varieties you grew in this *_____ season before 19** ? (check below)

3. What are the main constraints in getting higher yields from MV's and other varieties you grew this past *_____ season? (check below)

4. Do you plan to take any action to overcome the difficulties you mentioned that you had this past *_____ season? Yes/No _____ (If yes, specify in col. 3 below)

Check list	Before 19__	This season MV's	This season Other	What action farmer plans to take to overcome these
Pre-harvest				
Obtaining seed				
Obtaining fertilizer or chemicals				
Obtaining credit				
Water-irrigation				
Disease-insects				
Pests				
Other				
Harvest and post-harvest				
Harvesting				
Threshing				
Hauling				
Drying				
Storage				
Selling				
Processing				
Other				

5. If rice farming in this village is to be improved, what is the most important thing that must be done? _____

VII. Benefits and expenditures

A. *Compared to the period before 19**.*

	Higher	Lower	Same	If higher or lower, why?
Are your profits from rice NOW				
Is your level of living NOW				

B. *Compared to the period before 19**, have you*

	Yes	No	If yes, How (what new income)?

1. increased your food consumption or improved
   your diet?   ___ __ _____

   Check if any item
      increased

   rice   _____
   vegetables   _____
   fish   _____
   eggs   _____
   chicken   _____
   pork   _____
   beef   _____
   canned goods   _____
   milk   _____
   coffee   _____
   cooking oil   _____
   other (specify) _____

2. increased the amount of
   money spent for your
   children's education   ___ __ _____

3. improved your house or
   built a new house?   ___ __ _____

4. bought household
   furniture or
   appliances (specify)   ___ __ _____

        check if purchased

   a. radio   ____
   b. sewing machine   ____
   c. living room set   ____
   d. dining room set   ____
   e. clothes cabinet   ____
   f. gas or electric stove ____
   g. bed   ____
   h. other _____   ____
      _____

5. bought a bicycle?   ___ __ _____

6. bought a motorcycle or
   motor scooter?   ___ __ _____

7. bought a tractor or other ___ __ _____
   farm implement?
   (specify) _____   ___ __ _____

8. increased your savings   ___ __ _____

9. paid off any long-term
   debts?   ___ __ _____

10. started any new farm
    enterprises (specify)   ___ __ _____

C. *Do you expect your yearly income over the next five years to be higher
than it is now? Yes/No* ____
If yes, why? _____
If yes, how do you expect to spend the extra income? _____

Table 1. For ____ season (last season harvested)

Rice varieties (by name)	AREA[a] Irrig.	AREA[a] Non-irrig.	SEED[a] Amt	FERTILIZER[b] Amt	FERTILIZER[b] Type	Produc-tion	Identify best plot before 19** [d] Produc-tion	Identify best plot before 19** [d] Fertilizer Amt.	Identify best plot before 19** [d] Fertilizer Type
a. Modern varieties									
_____									
_____									
_____									
b. Improved local									
_____									
_____									
_____									
c. Traditional									
_____									
_____									
_____									
TOTAL									

[a]Question I.A4:   If the same variety is planted on both irrigated and non-irrigated areas, use a separate row for each so seed, fertilizer, and yield will be separated.

[b]Question I.A10

[c]Question III.C1

[d]Question III.C2

Table 2. For previous season

Rice varieties	AREA[a]		FERTILIZER[b]	
	Irrigated	Non-irrigated	Amount	Type
a. Modern varieties				
	_____			
	_____			
	_____			
b. _____				
	_____			
	_____			
c. Traditional				
	_____			
	_____			
	_____			
TOTAL				

[a]Question I.A5: If the same variety is planted on both irrigated and non-irrigated areas, use separate row for each so fertilizer will be separated.

[b]Question I.A11.

SECOND ROUND SURVEY QUESTIONNAIRE

Repeat these questions from First Round Questionnaire

I.A, 1, 2, 3, 4, 9, 10, 12, 13, 14

II.A. 5

III.A. 2,3; B. 1,2; C. 1,2

IV.A.; B.; C. 1,2,3

V.B

VI.

Add these questions.
1. Did the MV's give higher _____, lower _____, or the same _____ yields in this season as compared with last season?
   (If different) why is there a difference? _____
2. What can you do to improve yields from MV's in the _____ season next year? _____
3. Based on your past experience, what do you think are the most important things to remember about growing MV's successfully? _____
   How do they differ from growing other varieties? _____

Appendix B. List of Basic Descriptive Data Collected

To compare the conditions among the rice growing areas studied, data were collected and description of the physical and cultural environment was prepared for each of the study areas. All of the materials included in the 'list of basic description data collected' was gathered by talking with officials at the village (V), district (D), regional (R), or national (N) level. This information was used not only to describe the environment, but also to identify those factors which could be regarded as constraints to achieving higher yields.

A. The physical environment
1. *Topographical description*   V
2. *Climate*   V (D)
   Rainfall and temperature, for the 'survey year,' plus annual and seasonal averages.
3. *Soil characteristics*   V
   General nomenclature — heavy clay, clay loam, sandy, and other types — and some indication of water-holding capacity.
4. *Special difficulties*   V (D)
   Major rice pests and diseases and losses therefrom; typhoons, floods — in the 'study year' and including notation of any catastrophe year.
5. *Irrigation drainage*   V (D)
   Type(s) of irrigation system(s); periods of water availability; person(s) or authority controlling water allocation; drainage adequacy.
6. *Varieties planted in area*   V (D)
   Classified as high yielding or modern, improved local, or traditional, and other special plant characteristics were noted.

B. Other infrastructure (Diagram model used)
1. *Transportation*   V (D)
   Roads and waterways; availability of buses, trucks, carts, boats, and other modes of transportation; railroads, quality of roads — paved or not; year-round use, and related information.
2. *Storage, processing, and marketing facilities*   V (D)
   Types that serve the villages selected for study; dryers included; notation of any increase in total milling capacity of mills in local market center in the period following the introduction of the MV's; information on local volume and weight measures, and in milling outturns.
3. *Banks and other credit facilities*   V (D&R)
4. *Other government facilities for production*   V (D&R)
   Experiment station(s); demonstration trials; extension service(s).
5. *Schools, clinics, postal services, and others*   V (D)
6. *Communications media*
   Press, radio, and other forms of mass media, extent of news of direct interest to farmers; market news service.
7. *Electricity*   V

C. Demographic and land use
1. *Village population*   V
   Total, and percentage change in last 10 years; main sources of livelihood – farming and non-farming.
2. *Other census data*   V
   Religion, ethnic group, castes, and others.
3. *Village settlement pattern*   V
   Along road, with house gardens, cluster, isolated, etc.
4. *Land use pattern*   V
   Land use map where possible; man-land ratio.
5. *The agricultural year including pre- and post-harvest activities.*   V
   Rotations; growing period of new varieties compared with local varieties; changes in timing of harvest periods are shown schematically

D. The economic environment
1. *Prices*   V (D)
   By month from nearest rice mill or rice dealer for survey 'year' for 2–3 main types of rice, including one MV; also for other years when available; prices at nearest dealer or cooperative for fertilizer and other important inputs; data on price differentials between local and major markets.
2. *Wages*   V
   Wage rates; systems of wage payment; changes over time*
3. *Interest*   V
   Rates usually paid on loans from different sources; changes over time*.
4. *Rent*
   Rates per season, year, and others; in cash or kind; fixed or share; changes over time*
5. *Taxes*   V
   Types and totals; paid to village or other agency; changes over time*
6. *Land prices*   V
   Average, for major land types; changes over time*.
7. *Irrigation costs*   V
   Government irrigation fees and normal collection rates; normal cost of private irrigation systems, if any.
8. *Seed*   V (D)
   Availability, source, quality, and prices.
9. *Power*   V
   Typical farm power requirement and investment for land preparation, also rental rates for tractor and animal services.

---

*Changes over time since the introduction of modern varieties.

E. Institutional factors
1. *Farmers' organizations*   V
   Cooperatives, farmer associations, and similar
   bodies; other types of joint or group activities,
   changes over time*.
2. *Brief description of the way in which MV's were*   V
   introduced into the area.
3. *Extension services; also credit, and other services*   V (D&R)
   Number of agencies that provide services; quantity
   and quality of services; main complaints of farmers
   regarding agency programs; if, and to what extent,
   farmers realized profits from MV programs.
4. *Special government programs*   V
   Land reform, land consolidation, crash programs,
   and others.
5. *Kinship*   V
   Role in inheritance, cost of ceremonies, etc.; also
   factionalism
6. *Leadership in agriculturally relevant activities*   V
7. *Attitudes and values affecting development*   V
   Change in size and cost of ceremonies; evaluation
   as to whether farming is a preferred occupation
   and similar assessments.

F. The policy framework
1. *Aims of national policy for rice*   C
2. *Policy measures*   C,R,D,
   Price policies – input and output; restrictions on
   input and output marketing, if any; package
   programs, etc.
3. *Importance of rice as compared with commodity*   C
   production program

Appendix C. List of Varieties and Their Basic Characteristics

ADT-27. 1965. An indica x japonica hybrid of early maturity and intermediate height released by the Madras State of India. It is moderately responsive to nitrogen and has small, roundish grains. The cooking quality is good.

Apostol. A tall traditional variety of the Philippines which is strongly sensitive to photoperiod.

Bahagia. 1968. A sister selection of IR5 released by West Malaysia. It is intermediate in plant type and maturity.

BAM 3. A selection from a tall traditional variety suited to low-lying areas. Released by the Orissa State of India. The cooking quality is good.

Basmati 370. 1933. A selection from the Basmati variety of old India, known for its aroma and kernel elongation character. It is late in maturity and low yielding. It commands a high market price in South Asia and East Africa.

Bengawan. 1941. Released by the Central Research Institute of Agriculture, Indonesia. It is a tall variety which is weakly sensitive to photoperiod and is noted for its good eating quality. It is medium responsive to fertilizer.

BPI-76. 1960. An intermediate variety developed by the Philippine Bureau of Plant Industry. It is strongly sensitive to photoperiod and has slender grains.

C4-63. 1967. An intermediately tall variety developed by the University of the Philippines College of Agriculture about 1967. It is weakly sensitive to photoperiod and is noted for its good eating quality.

C4-63G. c.1968. A pure line selected from C4-63 (see preceding) having green basal leaf sheath (green base).

C4-137. 1969. An intermediately tall variety released by the University of the Philippines College of Agriculture. It is weakly sensitive to photoperiod.

CO-29. c. 1960. A hybrid variety of Madras State (India) having early maturity and blast resistance. It is moderately tall in stature and has medium grain quality.

CO-33. c. 1970. A semidwarf variety of Madras State (India) originating from IR8 x ADT27. This variety, also known as Karuna, is early maturing and responsive to nitrogen. It has small, roundish grains and good cooking quality.

Dara. 1960. A tall variety released by the Central Research Institute of Agriculture, Indonesia. It is relatively insensitive to photoperiod and has medium grain quality.

Dee-geo-woo-gen. A semidwarf variety of Taiwan, which is insensitive to photoperiod. Taichung Native 1, IR8, and many semidwarf lines were derived from it.

GEB-24. c. 1930. A spontaneous mutant selected from a traditional variety of Madras State (India). It has good grain quality and a 150-day maturity. It is parent of many Indian varieties. Although low yielding, it commands a higher price than do the MV's.

Intan. 1940. A tall variety released by the Central Research Institute of Agriculture, Indonesia, but is grown also in the Philippines. It is weakly sensitive to photoperiod.

IR8. 1966. A semidwarf variety. It is the first variety named by the International Rice Research Institute (IRRI). It is relatively insensitive to photoperiod and exhibits an outstanding response to nitrogen. It has poor grain type. It lacks resistance to bacterial blight, tungro virus, brown planthopper, and grassy stunt virus.

IR5. 1967. Developed at IRRI. It is intermediate in height and weakly sensitive to photoperiod. It has poor grain type. It is more resistant to adverse weather conditions than other IRRI semi-dwarf varieties, but lacks resistance to tungro, brown planthopper, grassy stunt, and the stem borers.

IR6. 1970. A name given to the breeding line IR6-156-2 before it was named as Mehran 69 in Pakistan.

IR20. 1969. A semidwarf named by IRRI. It is weakly sensitive to photoperiod and is moderately resistant to tungro and the leafhoppers. The grains are medium in length and slender in shape.

IR22. 1969. A semidwarf named by IRRI. It is weakly sensitive to photoperiod and has slender grains. It is susceptible to tungro and the leafhoppers.

IR24. 1971. A semidwarf named by IRRI. It is relatively insensitive to photoperiod and has a soft and moist cooking quality. It has moderate resistance to tungro and the leafhoppers.

Jaya. 1968. A semidwarf variety released by the All-India Coordinated Rice Improvement Project. It is relatively insensitive to photoperiod. It has poor grain type.

Jhona 349. 1933. A selection from Jhona, a traditional variety of the Punjab area (India and Pakistan). It has a higher yielding ability than other local varieties but poor grain quality.

Karuna. See CO-33. c. 1970.

Kullakar. A traditional variety from which ADT-23 was isolated. It is native of Madras State of India and matures in 130 days. The grains are short and red.

Malinja. 1964. A moderately tall and relatively early maturing (though sensitive to photoperiod) hybrid developed in Malaysia. It is highly susceptible to diseases.

Mashuri. 1966. An intermediate variety released by the Rice Department of Malaysia. It is relatively insensitive to photoperiod and is priced for its fine grains.

Mayang Ebos. A tall and late traditional variety of Malaysia which has very strong grain dormancy. It is sensitive to photoperiod.

Mehran 69. 1970. A semidwarf selection from IR6-156-2 released in Pakistan. It has long and slender grains.

Palman 246. 1939. A selection from Palman, a traditional variety of the Punjab area (India and Pakistan). It has good-looking grains but poor cooking quality.

Pankaj. 1969. A sister line of IR5 selected in India.

PB5 (Peta Baru 5). Indonesian name for IR5.

PB8 (Peta Baru 8). Indonesian name for IR8.

Pebifun. A relatively early, moderately tall, indica variety of Taiwan. This major variety was widely grown in the double-cropping area of West Malaysia during 1942–1964.

Pelita. 1971. Released by the Central Research Institute of Agriculture, Indonesia. It is weakly sensitive to photoperiod. The grain appearance is relatively more attractive than PB5 or PB8.

Peta. 1941. A tall variety released by the Central Research Institute of Agriculture, Indonesia, but also grown in the Philippines. It is weakly sensitive to photoperiod.

Ratna. 1970. A semidwarf variety released by the Central Rice Research Institute, India. It is weakly sensitive to photoperiod and is noted for its high grain quality.

RD-1. 1969. A Thai semidwarf variety. It is the first hybrid variety named by the Rice Department (Now Rice Division) in Thailand. It has long and slender grains and is higher yielding than traditional varieties.

RD-3. 1969. A Thai semidwarf variety, which is similar to RD-1. It is also non-glutinous. It is higher yielding than the traditional varieties and has long and slender grains.

RD-5. 1973. A moderately tall Thai hybrid variety having a plant type inter-mediate between the tall traditional type and the semidwarf. It is weakly sensitive to photoperiod, and has long and slender grains.

Ramadja. 1954. A tall variety released by the Central Research Institute of Agriculture, Indonesia. It is weakly sensitive to photoperiod.

Ria. 1966. IR8 under a Malaysian name.

Rojolele. A tall traditional variety of the bulu type; purified from a farmer's variety. It is relatively insensitive to photoperiod. Its bold grains command a higher price than PB5.

Siam 29. A tall traditional variety which is sensitive to photoperiod. Both the Malaysian and Thai strains have the same name. It has slender grains.

Sigadis. 1954. A tall variety developed by the Central Research Institute of Agriculture, Indonesia. It is relatively insensitive to photoperiod and has medium response to fertilizer. Its eating quality is good.

SLO-13. c. 1950. An intermediately tall strain selected from a traditional variety. It was developed in Andhra Pradesh, India.

SLO-19. c. 1950. A tall and early maturing strain selected from a traditional variety. It was developed in Andhra Pradesh, India.

Syntha. 1963. A tall variety developed by the Central Research Institute, of Agriculture, Indonesia. It is weakly sensitive to photoperiod, and has medium response to fertilizer. It has slender grains with good eating quality.

Taichung 65. 1927. A ponlai (japonica) variety of Taiwan. It is well adapted to double cropping in the subtropics and tropics.

Taichung Native 1. 1960. The first semidwarf variety released by the Taiwan Provincial Department of Agriculture. It is relatively insensitive to photoperiod and is susceptible to many diseases and insects. It has poor grain type.

Tangkai Rotan. A traditional variety of Malaysia and parent of IR5. It has relatively erect leaves and intermediate height and maturity.

Tjeremas. c. 1940. A tall variety developed in Indonesia which has the same parents as Peta. It is also grown in the Philippines. It is weakly sensitive to photoperiod.

TKM-6. c. 1950. A relatively early and tall hybrid derived from GEB-24 x CO-18, developed in Madras State, India. It has slender grains and moderate resistance to stem borers.